WARSHIP 1994

WARSHIP 1994

Edited by John Roberts

CONWAY
MARITIME PRESS

Frontispiece caption:
Kite going aloft from the quarterdeck of the Revenge *on 2 September 1908 in a test which substituted a breeches buoy for* *the basket. The destroyer* Recruit *is in the background.* (RAE Museum)

© Brassey's (UK) Ltd 1994

First published in Great Britain by
Conway Maritime Press
An imprint of Brassey's (UK) Ltd
33 John Street
London WC1N 2AT

British Library Cataloguing in Publication Data
Warship . .
    1994 –
    1. Warships
    623.825

    ISBN 0–85177–630–2

Design, typesetting and page make-up by
The Word Shop, Bury, Lancashire
Printed and bound in Great Britain by
Butler & Tanner Ltd, Frome

CONTENTS

EDITORIAL

It is now twelve years since I was last the editor of *Warship*, and during that period much has changed both with the publication itself and with naval publishing in general. With regard to *Warship* the style and content have altered substantially and, I think, for the better, the credit for which must go to Robert Gardiner who, after editing five volumes of the annual, has turned his talents full time to Conway's book production. There has also, of course, been the major move from quarterly to annual which still causes some controversy, as there are many who express a preference for the older style but, like much else in the modern world, *Warship* is subject to the changing economic environment and as an annual it is a much more viable proposition – better the minor disadvantages of less frequent publication than no publication at all! The annual also makes it much easier to provide a reasonable balance of articles covering a variation of time, ship types and nationality, and subjects from out-of-the-way items, which might not otherwise be published, to the more popular mainstream items that are the mainstay of naval technical history.

On a broader front the changed circumstances of east/west relations have opened up the possibility of a vast new source of information on the Russian Navy. This is reflected in the article from Renè Greger and his Russian co-author, V V Jarovoj, covering the design history of the last conventional Soviet cruiser classes. More information of this type should become available in future years.

It is noticeable that during the many years that I have been interested in the development of the warship the quality of information that has been published on the subject has steadily improved. What was once largely restricted to fleet lists and the general particulars of ships has expanded into in-depth studies of warship designs and their *raison d'être*, covering not only technical developments but national and international political background. In this process many errors and misinterpretations have and are being corrected and several myths overturned. There are several examples of this in the present publication, the most obvious being the multi-authored article detailing the damage to the battleship *Bismarck* using the exploratory work of Dr Ballard. Although there are limitations – a great deal of the wreck, particularly the main belt, cannot be examined – the authors show that the ship's armour was penetrated and that she was severely damaged by British shell fire, demonstrating that she was not the 'super' ship that wartime propoganda (both British and German) made her out to be. At the same time the authors have avoided going to the opposite extreme and give a much more believable picture of a first class ship defeated by a combination of technical problems, bad luck and an enemy superior in numbers.

A similarly controversial subject, although less debated, is covered by Stephen McLaughlin in his description of the design rationale of the first Russian dreadnoughts. He argues that their evolution was much more logical than is generally supposed and in so doing provides a clearer understanding of the qualities and potential of these much criticised ships whose design was, in fact, matched precisely to their intended role. Correction of misinterpretations of the origins of a design are also to be found in Norman Friedman's description of the postwar development of US minesweepers while, stepping much further back in time, S Marthinsen, in detailing the development of the French ship-of-the-line, shows that, despite indications to the contrary, the French Navy continued to represent a potentially formidable force after Trafalgar.

In the area of factual corrections, Richard Wright demonstrates, in his article on the Royal Navy's fast minelayers, that the reported/rumoured speeds of these ships have been greatly exaggerated. This in itself is not too surprising; what is, is that it takes so long to get the true facts generally accepted. Like much else of this nature, I have no doubt that the speed of the *Abdiel* class will continue to be given in new publications as 'over 40kts' for some considerable time to come. Unfortunately, the effect of establishing the truth tends to degrade such ships in peoples minds and misses the point that they *were* very high speed vessels for their size.

Less obvious in the area of improving the quality of available information is Daniel Harris' article on the Swedish monitors designed by John Ericsson in the mid-nineteenth century. Very little detail has previously been available on this group of vessels, at least in English language publications. Much of what has previously been published was both limited and incorrect, particularly with regard to the vessels' dimensions (partly due to the Swedish employing their own 'foot' measurement at this time – slightly shorter than an English foot – which was subdivided by ten rather than twelve). I also noticed that the small monitor *Garmer* is often listed together with other ships to form a single class when she was in fact of a totally individual design. Although, I have never taken any great personal interest in minor navies and their ships, I must admit that I found the Swedish monitors quite fascinating. One must suppose that, like many subjects, if they do not have that indefinable 'glamour' which places them in the popular class, they tend to be ignored whether their stories are interesting or not. *Warship* exists to help to fuel the interest that these many and varied subjects deserve.

John Roberts

FRENCH SAIL-OF-THE-LINE
in the Napoleonic Wars (1792–1815)

Largely ruined by the destructive Revolution, the French Navy was to find itself in the unenviable position of not being able to function anywhere near the level required of it during the long Napoleonic Wars. Steve Marthinsen describes how, hampered by poor officers who preached poor strategy and incorrect tactics, Napoleon had to put his greatest efforts into rejuvenating the navy of France and providing the groundwork for its eventual recovery after his fall.

'The French Navy is called on to acquire a superiority over the English. The French understand building better than their rivals, and French ships, the English themselves admit, are better than theirs. The guns are superior in calibre to those of the English by one fourth. These are two great advantages.'

– Napoleon

The history of the French Navy during the Napoleonic Wars is a tale unlike that of other countries' fleets who fought during the period. It is remarkable that the fleet had held together at all during the period of the Revolution. Before it began, France had had a navy she could be justifiably proud of. Excellent ships manned by well-trained crews made her a force to be reckoned with and the fact that she had fought the English to a virtual standstill tactically and had beaten her strategically during the American Revolution were enough to rank her very close, if not on a par, with the Royal Navy of Britain. However, like the French Royal Army, the internal organization of the Navy was such that it was ripe for the picking when the Revolution began. The Navy, perhaps even more than the Army, was officered almost entirely by aristocrats with little room for the advancement of anyone whose blood was anything less than royal blue. The French Revolution quickly and bloodily changed the entire picture, opening the way for anyone (and sometimes this was literally true) to become an officer of a man-of-war. Tragically, this upheaval in organization did not recognize the plain fact that when dealing with a technical piece of equipment (and a ship-of-the-line was certainly that), one could not replace knowledge and experience with revolutionary fervour and hope to win any battles. In addition, the revolutionary government seemed to forget that, unlike an army living off the land, a fleet had to be supplied with all manner of equipment. In the past this had been provided from well-stocked arsenals but the major arsenals began to deteriorate immediately after the beginning of the Revolution.[1]

The chaos of the first years of the Revolution proved to be an enormous obstacle to naval recovery, as everything had to be started again from scratch under a revolutionary government that had no idea how to supply, let alone use, a once mighty fleet. The disaster that was the French Navy of the Revolution was to leave an indelible imprint on the fleet that would emerge later under Napoleon.

One of the first tasks Napoleon undertook when he came to power was to rebuild the Navy and try to make it into a force that could, one day, make a difference in the affairs of France. He was under no illusions about the task ahead; it would take years to build ships, cost a great deal of money and probably not bear any fruit for a long time. These facts, something that the revolutionary governments could not fathom, did not deter him and he set a programme in motion to produce a fleet that would one day surpass the strength of the prewar Navy and, just maybe, secure him enough time to pull off a cross-Channel invasion of England. At the very least, this 'fleet in being' would tie down large numbers of English ships in an expensive blockade of French ports. The aforementioned facts show that Napoleon was strongly committed to the Navy and understood the position it could occupy in France's affairs. With these ideas in mind, he set his zeal and organizational skill to work. His reforms would touch every aspect of naval life.

Napoleon knew that in order to have an effective Navy, he would have to improve the basic weaknesses that were afflicting the service. One of the first things he did was to shake up the officer corps and make sure that it was composed of men who were actually qualified or had the promise to do the job.[2] Consequently, the Navy was turned inside out and released of all of its poorer performers; too many times in the past years negligent captains had allowed their vessels to be captured after a

Le Northumberland *and* L'Impétueux. *Both ships were captured at the 'Glorious First of June' Battle in 1794.* (NMM)

pitiful defence, even when their ship was by far the stronger of the two contestants.[3]

Next, the country was divided into five *arrondissements maritimes*, or naval districts, so that Napoleon could exercise greater control over the major naval arsenals that each district contained. The district prefects whom he selected performed their jobs in the same manner for their districts as Napoleon did for the country as a whole; within each district, the prefect concerned himself with ship construction, naval supplies and, most importantly, manpower. This last item was controlled by registering all men in the district who had anything at all to do with the sea so that when the time came they could be called up to serve in a new ship or for service in the dockyards. Finally, Napoleon took a great step forward by insisting on having permanent crews for his ships, much as the soldiers in his army served in their respective regiments. This order, which at the time was nearly incomprehensible to naval people, was followed up in 1808 with a more formal decree by which the sailors were organized into numbered battalions, called *Equipages de Haut-Bord*, and then assigned to various vessels in the fleet. Given a few years of peace so that these measures could take effect, the Navy could have performed at a level not seen for many years. In fact the Navy did improve in performance, and the victories in the Indian Ocean[4] and the short fleet actions in 1813 and 1814

showed what could happen; however the respite that was so needed never came and it was not until several years after Napoleon's second abdication that the Navy began to revive. Ironically, the Bourbons, who came to power again after Napoleon's abdication in 1815, re-adopted the idea of permanent ship crews and were later imitated by most other countries.

The Battle of Trafalgar: an End or a Beginning?

There are many legends and myths surrounding this battle, but one myth that needs to be struck down is the state of the French Navy *after* the Battle of Trafalgar. Standard histories (many of which are highly regarded) usually end their commentaries with this famous action but few seem to realize that the French Navy did not vanish but surged on to new strengths, especially after the incorporation of Holland into France. In 1813, the French fleet matched the strength of the pre-revolutionary Navy and had more new ships with heavier armaments. Napoleon's ship-building programme was in full swing by this time and even at the time of his first abdication in 1814 there were thirty-seven ships building in the various ports of the Empire which, had they been completed,

Le Montebello. *The ship is seen in her postwar configuration.* (Watercolour by F Roux)

would have given France a fleet of well over one hundred sail-of-the-line. In this sense, the Battle of Trafalgar was more a blow to the morale of the Navy than to its strength but perhaps the greatest damage was the continued erosion of the French sailor's confidence in his superiors. Villeneuve and Dumanoir would be the culprits for this at Trafalgar but the same tendencies would be found again in Linois, the victor of Algeciras in 1801, when he engaged a fleet of East Indiamen only to be bluffed into retiring by their showing a bold front. Napoleon, a man who knew better than most the value of morale, remarked that Linois 'lacked courage of the mind' and this showed why his fleet could win virtually no battles.

It has been said that Napoleon never understood naval warfare but the French Emperor knew a great deal more about the matter than is generally credited. Unfortunately for him, his available admirals lacked the dash that made successes out of men like Britain's Nelson and Cochrane. Perhaps his admirals viewed it as realism in the circumstances but their subsequent neglect often caused utter disaster to strike; the best cases were at two of the major actions of the war: the Nile in 1798 and Trafalgar in 1805.

In the first case, Vice-Admiral Brueys should have entered Alexandria or sailed to Corfu, as Napoleon (then General Bonaparte) later ordered. Instead, he chose the small bay of Aboukir which, if properly defended, would not have been a bad choice. However, his conduct here,

though courageous in battle, left much to be desired as he allowed himself to be surprised (all of his light ships were in the harbour and therefore useless for scouting) and then, because of his ships' placement too far from the shore, he had his force destroyed piecemeal. His ships fought well, as French ships always seemed to be able to take tremendous punishment, but in vain.

The second battle, Trafalgar, was another example of poor overall leadership leading to disaster. Vice-Admiral Villeneuve should never have sailed from Cadiz harbour in the first place as his replacement, Vice-Admiral Rosily, was on his way south to take over. While it is true that Napoleon's orders to Villeneuve told him to engage equal or inferior fleets, the French admiral must surely have known that his leader counted every two Spanish ships as one Frenchman and that accordingly he should not have engaged. Napoleon knew his fleet was still weak from many years of mismanagement and he also knew that the Spanish Navy was virtually worthless as a fighting force; Villeneuve knew this too, but of all the options available the unfortunate admiral chose precisely the wrong one, a trend all too common with the French Navy. Secondly, once the fleet had sailed, why did he attempt to get back to Cadiz? Would it not have been better to keep going in the hope of escaping with some force rather than risk losing it all? (In the event this is what happened. Every French ship involved in the battle was lost; the ones that made it to port were taken over by the Spanish in 1808.) These questions cannot of course be answered but seem to underline the fact that at sea Napoleon had no Davout or Lannes.[5] Indeed, he himself admitted on St Helena that 'I especially liked sailors . . . but I never found between them and myself the man who would have made them worthy . . .' This fact, perhaps more than any other, was the ultimate result of the Revolution and the damage it caused to the navy of France under Napoleon.

Article 15 of the Peace Treaty of 30 May 1814

When Napoleon abdicated for the first time in 1814, the British saw to it that the powerful navy he left to France was reduced in strength by stripping away many of the ships residing in what were now considered foreign ports (eg Antwerp and Venice) and by breaking up all the ships being built at these ports (see Table 1). As a result of this article in the peace treaty of 30 May 1814, the French Navy lost nine ships-of-the-line that were already built and seventeen that were in various stages of construction. It is interesting to note that, of the thirty-seven ships being built, well over half of them would have been of eighty guns or more, anticipating what would happen in post war ship-building.

Table 1: *SHIPS UNDER CONSTRUCTION ON 30 MAY 1814*

Antwerp		Rochefort		Venice	
Hymen	110	Tonnant	118	Saturne	80
Monarque	110	Ville de Vienne	118	Arcole	74
Neptune	110	Iena	110	Duquesne	74
Terrible	110	Glorieux	74	Montenotte	74
Alexandre	80	Venitien	74		
Atlas	80			**Brest**	
Fougeux	80	**Lorient**			
Mars	80			Sans Pareil	118
Tibre	80	Algeciras	80	Couronne	74
Aigle	74	Brabanon	80		
Alcide	74	Magnifique	80	**Genoa**	
Belliqueux	74	Jean Bart	74		
Impétueux	74			Brave	74
		Cherbourg		Brillant	74
Toulon					
		Inflexible	118		
		Centaure	80		
Formidable	118	Jupiter	80		
Souverain	118	Généreux	74		
Provence	74				

Notes:

All ships building at Antwerp and Venice were broken up on the stocks. All other ships completed after the wars were over.

L'Achille. (Musée de la Marine, Paris)

L'Ocean. (Musée de la Marine, Paris)

Sail-of-the-Line of the French Navy

France entered what would become known as the Napoleonic Wars with seventy-six sail-of-the-line available for service all of which, save one, carried seventy-four or more cannon. The 64-gun ship-of-the-line, a ship class that still endured in many other navies, had all but disappeared from the French active fleet lists and for good reason. France had standardized her ship designs into four basic types: 118-, 110-, 80- and 74-gun ships-of-the-line. This simplification, coupled with master plans produced by the great naval architect Sané, helped streamline production and gave all the ships of the same type similar characteristics. In the original French naval registers, which record the sailing qualities of each ship, there is a noticeable and unmistakable trend in that most of the ships designed to the plans of Sané are described as behaving quite well under sail while many of the captured types are described as poor sailers. This may well be bias but the fact that not all of the enemy ships are described thus (the British *Hannibal*, captured at Algeciras in 1801, being so favoured) leads one to believe that the judgements are fair, especially since these papers could be reviewed at any time by Napoleon whose critical eye for detail would have picked up anything resembling bias; the

Emperor might publish Bulletins for the masses to consume but in his own internal affairs he demanded accuracy and truth lest the individual concerned run the risk of the imperial wrath.

The most powerful ships of the Napoleonic Wars were France's 118-gun ships-of-the-line of which there were ten serving during that time. Fine ships capable of manoeuvring quite well for their size,[6] their punishing broadsides could lay waste to enemy vessels, as happened to the British *Bellerophon* at the Battle of the Nile in 1798. These ships, however, were expensive in terms of building materials, artillery and manpower and were reserved for admirals as fleet flagships. It is interesting to note that, though these ships were costly, their design was enlarged in terms of overall tonnage, with the introduction of the *Impérial* in 1803. Mounting 18pdr cannon on her third gun-deck (unheard of in three-decked ships of the period), she would set the standard for all future French 118-gun ships.

The 110-gun ship-of-the-line had been the standard large three-decker in the 1780s but by the time Napoleon took power they had become something of an anachronism; only two more of this type were completed after 1799. Large and impressive, the ships of this class gave a good account of themselves during the wars and none was ever

Le Bucentaure, *Villeneuve's flagship at Trafalgar.* (Musée de la Marine, Paris)

captured during the entire period. The 110-gun sail-of-the-line was almost reborn at the end of the war: four of shallow draught were being constructed at Antwerp in 1814, but these ships were broken up on the stocks by the allies and never finished.

France had been instrumental in the advancement of warship design and this was clearly shown by their early elimination of the weak 64-gun ship in favour of the 74-gun ship. More pointedly, the adoption of the later postwar standard 80-gun ship was almost entirely due to its general use by the French fleet who recognized its great advantages over the other standard line ships in use during the period. To get a better appreciation of this, one must know some of the details of French on-board artillery. The French pound of the period was significantly heavier than its English equivalent and this had always allowed the French to have heavier broadsides when two ships of the same type engaged one another.[7] This state of affairs lasted well into the 1790s when British designers tried to close the gap by introducing a 74-gun ship that mounted 24pdr cannon on her upper deck. While few of these ships were actually built (later classes mounted 18pdr cannon once again) this may well have provided the impetus for the French to begin concentrating on their 80-gun ships which already mounted 24pdrs on their upper decks. French 80-gun ships were fine vessels and were well known for their ability to absorb tremendous punishment;[8] virtually every ship of this type captured by the British was put back into service by them and one, the *Franklin* of 1797, became the basis for an entire class of British ships after the wars were over.[9] Given their armament, strength and excellent handling characteristics, the versatile French 80-gun ships were easily the best ships-of-the-line built during the entire Napoleonic Wars.

The 74-gun ship, the standard battleship of virtually every navy, had been the pride of the French fleet for many years. Fast and well armed, capable of taking and dishing out heavy damage, they formed the backbone of Napoleon's fleet during the entire period. These ships came in two distinct types. The first type was the standard deep water port '74' which made up the bulk of the fleet. The second type grew out of the need to build sail-of-the-line in ports whose depth was not entirely suitable for the task. These ships, called *petites modéles*, were shorter in length and drew slightly less water while keeping the same armament. The *petite modéle* 74-gun ship *Borée* was the test ship for this design and was completed at Toulon to the plans of Sané in 1805. Thenceforth, the ships of this type came out of Antwerp, Genoa and Venice.

The French Navy had one 64-gun ship in commission,

STRENGTH OF THE FRENCH NAVY 1792–1815

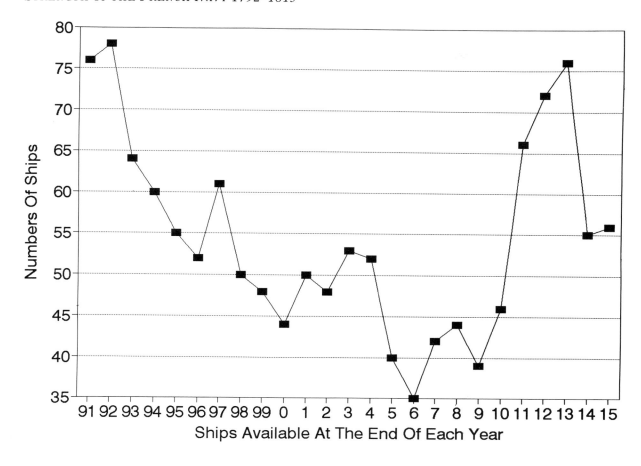

the *Brillant*, when the wars began and, though more would be captured and acquired during the period, this one small two-decker would be broken up by 1794. No other 64-gun ships were built for the French Navy.

Armaments of French Sail-of-the-Line

Table 2 details the armaments of French sail-of-the-line during the period. The last entry for each ship shows the additional carronades fitted during the early 1800s. Note that the number of cannon in the earlier ships more closely reflects the stated nominal number of guns of the class while in later vessels it bears no relation to them at all. For this reason, many histories list French 74-gun ships as 80 plus-gun ships which is true in the sense of number of guns but absolutely false when comparing ship types. Generally, French 80-gun ships displaced nearly 400 tons more than 74-gun ships.

Table 2: *ARMAMENTS OF FRENCH SAIL-OF-THE LINE*

Ship Type	36pdr	24pdr	18pdr	12pdr	8pdr	6pdr	36pdr carronades
118	32	34		34	18		4
118	32	34	34		14		12
110	30	32		32	16		
110	30	32		32	6		18
80	30	32		18			
80	30	32		14			14
74	28		30		16		
74	28		30		14		14
64		26		28		10	

La Ville de Marseille. (Watercolour by F Roux)

Le Friedland. (National Library of Canada)

Table 3: *SAIL-OF-THE-LINE OF THE FRENCH NAVY FROM 1792–1815*

Name	Built at	Guns	Launched	Fate	Known aliases
Achille	Brest	74	1778	L1794	
Achille	Rochefort	74	1804	L1805	
Agamemnon	Genoa	74	1812		
Aigle	Rochefort	74	1800	L1805	
Ajax	Rochefort	74	1806		
Albanais	Antwerp	74	1808	Article 15	
Alcide	Toulon	74	1782	L1795	
Alcide	Lorient	74	1807	L1809	1807 *D'Hautpoult*
Alexandre	Rochefort	74	1793		1793 *Jemmapes*
Alexandre	British	74	Captured 1794	L1795	
Algeciras	Lorient	74	1804	L1808	
Alliance	Spanish	74	Acquired 1799	B1807	Spanish *San Sebastian*
America	Brest	74	1788	L1794	
Amsterdam	Dutch	80	Acquired 1811	T1814	
Annibal	British	74	Captured 1801		
Anversois	Antwerp	74	1807		1814 *Eole*
					1815 *Anversois*
Apollon	Rochefort	74	1788	B1797	1794 *Gasparin*
					1795 *Apollon*
					1797 *Marceau*
Aquilon	Rochefort	74	1789	L1798	
Argonaute	Rochefort	74	1781	B1794	1794 *Flibustier*
Argonaute	Lorient	74	1798	T1806	
Athénien	Maltese	70	Captured 1798	L1800	Maltese *San Giovanni*
Atlas	Spanish	74	Acquired 1801	L1808	Spanish *Atalante*
Audacieux	Lorient	74	1784	B1802	
Audacieux	Antwerp	74	1807	Article 15	1807 *Pultusk*
Auguste	Brest	80	1778	W1795	1793 *Jacobin*
					1794 *Neuf Thermidor*
Auguste	Antwerp	80	1811	Article 15	
Austerlitz	Toulon	118	1808		
Banel	Venitien	64	Captured 1797	W1802	Venitien *Gloria*
Barra	Toulon	74	1794	L1798	1795 *Pegase*
					1797 *Hoche*
Berwick	British	74	Captured 1795	L1805	
Beyrand	Venitien	64	Captured 1797	W1799	
Borée	Lorient	74	1785	B1803	1794 *Ca Ira*
					1794 *Agricole*
Borée	Toulon	74	1805		
Brabant	Dutch	74	Aquired 1811	T1814	
Brave	Rochefort	74	1781	B1797	
Bretagne	Brest	110	1766	W1796	1793 *Révolutionnaire*
Brillant	Brest	64	1774	B1794	
Brutus	Lorient	74	1803	L1806	1803 *Impétueux*
Bucentaure	Toulon	80	1803	L1805	
Calcutta	British	54	Captured 1805	L1809	
Castiglione	Venice	74	1812	Article 15	
Causse	Venitien	64	Captured 1797	L1801	Venitien *Vulcano*
Censeur	Rochefort	74	1782	T1799	1799 *Alliance*
Centaure	Toulon	74	1782	L1793	
César	Antwerp	74	1807	Article 15	
Charlemagne	Antwerp	74	1807	Article 15	
Chatham	Dutch	80	Acquired 1811	Article 15	
Colosse	Toulon	74	1813		
Commerce de Bordeaux	Toulon	74	1785	L1798	1794 *Timoleon*
Commerce de Lyon	Antwerp	74	1807		
Commerce de Marseille	Toulon	118	1788	L1793	
Commerce de Paris	Toulon	110	1806		
Conquérant	Brest	74	1746	L1798	

Name	Built at	Guns	Launched	Fate	Known aliases
Conquérant	Spanish	74	Acquired 1802	P1807	Spanish *Conquistador*
Conquérant	Antwerp	80	1812		
Courageux	Lorient	74	1806		
Couronne	Brest	80	1749	L1795	1792 *Ca Ira*
Couronne	Dutch	74	Acquired 1813	T1813	
Dalmate	Antwerp	74	1808		1814 *Hector*
					1815 *Dalmate*
Danube	Toulon	74	1808		
Dauphin Royal	Toulon	118	1791	L1798	1792 *Sans Culotte*
					1795 *Orient*
Dego	Maltese	64	Captured 1798	L1800	Maltese *Zacharie*
Desaix	Spanish	74	Acquired 1802	B1804	Spanish *Pelayo*
Destin	Toulon	74	1777	L1793	
Deux Frères	?	80	1784	L1794	1792 *Juste*
Diadème	Brest	74	1756	B1793	1792 *Brutus*
Diadème	Lorient	80	1811		
Dictateur	?	74	1781	L1793	1792 *Liberté*
Dix Août	Lorient	74	1795	L1806	1795 *Cassard*
					1798 *Dix Août*
					1803 *Brave*
Doggerbanck	Dutch	64	Acquired 1811	T1814	
Donawerth	Toulon	80	1808		
Droits de l'homme	Lorient	74	1794	L1797	
Dubois	Venitien	64	Captured 1797	B1800	Venitien *Fama*
Duc de Bourgogne	Rochefort	80	1751	B1800	1792 *Peuple*
					1794 *Caton*
Duguay Trouin	Brest	74	1788	L1793	
Duguay Trouin	Rochefort	74	1800	L1805	
Duguay Trouin	Cherbourg	74	1813		
Duguesclin	Antwerp	74	1807		
Duquesne	Toulon	74	1788	L1803	
Duquesne	Russian	74	Acquired 1809	S1811	Russian *Moscow*
Entreprenant	Lorient	74	1787	B1802	
Eole	Brest	74	1788	B1806	
Etats de Bourgogne	Brest	118	1790		1793 *Côte d'Or*
					1793 *Montagne*
					1795 *Peuple*
					1795 *Ocean*
Evertsen	Dutch	80	Acquired 1811	T1814	
Expérimente	British	50	Captured 1779	B1795	
Ferme	?	74	1785	L1793	1792 *Phocion*
Formidable	Toulon	80	1794	L1805	1794 *Figuières*
					1795 *Formidable*
Foudroyant	Rochefort	80	1799		1797 *Dix huit Fructidor*
					1800 *Foudroyant*
Fougueux	Lorient	74	1784	L1805	
Franklin	Toulon	80	1797	L1798	
Frontin	Venitien	64	Captured 1797	B1806	Venitien *Medea*
Gaulois	Antwerp	74	1812		
Généréux	Rochefort	74	1785	L1800	
Genois	Genoa	74	1805		
Glorieux	Lorient	74	1808		1807 *Polanais*
					1814 *Lys*
					1815 *Polonais*
Guerrier	Toulon	74	1753	L1798	
Guillaume Tell	Toulon	80	1795	L1800	
Hercule	Rochefort	74	1778	B1797	1794 *Hydre*
Hercule	Lorient	74	1797	L1798	
Héros	Toulon	74	1778	L1793	
Héros	Rochefort	74	1801	L1808	

Name	Built at	Guns	Launched	Fate	Known aliases
Héros	Toulon	118	1813		
Heureux	Toulon	74	1782	L1798	
Hollandais	Dutch	80	Acquired 1811	Article 15	
Illustre	Rochefort	74	1781	W1796	1794 *Scevola*
Illustre	Antwerp	74	1807		1807 *Dantzick*
					1814 *Achille*
Illustre	Antwerp	80	1810	Article 15	1807 *Friedland*
Illustre	Antwerp	80	1811		
Impérial	Toulon	118	1811		1814 *Royal Louis*
					1815 *Impérial*
Impétueux	?	74	1788	L1794	
Indivisible	Brest	80	1799	L1806	1803 *Alexandre*
Indomptable	Brest	80	1788	W1805	
Inflexible	Lorient	74	1809	W1814	1807 *Golymin*
Intrépide	Spanish	74	Acquired 1801	L1805	Spanish *Intrepido*
Invincible	Rochefort	110	1780	B1808	
Jean Bart	Lorient	74	1788	W1809	
Jean-Jacques Rousseau	Toulon	74	1795	L1806	1802 *Marengo*
Jean de Witt	Dutch	64	Acquired 1811	T1814	
Jupiter	Brest	74	1789	B1807	1794 *Montagnard*
					1795 *Democrate*
					1795 *Jupiter*
					1797 *Batave*
Kremlin	Toulon	74	1815		1814 *Provence*
					1815 *Hercule*
La Harpe	Venitien	74	Captured 1797	L1799	
Languedoc	Toulon	80	1766	B1799	1794 *Anti-fédéraliste*
					1795 *Victoire*
Léander	British	50	Captured 1798	L1799	
Léopard	?	74	1787	W1793	
Lion	Brest	74	1794	L1795	1793 *Marat*
					1795 *Formidable*
Lion	Brest	74	1803		1795 *Glorieux*
					1798 *Cassard*
Lion	Rochefort	74	1804	L1809	
Lys	Rochefort	74	1785	L1793	1792 *Tricolore*
Magnanime	Rochefort	74	1803		
Magnanime	Brest	74	1803		1798 *Quatorze Juillet*
					1802 *Veteran*
Magnifique	Lorient	80	1814		
Majestueux	Toulon	110	1780	B1809	1797 *Républicain*
Marengo	Lorient	74	1810		
Marseillais	Toulon	74	1766	L1794	1794 *Vengeur du Peuple*
Mercure	Toulon	74	1783	L1798	
Monarque	Toulon	118	1810		1810 *Wagram*
Mont St Bernard	Venice	74	1811	Article 15	
Montebello	Toulon	118	1812		
Neptune	Brest	74	1778	W1795	
Neptune	Toulon	80	1803	L1808	
Nestor	Brest	74	1792	L1809	1797 *Cisalpin*
					1803 *Aquilon*
Nestor	Brest	74	1810		
Northumberland	Brest	74	1780	L1794	
Orion	Rochefort	74	1786	B1804	1793 *Mucius*
Orion	Brest	74	1813		
Pacificateur	Antwerp	80	1811		
Patriote	Brest	74	1785		
Peuple	Brest	118	1803	L1806	1794 *Vengeur*
					1805 *Impérial*
Piet-bien	Dutch	74	Acquired 1813	T1813	

Name	Built at	Guns	Launched	Fate	Known aliases
Pluton	Rochefort	74	1778	B1805	1797 *Dugommier*
Pluton	Toulon	74	1805	L1808	
Pompée	Toulon	74	1791	L1793	
Prince	Dutch	80	Acquired 1811	T1813	*Prince Royal*
Puissant	?	74	1782	L1793	
Pyrrhus	Rochefort	74	1791	L1805	1793 *Mont Blanc*
					1794 *Trente et un Mai*
					1795 *Républicain*
					1796 *Mont Blanc*
Quatorze Juillet	Lorient	74	1798	L1798	
Regulus	Lorient	74	1805	L1814	
République Français	Rochefort	118	1802		1803 *Majestueux*
Rivoli	Venice	74	1810	L1812	
Robert	Venitien	64	Captured 1797	B1804	Venitien *Eolo*
Robuste	Toulon	80	1806	L1809	
Romulus	Toulon	74	1812		
Rotterdam	Dutch	64	Acquired 1811	T1814	
Royal Louis	Brest	110	1780	W1794	1792 *Républicain*
Ruyter	Dutch	64	Acquired 1811	T1814	
Saint Esprit	Brest	80	1765	W1795	1794 *Scipion*
Sandos	Venitien	64	Captured 1797	B1798	Venitien *San Georgio*
Sans Pareil	Brest	80	1793	L1794	
Saturne	Lorient	80	1807		1807 *Eylau*
Sceptre	Brest	74	1780	B1802	1792 *Convention*
					1800 *Marengo*
Sceptre	Toulon	80	1810		
Scipion	?	74	1790	L1793	
Scipion	Lorient	74	1801	L1805	
Scipion	Genoa	74	1813		
Séduisant	Toulon	74	1783	W1796	1793 *Pelletier*
					1795 *Séduisant*
Souverain	Toulon	74	1757	L1798	1793 *Peuple Souverain*
Spartiate	Toulon	74	1797	L1798	
St Antoine	Spanish	74	Acquired 1801	L1801	Spanish *San Antonio*
St Pierre	Russian	74	Acquired 1809	B1814	Russian *St Peter*
Stengel	Venitien	64	Captured 1797	L1799	
Suffisant	Toulon	74	1782	L1793	
Suffren	Brest	74	1789	L1805	1794 *Redoutable*
Suffren	Lorient	74	1803		
Superbe	Brest	74	1784	W1795	
Superbe	Genoa	74	1808		1807 *Breslaw*
Superbe	Antwerp	74	1814		
Swiftsure	British	74	Captured 1801	L1805	
Téméraire	Brest	74	1782	B1803	
Terrible	Toulon	110	1780	B1804	
Themistocle	Lorient	74	1791	L1793	
Thésée	Rochefort	74	1790	P1805	1793 *Révolution*
					1803 *Finisterre*
Théséee	Antwerp	74	1807		1807 *Ville de Berlin*
					1814 *Atlas*
					1815 *Ville de Berlin*
Tigre	Brest	74	1793	L1795	
Tilsitt	Antwerp	80	1810	Article 15	
Tonnant	Toulon	80	1787	L1798	
Tonnant	Rochefort	80	1808	L1809	1808 *Ville de Varsovie*
Tonnerre	Brest	74	1808	L1809	
Tourville	Lorient	74	1788		
Trajan	Lorient	74	1788	B1805	1797 *Gaulois*
Trajan	Antwerp	74	1811		
Trident	Toulon	74	1811		

Name	Built at	Guns	Launched	Fate	Known aliases
Triomphant	Toulon	80	1779	L1793	
Triomphant	Rochefort	74	1809		
Tromp	Dutch	64	Acquired 1811	Article 15	
Tyrannicide	Lorient	74	1792	W1802	1800 *Desaix*
Ulm	Toulon	74	1809		
Ulysse	Spanish	74	Acquired 1801	S1814	Spanish *San Genaro* 1811 *Tourville*
Union	Lorient	74	1799	L1806	1803 *Diomede*
Utrecht	Dutch	64	Acquired 1811	B1813	
Vencedor	Spanish	74	Acquired 1806	L1808	Spanish *Vencedor* 1807 *Argonaute*
Vengeur	Brest	74	1789	W1793	
Viala	Lorient	74	1795	L1806	1795 *Voltaire* 1795 *Constitution* 1803 *Jupiter*
Victorieux	Rochefort	110	1814		1807 *Iena* 1814 *Duc d'Angoulême* 1815 *Iena*
Ville de Marseille	Toulon	74	1812		
Wattigny	Lorient	74	1794	B1809	
Zélandais	Cherbourg	80	1813		1814 *Duquesne* 1815 *Zélandais*
Zèle	Toulon	74	1763	P1805	
Zoutman	Dutch	80	Acquired 1811	T1814	*Amiral Zoutman*

Legend:
Article 15: Ships taken away due to the peace treaty in 1814

B:	Broken up	P:	Prison ship	T:	Transfer of ownership
L:	Lost in battle	S:	School ship	W:	Wrecked

Notes:
Some name changes occurred before the ship was finished.
Name changes in 1815 reflect Napoleon's return from Elba in March of that year.

Notes

[1] This state of affairs was to last well into the years of the Empire.

[2] It is interesting to note that this was not the first time the officer corps had been 'shaken up' but it would be the last time during the wars.

[3] Of the twenty-six captains serving at the 'Glorious First Of June' in 1794, eleven of them had never been any form of officer aboard a warship and many of the others, including Contre-Amiral Villaret-Joyeuse, had been lieutenants only a few years previously.

[4] The multiple frigate action at Grand Port in 1810 was the one clear French naval victory of the entire war.

[5] Both these men were marshals of France and were to lead brilliant careers on the continent.

[6] The *Commerce de Marseille*, captured intact at Toulon in 1794, impressed her captors considerably and was declared a fine sailing vessel, especially easy to handle for her size.

[7] As an example, the French 36pdr shot weighed nearly 39 English pounds.

[8] The *Tonnant*, lost at the Nile in 1798, was a good example of a very badly battered ship which nevertheless served her captors well in the years ahead.

[9] The *Canopus* class of ships was designed to the lines of the *Franklin*.

Bibliography

France: *Archives Nationales*, Paris. Cartons BB5-6, BB5-11 and BB5-223 provided the bulk of the information found in the fleet list.

Chartrand, René, *Napoleon's Sea Soldiers*, Osprey Publishing Ltd, (London 1990).

Elting, John R, *Swords around a Throne: Napoleon's Grande Armée,* The Free Press, (New York 1988).

Hampson, F, *La marine de l'an II,* (Paris 1960).

James, William M, *The Naval History of Great Britain,* (London 1837).

Jenkins, E H, *A History of the French Navy,* Macdonald and Jane's, (London 1973).

Lavery, Brian, *The Ship of the Line,* Conway Maritime Press Ltd, (London 1983).

Neptunia, Nos 102 and 142.

Vichot, Jacques, *Repertoire des navires de guerre français,* Association des Amis des Musées de la Marine, (Paris 1967).

THE SWEDISH MONITORS

In the mid nineteenth century, as a result of the activities of foreign fleets in the Baltic during the Crimean War and a constant fear of Russian expansionism, Sweden carried out a review of its defence forces. The leading strategists of 1860 criticised the existing and overrated system of central defence, based on the Karlsborg fortress on Lake Vätter (over 200 kilometres from Stockholm), and held that the nation's defences ought to begin at the country's coastal land frontiers. Daniel G Harris examines the effects of this change in strategic thinking on the development of the Swedish Navy and, in particular, its adoption of the Ericsson monitor.

In 1861, parliament[1] set up a special committee to determine the state of the fleet in Karlskrona and Stockholm. That committee found that 'the fleet consists of vessels belonging to a bygone age – it includes two hundred rowing craft.' The committee recommended that the fleet should consist entirely of steam vessels and that armoured ships should be included. The special committee's 1862 report to parliament proposed that the Navy's responsibilities should be:

1. To provide coast defence and to carry out warlike activities beyond the coast.
2. To be a strong and modern defence force suitable for operations in the Swedish skerries and large lakes.
3. To assist in the blockade of enemy ports, uphold respect for the Swedish flag in distant waters, assist Swedish merchant vessels when needed, and to train naval personnel.
4. To aid defence by moving troops quickly from one place to another and in support operations requiring rapid deployment.

To meet these requirements, the committee recommended that the fleet should consist of steam frigates for offshore defence, steam corvettes for trade protection, steam schooners to act as troop transports, and iron steam-gunboats for inshore defence. Moreover, it concluded that sailing ships had no value as warships and that all new vessels should be built of iron. The 1862–63 Parliamentary Defence Committee agreed and decided that all vessels should be steam-powered, have 4½in armour and be built of iron.

The news of the success in action of John Ericsson's *Monitor* against the rebel states *Virginia* (ex-*Merrimac*) aroused much interest in Sweden as this new type of vessel, with its small target area, rotating turret and no rigging, seemed ideal for the country's inshore defence. One Scandinavian defence expert wrote that the monitor-type vessel was a 'David able to defeat Goliath' – including frigates and ships-of-the-line.

The Swedish *Royal Society for Naval Science's*[2] journal for 1862 noted the *Monitor* action and suggested that America now challenged the naval supremacy of Britain and France. The journal compared Stevens battery, a 400ft iron vessel, protected with 1½in–6½in plate, armed with two 20in and five other guns and propelled by an 860hp engine, which was begun in America in 1854 but never completed, with Cowper Coles' turret vessel and Ericsson's *Monitor*. It dismissed the Stevens vessel as impractical, found Coles' proposals practical but held that the Ericsson vessel, with its 18in freeboard, heavy armour and 15in guns firing 252kg projectiles, would be ideal for coast defence. In addition, it estimated the cost of the monitor-type craft would only be 600,000 *riksdaler*. The author, Captain K Adlersparre, considered that armoured frigates, similar to those under construction in France and Italy, presented too large a target and would be unseaworthy. He also believed that vessels with rotating turrets and 15in guns could severely damage ironclads like the French *La Gloire*.[3]

The New Ships

John Ericsson,[4] born in 1803, had served in the Swedish Army and had acquired recognition for his fine mechanical drawings. He designed a steam locomotive for the 1829 Rainhill trials and received part of the British Admiralty prize for inventing the screw propeller. Ericsson emigrated to the United States in 1839 and set up an engineering business, specialising in iron ships. Although he became an American citizen in 1848, he offered his services to Sweden at the time of the Crimean War. The American government accepted the Ericsson-designed turret vessel in 1861–62 and this became the prototype for

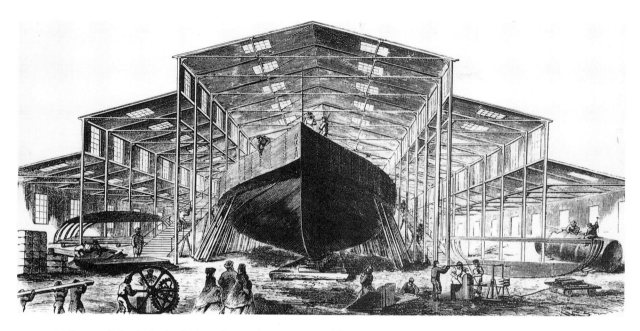

The monitor John Ericsson *on the stocks at the Motala Yard in 1865*. (Sjöhistoriska Museet, Stockholm)

many similar craft built in both America and northern Europe. Ericsson, in a letter dated 6 June 1862, to the Swedish Minister for the Navy, wrote:

> Should you decide to build gunboats of the *Monitor* type, may I contribute in the implementation of such plans. I need to know about the principal dimensions of any planned vessels. Sweden's coasts will be better defended by *Monitor*-type vessels than by costly frigates. Sweden has the richest ore for making iron.

Early in 1862, before the receipt of Ericsson's offer, Deputy Minister C Ehnemark had instructed Captain K Adlersparre, then visiting America in the frigate *Nörrköping*, 'to obtain draughts of the Ericsson batteries while his ship was visiting Boston.' The Deputy Minister reminded Adlersparre that, following the *Monitor*-

Virginia engagement, 'the rowing fleet is useless to defend the Skerries – even as floating batteries'. Adlersparre visited Ericsson in New York on 14 April 1862 and, as a result of his report, parliament released funds to enable J C A d'Ailly,[5] of the Naval Construction Corps, to visit America and meet both Ericsson and the Secretary of the US Navy. In July, d'Ailly arrived in New York and duly met Ericsson.

In his first report,[6] dated 26 September 1862, d'Ailly wrote:

The John Ericsson *at anchor in the Stockholm Skerries in 1867*. (Sjöhistoriska Museet, Stockholm)

A model of John Ericsson *showing the modifications made to the monitor in 1877.* (Sjöhistoriska Museet, Stockholm)

there is great confidence in the vessels designed by Captain Ericsson and now building here. One would have thought that more time on experiments would have been necessary but the *Merrimac* affair has proved that all navies must consist of ironclad vessels . . . A committee asked American engineers to submit plans for suitable armoured vessels – many were received but none were equal to those of John Ericsson. He has held back no details from me. A special group of engineers tested USS *Monitor* and, after trials, gave glowing reports. Several of this type are now under construction. I attach a list, and a drawing of a new, so-called, *River Monitor.*

D'Ailly continued:

Special care is necessary in the relationship between Captain Ericsson and myself. I have to copy each drawing personally and that takes most of my time. I shall, under Captain Ericsson's direction, design a gunboat suitable for Sweden; for that I need particulars of the locks giving access to Lake Malar.

D'Ailly also described a visit to Philadelphia, to see the new frigate *Ironsides* and discussed the recoil problems of the Dahlgren and Parrot guns. He attached a list of eight Ericsson-designed *Monitor*s and stated that '31 vessels now building will have Ericsson-type turrets; 19 of these are *Monitor*s.'

D'Ailly's later dispatches, of 21 October and 27 November 1862, described visits to mills for rolling armour plate and casting guns. In addition, he gave particulars of the *Dictator*, building in New York, which was to have 2ft freeboard and 10in armour. The armour consisted of six 1in rolled plates covered by 4in forged plates and backed by 12in oak. The vessel's engines were 8000ihp to give a speed of 14kts, and she could carry 1000 tons of coal. The builder believed that *Dictator* could easily cross the Atlantic.

D'Ailly's December 1862 report covers the Ericsson shallow draught (6ft) *Monitor*s fitted with turrets. The hulls were to have elliptical, rounded bows and sterns, were to be wall-sided and have flat bottoms. The armour was to consist of three layers of 1in iron plates bolted to a timber backing. They were to have twin screw propulsion and were intended for river service. During January 1863, d'Ailly was present at the launch of the *Keokuk*, a 159ft vessel which 'lies in the water like a *Monitor*'.

D'Ailly's last dispatch of 27 January 1863 describes the *Monitor*'s loss off Cape Hatteras. He wrote:

the loss has caused some pause in the construction of new gunboats. Possibly it is because the form of the hulls is so different from that of ordinary ships – safety from shells was the most important feature. However, the similar gunboats, *Weehawkin* and *Nahant*, rode out the storm. The design intends that the sea should roll over the decks but, in the most severe weather, it is important that the seas do not reach the turrets' tops. Changes are being made in the *Dictator* and *Puritan* as a result of the *Monitor*'s loss.

D'Ailly returned to Sweden with sets of drawings prepared under Ericsson's direction. The American Naval Secretary raised no objection to Sweden having the particulars of the revolving turret but he had refused to allow Denmark access to the same technical data.[7] Consequently, Denmark's first turret ship, *Rolf Krake* built by Napiers in Britain, had Coles turrets. The Deputy Minister wrote to Ericsson on 27 July 1863, expressing his 'special recognition for the willingness and frankness shown to d'Ailly concerning the design and construction of the monitors that you have invented'.

The Fleet's Reorganization

In July 1862, Baltzar J von Platen[8] became head of the Navy Department. He was determined to divide the Navy into two separate forces; one to defend the coast and outer Skerries, the other, to be called the Royal Skerry Artillery, to defend the inner leads and lakes. The outer fleet was to include fast steam corvettes and, if the monitor system was developed, armoured turret ships. The Royal Skerry Artillery was to have shallow draught, armoured, steam vessels able to pass through the Göta canal system,[9] and small craft to move artillery. The steam vessels were to provide flank defence to the Karlsborg fortress and defend Göteborg and Stockholm. The last act of the old four-estates parliament approved Platen's reorganization plans in 1865. This unfortunate division of naval forces, opposed by the press, was to last until 1873. Among the extraordinary results were that the outer fleet retained responsibility for pilotage services but the new force was to carry out all the hydrographical surveys!

In September 1863, the Board of Naval Administration filed the drawings and specifications, prepared by d'Ailly under Ericsson's supervision, with the Navy Minister. Although the *Monitor*'s loss had raised some doubts about the seakeeping qualities of these new ships, the Minister obtained parliamentary approval to release funds for the construction of three (later increased to four) turret vessels. At about the same time, the Norwegian government agreed to purchase a similar turret ship, to be built by the same yard as that chosen for the Swedish ships.

When the Navy Minister authorised the Naval Board of Administration to obtain tenders for the new ships, his instructions were that they were not to simply accept the lowest bid but must choose a shipyard known for quality workmanship and with experience in iron construction. The Motala yard at Nörrköping fulfilled these requirements and, in February 1864, the Crown and Motala signed a 290-page contract for the first three ships. At the same time, the Minister instructed the Karlskrona Royal Dockyard to dismiss all personnel qualified only in the construction of wooden vessels.

In 1864, the Crown set up an open design competition for an armoured craft suitable for the defence of the inner Skerries and Lakes. It decided none of the competitors' proposals met the requirements (but, nonetheless, paid out some prize money) and instead the Navy Minister instructed the Corps of Naval Constructors to design suitable vessels.

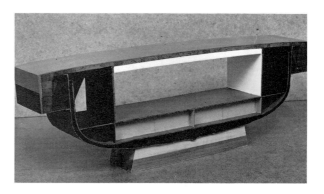

Model showing the midship section of the John Ericsson *class monitors*. (Sjöhistoriska Museet, Stockholm)

The Large Monitors

Following the launch of the *John Ericsson*, the first of the four large turret vessels – now officially designated monitors – in March 1865, Platen made a special report to parliament to correct alleged 'misinformation appearing in the press'. The report described the vessel's construction in detail as follows:

> The hull is broad amidships and narrow at the bow and stern. The keel is made of 0.65in iron plate bent in the form of a channel; wide enough for double riveting of the lowest plates and frames. The forward end of the keel has the same form as the stem post which is made of forged iron 2.5in thick. The stern post has the same form as the stem post and is of forged iron 2.57in thick. The frames are fitted with 3.3in x 2.9in flanges strengthened by floor plates and are 1.5ft apart. The width of the frames varies from 6in to 7in and their edges are strengthened by double-angle brackets. The space

The John Ericsson *in 1891, with her new superstructure and the turret converted into a barbette.* (Sjöhistoriska Museet, Stockholm)

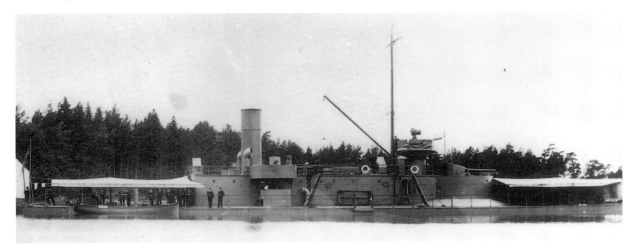

below the orlop deck is strengthened by cross plates. The outer skin is of 0.42in plate. The deck beams are generally of 10in square oak, with 2ft spaces between them, but heavier beams support the armoured funnel. The deck planking is of 6in pine – or oak when available. The vessels will have 8 watertight bulkheads. The stern has a 20ft overhang to protect the propeller and the rudder – the under body has a whale form to provide an air cushion to facilitate launching. Motala has forged two Trotman anchors for each hull. Each vessel will have 450ft of chain, also forged by Motala.

The Turrets and Conning Towers The Ericsson-designed turrets for the Swedish and Norwegian monitors had an inner diameter of 6.4m (21ft) and a height of 2.74m (9ft). The Navy Minister's 1866 report to parliament described the turret's operating mechanism as follows:

The Ericsson turret is located 22ft ahead of the vessel's midships. It revolves around a fixed forged iron shaft 8–10in in diameter. The machinery that turns the turret comprises a gear train just below the turret floor. This is driven by two 17ihp steam engines, placed at right angles to each other and driving a common crank, in the after section of the turret's lower compartment. A gear at the end of the crank shaft drives, through gearing, a vertical shaft which passes through the turret chamber to a point just above the deck beams. The upper end of this shaft has a pinion that drives on the rim of a 10ft 6in diameter, toothed wheel which is fixed to the central shaft of the turret. Levers, on each side of the turret, open or close each engine's valves when movement is required.

The turrets' interiors were lined to a height of 1.22m (4ft) with mattresses as protection against splinters. The conning tower, above the turret, was 1.83m (6ft) in diameter and was protected by layers of forged iron plates with a total thickness of 225mm (8.9in). This also had a

A model of the 15in Dahlgren gun fitted in John Ericsson. (Sjöhistoriska Museet, Stockholm)

Table 1: *PARTICULARS OF* JOHN ERICSSON *CLASS MONITORS*

Full load displacement:	*John Ericsson* 1522 tons; *Thordön* 1501 tons; *Tirfing* 1511 tons; *Loke* 1594 tons
Dimensions:	60.88m (oa) × 13.54m (max) × 3.4m (199ft 9in × 44ft 5in × 11ft 1in); *Loke* 64.4m (oa) × 13.47m (max) × 3.6m (205ft × 44ft 2in × 11ft 10in)
Machinery:	2, fire-tube boilers; twin-cylinder, horizontal trunk engine (87cm dia pistons × 47.75cm stroke, 34.23in × 18.8in); 380ihp = 6.5kts (des), 7.5kts (max, trials); single 4-bladed propeller, 3.75m (12.32ft) dia
Auxiliary machinery:	9hp steam engine for ventilation fans; 5hp steam engine for vacuum pump (not in *Loke*); steam-operated bilge pump in engine room; steam-operated centrifugal pump in turret chamber
Coal stowage:	110 tons
Endurance:	6 days at 6.5kts (max radius of action = 950nm)
Armament (as completed):	*John Ericsson* 2 × 15in SB, ML; *Thordön* and *Tirfing* 2 × 26.7cm SB, ML; *Loke* 2 × 24cm BLR
Armour:	124mm (4.9in) belt; 2.6mm (0.85in) deck; 120mm (4.7in) funnel – to 50% of height; 270mm (10.6in) turret walls (381mm side and 447mm face in *Loke*), 127mm (5in) turret roof and base; 225mm (8.9in) CT
Complement:	5 officers; 6 WOs; 1 surgeon; 5 engine room personnel; 63 other ranks. Total 80 (increased to 104 by 1904)

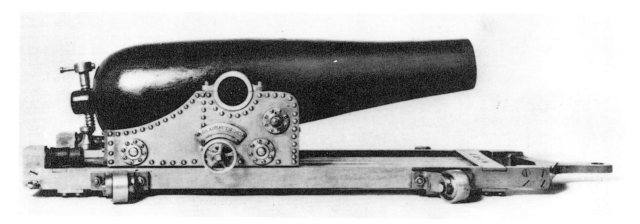

lining of mattresses to give splinter protection. A hatch in the floor gave access to the turret.

Armament In 1865 two 15in smooth bore Dahlgren ML (muzzle loading) guns, given to Sweden by John Ericsson, were transported from New York to Nörrköping in the frigate *Vanadis*. The guns were exempted from customs duty by special legislation and were mounted in the monitor bearing Ericsson's name by the Motala Yard. The total weight of the turret and guns was about 220 tons.

After firing, the guns recoiled into the turret for reloading and the gun-ports were closed with forged iron doors; smoke was cleared from the turret by steam-operated ventilation fans. These guns were obsolete by 1865 and firing trials proved that they could not penetrate the stone walls of the old Vaxholm fortress at a range of about 200m (219yds). In 1881, two 24cm (9.4in) BLRs (breech-loading rifles) replaced the Dahlgrens which became part of the Ericsson monument at Filipstad. In 1894, the 24cm guns were, in turn, replaced by two 15cm (5.9in) guns, mounted on a turntable and arranged to fire over the turret walls – *en barbette*. In 1877, two 12mm (0.47in) ten-barrel machine guns had been mounted on the superstructure (the superstructure was added in stages, between 1867 and 1880) and in 1881 these were replaced by two 25mm (1in) guns. In 1895, six 57mm (2.24in) Nordenfelt guns and a searchlight were mounted on the superstructure.

Machinery The design of the propulsion machinery was prepared by Ericsson himself and the trunk engines included an oscillating lever of his own design.[10] The *John Ericsson* class monitors could carry 110 tons of coal which was sufficient for six days steaming at 6.5kts. The contract speed was 6.5kts and the highest speed reached on trials was 7.5kts. The only change to the engine room during the vessels' service was the installation of ash chutes in the 1870s.

The Sister Vessels Motala laid down two sister monitors, *Thordön* and *Tirfing*, in 1864 and delivered them in 1866–67. Motala had contracted to build the two vessels for 864,285 and 881,337 kronor respectively. Their

The Norwegian monitor Mjølner *in 1906, showing her final appearance.* (Courtesy Captain S Moen, RNorN Horten)

original armament was two turret-mounted 26.7cm (10.5in) smooth-bore, ML guns but, in 1869, these were replaced with 24cm (9.4in) BLRs. During 1892–95, two 12cm (4.7in) QF (quick firing) guns displaced the 24cm. Both ships originally had the same number and type of machine guns as *John Ericsson*. The installation of flying bridges and superstructures in 1902–05 enabled the addition of eight lighter guns: 47mm (1.85in) on *Thordön* and 57mm (2.24in) on *Tirfing*. Both vessels received two 60cm (24in) searchlights.

Motala contracted to build the fourth of the class, *Loke*, for 1,200,422 kronor in 1867, but did not complete the vessel until 1871. She was generally similar to the earlier vessels but displaced 1594 tons and had dimensions of 62.79m (206ft) oa x 13.82m (45ft 4in) max x 3.7m (12ft 2in). Other variations included the omission of the vacuum pump for the machinery and the increase in the turret armour to 381mm (15in) on the sides and 447mm (17.6in) on the front. The initial armament of two 24cm (9.4in) guns was replaced by a later mark in 1882 and she was fitted with the same type of machine guns as *John Ericsson*.

The Norwegian Sister: KNS Mjølner In 1867, the Norwegian parliament authorised the construction of a monitor by Motala's Nörrköping yard at a cost of 1,102,000 Norwegian kronor. This vessel, *Mjølner*, had the same dimensions, armour and machinery as the *John Ericsson*.[11] She was launched in 1868 and delivered on 7 September the same year. The armament in 1868 consisted of two 27cm (10.6in) MLR and one 8cm (3.15in) guns.[12] Two 12cm (4.7in) QF Cockerill guns, with Nordenfelt's screw breech, replaced the 27cm guns in 1897 when the turret was cut down to form a barbette. In the same year, two 12.4cm (4.9in) and two 65mm (2.6in) Cockerill guns, and two 37mm (1.46in) Hotchkiss revolver guns were mounted on the superstructure. The addition of a supply and secretariat officer increased the complement to eighty-one.

A hull model for the inshore monitor Garmer.
(Sjöhistoriska Museet, Stockholm)

Service Careers During 1867, *John Ericsson* underwent a refit that included the construction of a platform and superstructure between the turret and the funnel (on which the 57mm Nordenfelt guns were to be mounted in 1895).

In July 1867, the *John Ericsson, Thordön* and *Tirfing*, together with the Norwegian monitor *Skorpion* and the steam frigates *Vanadis* and *Thor*, left Stockholm for Helsingfors and Kronstadt under the command of Vice-Admiral C A Sundin.[13] On 17 July, Prince Oscar (later King Oscar II) inspected all the vessels and observed gun trials in the Stockholm Skerries. The group sailed for Helsingfors and Russia on 24 July. A Royal command (No 242 of 20 June 1867) required that the squadron stay five days in Helsingfors and twelve in Kronstadt. In addition, on arrival in Kronstadt, the Admiral was to obtain permission to moor the monitors in the inner harbour or alongside a mole. The ships arrived at Kronstadt on 3 August and left on the 17th. During their stay, they were visited by the Grand Duke Konstantin for two and a half hours (the Russians had already built the *Latnik* class monitors, based on American plans, prior to the Scandinavian visit). This was the only 'foreign voyage' made by the three vessels as, before 1905, visits to Norwegian waters, made for joint exercise purposes, were not considered voyages to foreign waters.

John Ericsson's later career was uneventful; she was part of the Karlskrona local defence force during 1913–18 and, in 1919, the Gotland Cement Company purchased the hull for conversion to a barge; she was still in that service some forty years later.

Thordön grounded and sank in the outer Skerries in July 1883, although part of the bow remained above water. The Neptune Salvage Company (which was to become famous some eighty years later for the raising of the *Wasa*) was able to raise her and, after temporary repairs, she was able to make the voyage to Karlskrona for a more extensive refit under her own power. The subsequent court-martial ended in *Thordön*'s commander being ordered to pay the costs of the salvage and repairs, despite the fact that the unfortunate officer was able to prove the grounding was caused by a misplaced spar buoy (some senior officers resigned in protest at the court's sentence).

The vessel was part of the local defence force for Göteborg during the 1914–18 war and was sold for scrap, for £2500, in 1922. *Tirfing*'s career, apart from the visits to Finland and Russia, was uneventful. She had a major refit in 1902 and during the First World War was stationed in the Göteborg Skerries. She was scrapped in 1922. After completion in 1871 *Loke*, for reasons that are obscure, was seldom in commission. She was laid up from 1880 to 1908 and then sold for scrapping.

The Norwegian *Mjølner* made occasional visits to the Swedish west coast ports during the 1870s and King Karl XV made a 3hr visit to her on one occasion. Thereafter, her services were confined to Oslo fjord. The Stavanger Shipbreaking Company dismantled her hull in 1909.

The Inshore Fleet: the Royal Skerry Artillery Monitors

In 1865, Baltzar Platen successfully persuaded the old estates general to establish a new force that was to be part of the army. During the years 1868–73, this new force consisted of ten small monitors whose purpose was to defend the inner waters and to act as a flank defence for the fortresses.

The first of these armoured vessels, *Garmer*, designed by Ericsson and d'Ailly, was the most curious of all those built. A report to parliament stated that the vessel had frames of forged iron, no keel, was flat-bottomed amidships and had a sharp bow and stern. In addition the deck extended about 3m over the stern to protect the

Table 2: *PARTICULARS OF* GARMER

Length (oa):	28.5m (93ft 6in)
Beam (max):	6.98m (22ft 11in)
Draught:	2.29m (7ft 6in)
Displacement (full load):	271 tons
Speed:	5.5kts
Armament:	1 × 26.7cm ML
Armour	
belt:	39mm (1.5in)
deck:	20mm (0.8in)
shield:	149mm (5.9in) face
CT:	208mm (8.2in)
Complement:	20 (2 officers, 4 WOs, 14 other ranks)

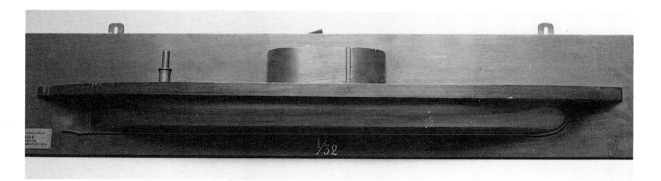

rudder and propeller. The intention was to employ *Garmer* as flank support to the Karlsborg fortress on Lake Vätter, and her small size enabled her to navigate the Göta canal system. Motala of Nörrköping launched the vessel in 1867 and delivered her in the following year.

Garmer's armament was one 26.7cm (10.5in) smoothbore, Ferlitsen system, ML gun made by Finspong, mounted in a cupola about 1.5m (4ft 11in) above the waterline. She was also fitted with a ten-barrel 12mm (0.47in) machine gun in 1877. She had a single boiler and a 90ihp steam engine, supplied from New York, designed for a contracted speed of 6kts but she made only 5.5kts on trials.

The *Royal Society of Naval Science*'s journal for 1878 describes the difficulties of operating *Garmer* as follows:

> The Commander is stationed inside a cupola and stands by the steering gear where he must control the vessel's movements at the same time as filling the touch hole and firing the gun. Sometimes there are difficulties with the engine. Since the gun is fixed, training is by the movement of the vessel.

Garmer became a naval unit on the abolition of the Royal Skerry Artillery in 1875 and was sold for scrap in 1893.

The second vessel built for inner defence was *Sköld*, designed by J C A d'Ailly, although John Ericsson had supplied the first draughts and a model. The iron-hulled vessel was built by Bergsund, Stockholm in 1868. The armament was originally a fixed 26.7cm (10.5in) gun, protected by an elliptical shield, but this was replaced in 1870 by a 24cm (9.4in) gun and a ten-barrel 12mm (0.47in) machine gun. John Ericsson designed, and had built in New York, a novel system of propulsion for *Sköld*. This,

Half model of the monitor Sköld. *Note the elliptical, fixed gun shield amidships, the single funnel aft and the raft hull.* (Sjöhistoriska Museet, Stockholm)

another of his many gifts to Sweden, consisted of a combined hand and steam-driven arrangement. In the vessel's stern, a row of six two-seat benches were positioned on each side of the propeller shaft. With a full crew of twenty-four men turning the shaft, by means of rowing levers and a crank, a maximum speed of about 1.5kts was possible and gave sufficient movement for training the gun. The steam plant, located close to the stern post, consisted of a large, semi-circular, fire-tube boiler, covered with heavy wooden lagging. The fire box and ash pit took up half the space at one side of the boiler, while a door to the smoke box gave access to the several hundred fire-tubes which occupied the other side. A horizontal steam cylinder and its slide valves were fitted to each side of the boiler and were cross-connected via a horizontal crankshaft which drove the propeller shaft through large bevel gears. The hand propulsion unit drove the propeller shaft via the same set of gears and was connected to the ends of the crankshaft. The maximum speed attained under steam was 4kts. Probably to the relief of *Sköld*'s crew, the hand-operating gear was removed early in the vessel's life. She became a naval unit in 1873, was placed in reserve in 1890 and was sunk as a target in 1907.

A model of the hand-driven propulsion system designed by John Ericsson for the Sköld *class – in its final form it differed in several details, including the number of benches.* (Sjöhistoriska Museet, Stockholm)

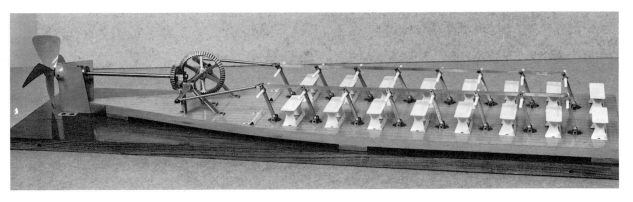

Table 3: *PARTICULARS OF SKÖLD CLASS*

	Sköld	Fenris
Length (oa):	31.93m (104ft 9in)	31.93m (104ft 9in)
Length (pp):	26.06m (85ft 6in)	28.8m (94ft 6in)
Beam (max):	6.81m (22ft 4in)	6.83m (22ft 5in)
Draught:	2.31m (7ft 7in)	2.31m (7ft 7in)
Displacement (full load):	250 tons	260 tons
Speed:	4kts	6kts
Armament:	1 × 26.7cm ML	1 × 24cm BL
Armour		
belt:	64mm (2.5in)	39mm (1.5in)
deck:	13mm (0.5in)	13mm (0.5in)
shield:	220mm (8.7in) face;	267mm (10.5in) face;
	93mm (3.7in) sides and rear	87mm (3.4in) sides and rear
CT:	178mm (7in)	205mm (8in)
Complement:	29 (designed for 40 with hand prop)	29 (designed for 36 with hand prop)

The third small monitor designed by d'Ailly was *Fenris*, which was also intended to navigate the Göta canal system. She was also designed with the hand propulsion system – although for only twenty men and with a different form of connection to the propeller shaft. Both Bergsund and Motala tendered for the vessel's construction but, after conflict arose between Motala and the Navy Department about material standards, the contract was placed with Bergsund, that laid down *Fenris* in 1870 and delivered her two years later.

As complete she mounted a single 24cm (9.4in) gun in a fixed shield, and a ten-barrel 12mm (0.47in) machine gun

Rear view of the combined boiler and two-cylinder engine designed by John Ericsson for the Sköld *and built in New York in 1870. Note the two large bevel gears, at the back of the boiler, which drove the propeller shaft and the hook-shaped arms at the ends of the crankshaft to which the levers from the hand-propulsion system were connected.* (Technical Museum, Stockholm)

was added in 1877. A single, fire-tube, boiler provided steam for a two-cylinder, half-trunk engine of 43ihp driving a single propeller for a maximum speed of 6kts. The vessel was sold in 1903 for conversion to a barge. Neither *Sköld* nor *Fenris* ever navigated the Göta canal system as units of either the Skerry Artillery Force or the Navy.

The Hildur *Class*

In January 1870, the head of the Navy Department, in a memorandum to the Minister, stressed the need for larger warships on Lake Mälar and in the Stockholm Skerries. These, he wrote, ought to have heavier armour than the three earlier vessels, be of monitor type and have more powerful engines. As a result, the Minister obtained parliamentary approval for the construction of two iron 'armoured vessels' to be named *Hildur* and *Gerda*. These were to be the first pair of a series of seven and were to be the last d'Ailly designs based on John Ericsson's proposals. The estimated cost for each ship was 210,000 riksdaler; Bergsund and Lindbergs of Stockholm laid the keels in the autumn of 1870 and delivered the two monitors in 1872. The original armament was a 24cm (9.4in) gun in a fixed elliptical shield plus a number of machine guns. In 1890, a 12cm (4.7in) QF gun and three 57mm (2.24in) pieces replaced the original armament. Two cylindrical boilers supplied steam to two Woolffs, twin cylinder, horizontal engines of 133ihp driving twin screws. The maximum speed attained was 8kts. In 1890 and 1908, both vessels underwent major reconstruction, which included the fitting of bow rudders, the replacement of the armoured decks (owing to the original wooden backings' rotting), and the erection of a 75mm (3in) armoured conning tower on the turret. At the same time, new galleys, ventilation and earth closets were added.

During *Hildur*'s gun trials in 1872, her 24cm shells succeeded in penetrating the Vaxholm fortress wall after firing three shots. *Hildur* and *Gerda* were discarded in 1919. *Hildur* became an oil barge, and *Gerda* was cut down and used as a moored torpedo-monitoring station until the mid 1930s.

In 1871, parliament authorized the construction of a further four small monitors, the *Ulf*, *Björn*, *Berserk* and *Solve*. Built by Motala, they were basically of the same design as *Hildur* except that they had bow rudders, and that the *Björn* and *Ulf* had a waterline belt of 95mm (3.74in) thickness. In addition, the Motala Verkstad provided them with more powerful machinery, which consisted of two twin-cylinder, horizontal engines of 155ihp driving twin propellers for a maximum speed of 8kts. All acquired a similar armament to *Hildur* after

Front view of the Sköld's *boiler/engine, showing the furnace on the right and the fire-tubes on the left.* (Technical Museum, Stockholm)

Table 4: *PARTICULARS OF* HILDUR *CLASS:* HILDUR, GERDA, ULF, BJÖRN, BERSERK, SÖLVE *AND* FOLKE

Full load displacement:	460 tons
Dimensions:	39.78m × 8.02m (max) × 2.7m, (130ft 6in × 26ft 4in × 8ft 10in)
Machinery:	2 shafts; 2 cylindrical boilers; two 2-cylinder horizontal steam engines; 155ihp (*Hildur* and *Gerda* 133ihp) = 8kts
Armament:	1 × 24cm BL
Armour	
belt:	76mm (3in) (*Folke* 76mm aft, 48mm for'd)
deck:	19mm (0.75in)
shield:	418mm (16.5in) face; 356mm (14in) sides;
CT:	254mm (10in)
Complement:	48 (*Hildur* and *Gerda* 42)

The Gerda, *as built, underway in the Stockholm Skerries in 1895.* (Göteborg Maritime Centre)

The hull structure in the engine room of Sölve. (Courtesy Mr C S Ohlsson, P Eng, Göteborg Maritime Centre)

reconstruction in the 1890s and the early 1900s. They were all placed on the sale list in 1919 and were subsequently converted to oil barges by their new owners. In 1992, the Göteborg Maritima Centrum acquired *Sölve* from Mobiloil, and it is planned to restore her to her original condition.

Folke, last vessel of the *Hildur* class, was the most unusual of all the monitors built for the Swedish inner defence. During her construction by Motala, members of the defence staff realised that circumstances could arise in which a group of monitors might be forced to retire from an engagement. In such a situation because the main armament was fixed and could only fire ahead, the *Hildur* class would not be able to reply and would probably be annihilated. They, therefore, decided that *Folke*'s single 24cm (9.4in) gun and two 75mm (3in) guns should fire astern, while the waterline belt was modified to 76mm (3in) aft and 48mm (1.9in) forward. When underway, smoke from the funnel must have made conditions for the 57mm guns' crews, and the watch, unpleasant at the least. *Folke*'s active service ended in 1919; she lay for some years in the Stockholm dockyard but was eventually converted into a heating plant for laid-up submarines and was finally sold for conversion to a barge in 1942.

New Policies

In 1873, Parliament abolished the Royal Skerry Artillery and the Navy took over its fleet and personnel. One consequence of this was the generation of new ideas about seaward defence and, in 1876, the new Minister for the Navy, C G von Otter, a retired naval officer, suggested an improved strategy. The Navy's role in defence was to be expanded to include the entire national coastline and would not be limited to the local defence of the archipelagos. For this the monitors, 500-ton gunboats and two wooden corvettes[14] were inadequate.

In 1879, the Minister called upon a committee of experts to determine which types of ships were required to prevent enemy landings and the blockade of the nation's major ports. It presented its reports in 1880 and concluded that the new fleet should comprise armoured ships of about 2600 tons displacement, torpedo boats of 36 tons displacement and minelayers.

In 1882, both houses of parliament accepted the committee's recommendations and authorised the immediate construction of three armoured ships, to be followed by eight more over a period of fifteen years, together with the building of several torpedo boats, one of which was to be purchased from Britain. King Oscar II approved the drawings for the new ships a year later and the reliance placed upon slow-speed monitors, stationed in the skerries as Sweden's first line of defence was finally abandoned.

Notes

[1]   In 1862 the Swedish parliament comprised four houses: nobles, clergy, citizens and farmers. It was replaced by a two-chamber parliament in 1865. Source: *Carlsson Svensk Historia* (Stockholm, 1961).

[2]   The *Royal Society for Naval Sciences* was founded in 1771. Its journals have followed world naval developments and it

has covered both technical matters and defence policies.
Source: B Broomé, *et al*, *KöS 1771–1971* (Östevåla, 1971).

3 *La Gloire*: the French wooden hulled ironclad built in 1858.

4 John Ericsson: born 1803; Swedish army officer, designed
steam locomotive Novelty for Rainhill trials 1829; awarded
20 per cent of the British Admiralty prize money for the
screw propeller; to USA 1839; American citizen 1848; died

A view of the fore end of Sölve *showing the framing and
chain lockers*. (Courtesy Mr C S Ohlsson, P Eng,
Göteborg Maritime Centre)

The Sölve *as an oil barge in Göteborg Harbour*. (Courtesy
Mr C S Ohlsson, P Eng, Göteborg Maritime Centre)

Two officers, wearing frock coats and playing chess, in the wardroom of Gerda *in 1914.* (Göteborg Maritime Centre)

9   The Göta Canal system connects the Baltic with the Skagerrack. It was built by the Swedish Army during 1810–1832.

10 *Tirfing*'s engines were on view at the 1866 Stockholm Industrial Exhibition and labelled 'According to Captain John Ericsson's design'.

11 Two sister ships, *Skorpionen* and *Thrudvang*, built by the Horten Royal Dockyard, Norway, differed in having five boilers.

12 Armstrongs supplied the 27cm (10.6in) ML guns. They were constructed of steel, built-up in coils, and had Armstrongs' helicoidale rifling. The total weight of each gun was 18.5 tons.

13 Admiral C Anders Sundin, 1816–1886: served in British Navy on China Station, 1840–42; as CO of the corvette *Najaden* visited South America; commanded Swedish Norwegian Squadron, 1867–78; Vice-Admiral at Karlskrona, 1868–78.

14 These were the wooden, steam corvettes *Balder* (1800 tons) and *Saga* (1500 tons) built in 1870 and 1878.

Sources
Naval Defence Policies
G Holmberg, *Svenskt Skeppsbyggeri* (Malmo, 1963).
R Lindsjö, *Försvars fråga* (Stockholm, 1978).
O Lybeck, *Svenska Flottons Historia, Vol III* (1945).
Riksståndernas Protokol, 1862–63.
Riksståndernas Protokol, 1865.
Tidskrifti, *Sjövåsendet* (1862).
P Wedin, *Admiralitets Kollegiets Historia, Vol III (Malmö, 1978).*

1889. Source: *Oxford Companion to Ships and the Sea* (Oxford, 1976).

5   Johan Christian August d'Ailly: born in Karlskrona 1822; cadet, Naval Construction Corps 1826; sub-lieutenant, Naval Construction Corps 1843; boiler inspector at Motala, Verkstad 1846–47; chief engineer of various steam vessels 1855–57; sent to America to meet Ericsson 1862; designed monitors for Sweden and Norway; head of Engineering Branch of Swedish Navy 1868; died 1878. Source: B Zetterström, *Skeppsbyggmastäre* (Stockholm, 1948).

6   D'Ailly Reports: the first report, dated 26 September 1862, contains a description of an experimental two-piece rudder fitted to a frigate and intended to give a better 'grip' on the water – d'Ailly did not believe it would work. The report also contained the names of eight Ericsson monitors under construction in the USA. In his report of 14 November 1862, he said he had little time to visit US naval establishments but his dispatch of 27 November mentions his visit to the Charlestown Navy Yard and describes progress in the construction of the US monitor *Passaic*. D'Ailly's last dispatch, of 27 December 1862, includes an account of his meeting with the US Secretary of the Navy, which had been arranged by Ericsson. Source: d'Ailly papers, held at the Royal Military Records Office (Krigsarkivet), Sweden.

7   R S Steensen, *Vore Panserskibe*, p209, (Copenhagen, 1968).

8   Baltzar J Von Platen, 1804–1875: former naval captain and diplomat of liberal views; Navy Minister 1862–68; Ambassador to London 1871–72. Held majority of Motola shares.

New Ships
(Negotiations with J Ericsson)
J C A d'Ailly, Reports of 26 September, 14 and 27 November and 27 December 1862 (held by Krigsarkivet, Stockholm).
(Construction – large monitors)
G Holmberg, *Svenskt Skeppsbyggeri* (Malmo, 1978).
R F Kronenfels, *Schwimminde Flotten Material des Seemachts* (Vienna, 1881).
Minister for the Navy, Reports to Parliament 1865–66.
K Westerlund, *et al, Svenska Örlogs Fartyg 1855–1905* (Karlskrona, 1992).
(Construction of inshore fleet)
J C A d'Ailly, Reports of 21 October – 27 December 1862 (held by Krigsarkivet, Stockholm).
R F Kronenfels, *Schwimminde Flotten Material des Seemachts* (Vienna, 1881), Extracts published in *Actuellt*, Marin Museum (Karlskrona, 1978).
Minister for the Navy, Report to Parliament 1865.
Tidskrifti, *Sjövåsendet* (1872).
K Westerlund, *et al, Svenska Orlogs Fartyg 1855–1905* (Karlskrona, 1992).
Tekniska Muséets, unpublished paper on *Sköld's* engines.
(Norwegian monitor *Mjølner*)
Captain S Moen, *Monitoren* (Horten, 1992).
K Westerlund, *et al, Svenska Örlogs Fartyg 1855–1905* (Karlskrona, 1992).

NAVAL KITE TRIALS

The kite, the oldest of mankind's aerial devices, has served a remarkably wide variety of purposes, in peace and war, for millennia. R D Layman describes the short-lived attempts to adapt one form of it for naval service around the start of the twentieth century.

It is generally agreed that the kite originated in China during the fourth or fifth centuries BC. Over the next two thousand years or so, it was widely diffused, as far east as Easter Island, as far west as North Africa.[1]

Military uses of the kite in Asian antiquity included signalling, measuring distances, carrying of messages, distribution of what today would be called propaganda, instilling psychological fear in an enemy and perhaps even dropping explosives.

How and when the kite arrived or was originated in Europe is a matter of dispute but it was well-established there by 1600 AD.[2]

It enters European naval history for what was probably the first time in 1806, when Captain Thomas, Lord Cochrane flew kites from the frigate *Pallas* to strew 'printed proclamations, addressed to the French people' [ie, propaganda leaflets] ashore along the Bay of Biscay. As he described the technique: 'To the string which held the kite a match was appended in such a way that when the kite was flown over land, the retaining string became burnt and dispersed the proclamations which thus became widely distributed over the country.'[3]

Nearly fifty years later, during the Crimean War, Admiral Sir Charles Cochrane devised a method of towing 'torpedoes' (casks packed with explosives) by kites and it was successfully tested. Naval interest in the kite lapsed thereafter, although several schemes for using kites as aids to shipwrecked mariners were advanced during the later years of the nineteenth century.

The Man-Lifting Kite

The kite's ability to lift objects from the earth's surface could be extended to include human beings if its dimensions were large enough. The existence of man-lifting kites in China is well authenticated, although its military use is doubted. In Japan, where the kite was adopted with avidity and remains an important cultural object, legends that may well be founded on fact tell of man-lifters taking warriors in or out of besieged cities.[4]

In Western society, there were a number of attempts to create man-lifting kites or kite-like devices during the nineteenth century – a fascinating subject but beyond the scope of this study.[5] Some of these were moderately successful but what made the man-lifter a truly viable

vehicle was the invention and development of the box kite by the Anglo-Australian aeronautical pioneer Lawrence Hargrave in the early 1890s. Hargrave altruistically refused to patent his device, with the result that it was widely duplicated – albeit with ever-increasing improvements.

The box kite is basically what its name implies: a square structure enclosed on four sides and open on two. This configuration creates an area of lifting surface that could be achieved otherwise only by enlargement of linear dimensions. If weight to be lifted exceeds the capability of one such kite, others can be added to its tethering line. In its final refinements, it was very aerodynamically efficient, stable in wind velocities that would cause a spherical balloon to sway or oscillate. Later types incorporated control systems making it to some degree dirigible (steerable), in that inclining its surfaces to various angles could regulate its ascent and descent and to some extent its lateral movement. It was, in short, a quite sophisticated craft, which with the addition of power was the basis for many early aeroplanes.

Disassembled Schreiber kites and their handling crew aboard an unidentified Russian warship, date and venue unknown. Two crewmen are holding the basket.
(RD Layman/Boris V Drashpil collection)

A Russian kite-launching crew in action on the quarterdeck of an unidentified warship, steadying the main line as the basket and its occupant go skyward. Date and venue unknown. (RD Layman/Boris V Drashpil collection)

The military value of the man-lifter as an aerial observation post was obvious, providing a steadier, more reliable, more manoeuvrable, less cumbersome, less expensive and safer platform than the balloon before the advent of the kite balloon.

An influential British exponent of the man-lifting kite was Captain B F S Baden-Powell of the Scots Guards,[6] who, following his first success with kites in 1894, succeeded in arousing War Office interest. Later, during the Boer War, he employed kites to loft wireless aerials, thereby extending transmission range to 85 miles. His kites, however, were of 'flat' (single plane-surface) configuration.

Baden-Powell appears to have been the first in modern times to experiment with kites for the Royal Navy, at the behest of Commander (later Admiral Sir) Reginald R G Tupper while the latter was commanding a division of destroyers. As Baden-Powell described it in 1929 (without, unfortunately, giving the date), Tupper asked him 'to try communicating with another ship' from the destroyer *Daring*.

> A bundle was made up to represent dispatches, and these were to be deposited on a lightship off Spithead. We got within perhaps 200yds of the lightship and I got the kite with the dispatches over

it. Then I 'tipped' the kite, making it fall down, but I slightly misjudged the distance and it fell in the water just beyond the ship. However, that was all right, because of course the string was on the deck, so they pulled the 'dispatches' on board. The authorities seemed quite pleased with the result.[7]

No further interest by the 'authorities', however, was immediately manifested.

The Kite Versus the Balloon

By 1900 several navies had experimented with captive balloons lofted from warships, although their operational use had been seen only during the American Civil War.[8] The man-lifting kite was perceived as having several advantages over the balloon for aerial observation at sea. Not only could it be lofted in winds too strong for a spherical balloon to withstand, it could be assembled and disassembled on decks too small to permit shipboard carriage of a balloon, it could be raised into the air in equal or less time than needed for balloon inflation, it eliminated the ever-present danger posed by highly flammable hydrogen (the balloon's most efficient and almost universally employed lifting element) and it required fewer personnel to operate. These advantages, once demonstrated, were sufficient to interest several navies in the man-lifter. The first was the Russian.

The Russian Experience

A naval balloonist, Leitenant M N Bolshev,[9] is credited with making the first Russian man-lifting kite ascents in the early 1890s at Sevastopol but, if so, the kites were probably of flat-surface type. He was assisted by naval Leitenant Nicholai N Schreiber, who later devised a man-lifting box kite system based on the Hargrave principle.

The Schreiber kites typically had an individual lifting surface of 84 sq ft and were usually lofted in units of six to eight. They were tested in shipboard experiments during 1901–03 in the Baltic from the torpedo gunboats *Leitenant Ilin* and *Posadnik* and the destroyers *Prytkii* (ex-*Sokol*) and *Prozorlivii* (ex-*Gagana*).[10] Both manned and unmanned ascents were made, the latter to ascertain the usefulness of the box kite for meteorological purposes. An official report concluded that the man-lifters were both useful and safe but, with the outbreak of the Russo-Japanese War, all work with them was suspended and was never resumed by the Imperial Navy.

The next navy to investigate the man-lifter was that of Great Britain, due to the work of one of the most fascinating figures in early aero history, the American expatriate Samuel Franklin Cody.

The Cody Kites

Cody's early life has been depicted as a series of colourful adventures on the plains of the American West and the wilds of frontier Alaska. However, it is probable that much of this story is exaggerated.[11] He arrived in England in 1890 as a 'wild west' performer, enthralling audiences with feats of horsemanship, roping and marksmanship. After two years of this he organized a performing troupe with which he toured the continent. Returning to Britain in 1896, he turned his showmanship to the stage, writing and acting in a series of sensational and well-received melodramas.

From this improbable background, he emerged in the early years of the twentieth century as one of the great pioneers of aviation, both lighter-than-air and heavier-than-air, and an influential figure in development of the airship and aeroplane in Britain, reputedly becoming (although the claim has been questioned) the first person to achieve powered heavier-than-air flight in the British Isles.

Cody's later aeronautical work stemmed from his interest in kites, which apparently began around 1900.[12] The box kite system he eventually devised was undoubtedly the most efficient and successful of all the man-lifters. While based on the Hargrave principle, the Cody kite was so radically modified and improved as to constitute a completely different type; in fact Cody received a patent on it (No 23566, issued in 1901). Before proceeding further, a description of it is in order, necessarily brief, for a full technical description is beyond the scope of this study and its complexity is better apprehended by photograph than by written word.

What Cody customarily called his 'war kite' or sometimes 'aeroplane' (a term frequently applied to any kind of plane-surface aerial device before aviation nomenclature had developed) consisted of a rectangular, fabric-covered structure fitted with horizontal, scalloped, sharply pointed extensions ('horns'). The uppermost of these, featuring dihedral, had a span long enough to constitute,

for all practical purposes, a wing (the exact dimensions of these are somewhat vague but seem in general to have varied between 8ft and 36ft). With its spike-like projections and graceful curves, a Cody kite bore some resemblance to a piece of baroque architecture adrift in the sky.

As noted earlier, a train of these kites had remarkable lifting power. There seems to be no record of the heaviest weight lofted but Cody, a large man of about 210lb (15 stone, 97kg), was easily taken skyward. Details of maximum altitude also are hazy; heights of more than 2000ft are known to have been achieved and an unofficial record of more than 3000ft has been reported. Most flights, however, would appear to have been under 2000ft.

The Cody system has been well described by Percy B Walker as 'in effect, an overhead railway leading up into the sky.' He continues:

> An aerial ropeway was installed similar to those that are so common in . . . mountainous countries, except that instead of being fixed to the top of a mountain it was fixed in the sky by a battery of powerful Cody kites. Along this ropeway ran a small wheeled trolley or 'traveller' from which was suspended a 'car', usually a kind of armchair or basket designed to avoid too much risk of a man falling out. The trolley with its human load was then towed skywards by still another kite.[13]

A Russian destroyer, probably Prytkii, *trailing a train of Schreiber kites and its observer in the Baltic, date and venue unknown. The top unit is probably a pilot kite. The line is secured close to midships rather than on the quarterdeck.* (RD Layman/Boris V Drashpil collection)

The 'ropeway' was reeled out by a winch or windlass or, on occasion, a team of men.

Three sizes of kites were employed: pilot, lifter and carrier. The pilot kite (the smallest) was sent up first; when it reached the desired altitude the lifters (which varied in number, usually from two to four) followed. Stops on the cable automatically fixed them in position. Finally, the carrier kite, to which was attached the basket, was lofted.

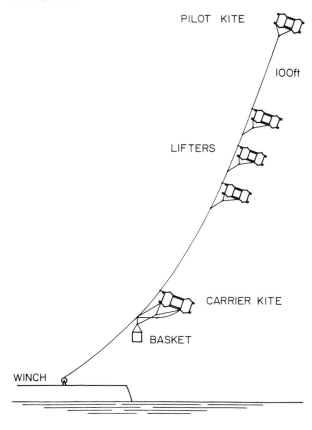

PILOT KITE

100ft

LIFTERS

CARRIER KITE

BASKET

WINCH

A schematic view of a typical Cody kite array as employed in the shipboard trials. Three lifters are shown but the number varied. (Drawing by Stephen McLaughlin)

Cody Kites and the Royal Navy: First Phase

On 6 February 1903, Cody, for reasons that can only be speculated on, wrote to the Admiralty to state:

> Having completed and patented an 'Aeroplane', or superior design of kite, suitable for signalling purposes, transmitting messages and light articles from one vessel to another, also capable of taking a man up for the purpose of reconnaissance, especially adapted as a look-out to guard against submarines, I should be pleased to bring the same before your notice . . . I am prepared to demons-

trate in the presence of any officials you may approve during the coming spring and summer.[14]

A reply to this invitation was assigned to Reginald Tupper (who now held the rank of captain and the post of Assistant Director of Naval Ordnance), probably because of his previously noted experience with Baden-Powell kites. The reply was negative, apparently because of an unfavourable opinion from Captain George Le C Egerton, commanding HMS *Vernon*, the torpedo school.

Undeterred, Cody arranged for a kite demonstration at Woolwich Common on 12–13 March and informed the Admiralty of it. At almost the last minute, Tupper was appraised that Baden-Powell had a high opinion of the Cody kite; consequently, he attended the demonstration. It should be noted here that initial Royal Navy interest in kites centred on their use for lofting wireless aerials, as Baden-Powell had shown this to be feasible.

Cody's demonstration was only moderately successful, for winds were light on both days. However, kites were flown and a few man-lifting ascents were made to a height of about 150ft. Tupper was highly impressed, as his separate reports on both days of the trials prove; he was soon to become the Navy's greatest exponent of Cody kites.

In his 12 March report, he declared: 'This is quite the best kind of kite I have seen, and I have every reason to think that it will be of use for supporting an aerial wire for W/T purposes, and that it can be easily handled and flown from the deck of a ship or even small craft. I have no hesitation in recommending a trial'.[15]

His report dated the next day continued: 'I think it would be quite practicable to use this system from a ship for reconnoitring purposes, such as examining harbours like Bizerta, and that it is always capable of being used from a ship, for if there is but little wind you can always make a breeze by steaming ahead – 3 or 4 kts would give sufficient breeze.' This passage shows that Tupper was one of the first to realise the importance of wind-over-deck (WOD) to the launching of heavier-than-air machines from surface vessels and how ship speed could create artificial wind.

Tupper noted:

> Mr Cody is most anxious to be allowed to try his system from a vessel, and wishes to place his invention at the disposal of the Admiralty; he says he has been in England for twelve years and considers himself an Englishman, and would be pleased to be naturalised if he could be employed by the Government in connection with his kites. [Cody did finally become a British citizen but not until 1909.] I have the honour to submit that the system might be very useful, and is worth a trial.

This recommendation caught the favourable attention of Prince Louis of Battenberg, the Director of Naval Intelligence, who on 18 March proposed that kite tests be carried out from land and sea by *Vernon*, for the lofting of aerials, and HMS *Excellent*, the gunnery training school at Whale Island, for man-lifting. This was so ordered on 25 March and trials began five days later.

Kites were sent up ashore at Whale Island during the first two days and flew successfully although there were strong winds, squalls and occasional rain; on the second day a 600ft W/T wire was raised. Flights were carried out on 1 April from the old ironclad *Hector*, one of the vessels of the *Vernon* establishment, and were continued at sea during the next two days aboard the destroyer *Starfish*. The tests ended on 4 April with more flights at Whale Island.

Captain Egerton, whose previous dim view of kites was noted earlier, now had a change of heart. In a report dated 7 April he pronounced the Cody craft

> immensely superior to any kites previously tried here, and even as fitted at present, are perfectly suitable for raising an aerial wire. I have no doubt that they could, after some experience, be still further improved.
>
> No difficulty was experienced in putting the kites up from a Destroyer, either at anchor or under way, and they were kept flying whilst leaving the harbour or steaming in any direction.

Prince Louis did not wait for Tupper's comments or even for the completion of the tests; on 6 April he recommended that the Government should consider purchasing Cody's patent and employing him as a kite instructor and constructor.

That same day, Cody addressed a letter to the Admiralty rehashing the work done at Whale Island, announcing that man-lifting demonstrations were soon to be carried out, declaring he was 'quite disposed to sell the patent outright' and adding the interesting thought that 'My kites can also be used from submarines . . . whilst the submarine is either above or below the water.'[16]

Man-lifting trials at the *Excellent* establishment, now under the command of Captain (later Admiral Sir) Percy Scott, the famous naval gunnery innovator, began on 13 April. On that day one of Cody's assistants made a 500ft ascent at Whale Island but, while he was descending, a sudden radical shift of wind threw the train into disarray and the basket fell. Its occupant alighted easily and safely, however, thanks to what Scott later described as the parachute-like action of the carrier kite. No attempt were made at man-lifting on the next two days due to 'unsteady winds'.

On the 16th, the kites were embarked on the 670-ton tug *Seahorse* for sea trials. The pilot kite and two lifters were lofted successfully but then 'Flight suddenly came down in a squall just before carrier kite left the deck. This was due to bridle of second "lifter" carrying away.' The next day saw greater success, although no manned ascents were made. As reported by Scott: 'Good results. With a flight of one pilot, two lifters and one carrier kite a weight of 140lb [a log] was sent up 300ft,' with 'Ship steaming 4 to 6 kts, head to wind or near'. Winds were insufficient for a final man-lifting trial on the 18th and the tests came to an end.

The trials could hardly be called outstandingly successful but at least they proved that the kites could indeed lift human beings and could function in moderately adverse

Schreiber kites going aloft from an unidentified Russian warship. The officer in the basket is believed to be Captain VA Semkovskii, acting chief of the Russian navy's Aeronautical Section, who made an ascent on 23 August (old style date) 1903.
(RD Layman/Boris V Drashpil collection)

weather. Captain Scott was favourably impressed, writing in his report on the tests:

> The results achieved by these kites are remarkable and they should prove useful, not only for wireless telegraphy but for distant signalling especially from destroyers.
>
> At present it cannot be said that they are to be relied on for man lifting either on land or at sea, except in very favourable weather, but as the inventor has only been working at them for two years there seems to be no reason why their efficiency should not eventually justify their use for this purpose also.

Samuel Franklin Cody, c1900, wearing the cowboy-style hat he habitually affected, even aboard ship. (Courtesy of Jean Roberts)

An ascent, minus the kite basket, during the 1903 trials. The headgear indicates the flyer is Cody. (Public Record Office)

Scott recommended further experiments but two developments brought everything to an abrupt halt. The first was a most unsagacious letter from Cody to the Admiralty on 21 April in which he asked for payment of £25,000 for his patent and employment of his services for five years or more at an annual salary of £1250, at the end of which he was to be paid an additional £25,000.

Appalled would be a mild description of Admiralty officials' reaction to this demand. The lump-sum payments and salary for a minimum five-year employment would have amounted to a total equal to two-thirds or more of the construction costs of a destroyer in 1903. Even Captain Tupper agreed that 'the terms of Mr Cody are excessive'. However, he continued in a memo of 24 April, 'from what I have heard from *Excellent* & *Vernon*, it seems desirable to engage Mr Cody's services & use his kites for further experiments if he can be induced to modify his terms to reasonable proportions'.

Apparently he did so but to no avail, for a highly adverse report on his kites was soon received. Before entering into negotiations, the office of the Director of Navy Contracts recommended an outside evaluation of the validity of Cody's 1901 patent. James Swinburne, a consulting engineer, was engaged for the analysis. Although aeronautics was obviously outside his field of expertise, Swinburne had no hesitation in judging the patent invalid because it was unoriginal, as well as condemning features of the kite system as impractical.

Mistaken as it was, his report, coupled with Cody's monetary demands, put paid to the matter. On 20 May Cody was informed that the Admiralty was rejecting his proposals but offering, in view of his services, to pay him £100 plus out-of-pocket expenses.

This was not quite an immediate end to kites in the Navy. On 3 July 1903 the Controller of the Navy informed the superintending admiral at Portsmouth of an 'order placed with Mr Cody for four sets of kites, each set consisting of four kites with small winch, wires, and tackle complete', to be issued to the battleships *Majestic* and *Revenge*, the armoured cruiser *Good Hope* and the second-class cruiser *Doris*. 'Officers and men from these ships have been undergoing instructions in London in the use of the kites . . .'

That at least one of these ships employed the kites is shown by a 15 August report to the admiral of the Channel Fleet from the captain of the *Majestic*:

> whilst using Cody Kites for wireless communication . . . on August 8th two kites (the light pilot and light carrier) together with 300ft of special aerial wire were accidentally lost overboard. The wind was light at the time and when the fleet slowed down the men at the winch were unable to heave in fast enough to keep the kite clear of the water.
>
> It is submitted that two more Cody Kites of similar pattern and 100 yards of special aerial wire may be supplied to replace them.

Records of what use the other three vessels may have made of their kites apparently have not survived.

Cody Kites and the Royal Navy: Second Phase

A kite aboard the destroyer Starfish *on either 2 or 3 April 1903. Cody (at right) is on the bandstand of the after 6pdr gun. The kite winch is in the lower left and one of the Portsmouth forts is just visible in the background.* (Public Record Office)

The story now moves ahead to 1907, by which time the British Army's aeronautical branch had adopted man-lifting kites to supplement its balloons. Cody, as a civilian employee, was serving as its kite instructor and construction supervisor at the Balloon Factory (the forerunner of the Royal Aircraft Establishment) and Balloon School at Farnborough (although on less favourable financial terms than he had asked of the Navy). He was also involved in development of airships and aeroplanes.

The reasons for the Royal Navy's renewed interest in kites that year remains unexplained; it can only suffice to say that it *was* rekindled, and in November Captain Osmond de Brock, the Assistant Director of Naval Intelligence, was dispatched to Farnborough to investigate developments. During the years since 1903 Cody had further refined his kites and their launching technique had become routine. A demonstration convinced de Brock of their value and feasibility for shipboard use. His report stressed the potential for aerial detection of submarines and mines. This undoubtedly reflected the RN concern over these underwater menaces that had developed since 1903. In that year the Navy had possessed only one experimental, American-built submarine but improved, British-built, craft had since been obtained and had begun to demonstrate potential, while the many mine-inflicted losses of ships of both sides during the Russo-Japanese War of 1904–5 showed how deadly these devices had become.

De Brock's report was forwarded to Captain Tupper, the erstwhile kite enthusiast who was now in command of HMS *Excellent*. He urged reinvestigation of kites and asked permission to conduct trials at *Excellent* the next year, suggesting that Cody's services be obtained for them. After considerable bickering over the financial arrangements, the War Office agreed to release Cody for a month. In April 1908 Tupper visited Farnborough to work out details and the next month two petty officers and six leading seamen from *Excellent* were sent there to be trained by Cody.

The actual trials, all conducted aboard ships attached to *Excellent*, began on 17 August and between that date and 7 October the kites were flown on nineteen days. The experiments are described clearly and in detail in daily reports written by one Lieutenant Usborne, who made several ascents during them.[17]

Unlike the 1903 trials, which were devoted more to the mere feasibility of kite-flying, those of 1908, while also directed to that end, tested practical application of man-lifters to naval purposes: general observation, spotting of gunfire, detection of underwater objects, signalling and photography. A detailed description of them, during which dozens of ascents under many weather conditions were made, would be tedious in the extreme (Usborne's reports run to more than twenty-six pages) so this narrative will focus on only the highlights and the conclusions drawn from them.[18]

The first day, 17 August, started inauspiciously aboard the battleship *Revenge*. The ship was steaming at 12kts into an 11kt wind, and Usborne reported that 'Difficulty was experienced getting the kite to leave the quarter deck when dead to wind, owing to the lee, a yaw of 3 to 4 points was necessary.'

The problem was caused by the distortion of wind flow by the ship's superstructure, a phenomenon that had not occurred (or at least had not been reported) during the 1903 tests. Unmentioned by Usborne (perhaps because not guessed at) but possibly another contributing factor might have been the flow of engine room gasses from the funnels. This was a problem that became evident during the many failed attempts to land aeroplanes on the afterdeck of HMS *Furious* in 1917 and would bedevil designers of aircraft carriers for many years.

At the time, however, the difficulty was attributed to insufficient 'total' wind, ie, the velocity of natural wind combined with that generated by the ship's speed. Consequently, Usborne wrote, 'It was decided that a Destroyer was necessary to find out exactly what total wind was required.' Thus the next day's experiments were made from the destroyer *Fervent*.

The same problem was encountered when the ship steamed dead into the wind but, by steering at an angle to it, the kites lifted easily under a 'total' wind of 21 to 25 kts. The success of this technique was confirmed on 20 August in ascents from *Revenge* and it became standard practice. Later, it was found that once the kites were aloft the ship could return to its original bearing, or any other, and

A kite being prepared for launching aboard the destroyer Starfish *during the 1903 trials. This view is taken from aft, looking forward.* (Courtesy of Jean Roberts)

could even make a 16-point turn while trailing kites – something that had earlier been thought impossible. As Usborne put it in his report of four man-lifting ascents (including one by Cody) from *Revenge* on 24 August, 'Once the man was clear of the ship's lee there was no difficulty.'

The 25 and 26 August flights were devoted to experiments in spotting gunfire from *Revenge* against a canvas representation of a torpedo boat towed by a destroyer[19] steaming at the same course and speed (not given) as *Revenge* at distances ranging from about 6100 to 7000yds. This may have been a landmark of sorts in aeronaval history. Although aerial spotting of naval gunfire against land objectives from balloons had been employed operationally during the American Civil War and experimentally by Russia during the Russo-Japanese War, the RN tests of August 1908 could well be (unless yet-undiscovered Russian records prove otherwise) the first application of the technique against a floating target.

The kite observers were Cody, an unidentified petty officer, a naval lieutenant, identified only as Yeats Brown, and Usborne. For comparative purposes, the splashes from one or more of the battleship's 6in guns were also noted by observers in *Revenge*'s foretop and aboard the towing destroyer. The results were relayed to *Revenge* by semaphore. Apparently a telephone line was fitted but not used because 'Mr Cody considered it unsafe to let so much telephone wire sag, and it would probably have carried away with the wind.' Cody suggested attaching the phone line to the cable by clips but it is evident this was not done.

Ten rounds of 6in were fired the first day and nineteen on the second. Usborne's reports include two tables listing the estimates from the three observation points of overs, shorts, rights and lefts of the fall of shot. There are wide discrepancies among them, and it is impossible to determine which were the most accurate. The results, however, were less significant than the fact that the concept of spotting from the air had been conceived and tried. Usborne's comments on the experiments, as expressed in his 'Remarks on Spotting from Kite', are prescient:

> All those who have been up in the kite are convinced that a more accurate estimate of the fall of shot can be obtained from there than from a control position . . . The [kite] observer would be clear of the smoke from his own guns and could probably see over the smoke made by the enemy's guns, and could get a very good look of what was going on on board the enemy.
>
> Supposing a case of an engagement with an enemy's fleet with a fair breeze, and that the Admiral was able to steam within a few points of the wind, an officer in a kite connected with a control position would be invaluable.

Even more prescient is Usborne's concluding paragraph:

> It is however in engaging shore works at long range that kites would be more useful. It would seem that they supply the solution to the difficulty of directing the fire on works hidden from the ship at long

A detailed view of the Cody kite, showing its construction and general configuration. The gentleman on the right is Cody himself. (RAE Musem)

ranges as the Japanese ships fired at, at Port Arthur. If they were useful for no other purpose I think that this alone would justify their being sup-plied [*sic*] to ships.

History has borne out the accuracy of this judgment. Direction of naval gunfire against 'shore works' became a major function of aircraft during the First World War, much more so in the Second, and continues to be important. The remotely controlled 'drones' that guided the gunfire of American battleships during the Persian Gulf War were far removed in time and technology from the man-lifting kites of 1908 but in principle and for purpose they were the direct lineal descendants.

The tests resumed on 28 August aboard the destroyer *Recruit*, but attempts to fly kites during a full gale caused two wire breakages and damage to one kite. Cody had a close call on the 31st during a flight from *Recruit* to determine if mines could be detected from the air (they could not, although weeds could be seen). He was suspended under a pilot kite and four lifters at about 800 ft when, as reported by Usborne:

> I observed that the basket was being greatly shaken about, then that pilot kite gave a great dive to the right. Then all the lifters dived to the right, nearly turning over. They again righted, but apparently owing to the erratic motion of the pilot kite dived ever again and began to come down.
>
> The descent was checked twice by a backward swing of the kites and the carrier kite struck the water at about the speed a man acquires when diving from a height of 20–30ft. The car turned over when it struck the water and Mr Cody dived out and then held on to the car which supported him. Meanwhile, the destroyer had reversed, cut

A kite, its basket manned, under tow by the battleship Revenge *during the 1908 trials.* (Courtesy of Jean Roberts)

A photograph of Revenge *taken from a kite, possibly by*
Cody. (RAE Museum)

the wire, and closed the kites, and picked up the
man who was none the worse.

The kites were damaged, although repairable, but 1000ft
of wire was lost.

As a result of this accident, Cody spent some time
readjusting the kites, including the addition of 'save-alls',
small extensions that acted as air brakes. Another result
was an experiment on 2 September aboard the *Revenge* in
which a breeches buoy was substituted for the basket. '[It]
was tested overboard with a man in it,' Usborne reported.
'It kept him well up in the water and he could get out of it
easily. But it was capable of being turned over. A little
lead was put in each foot.' The unidentified man was
probably Cody, for photos show him standing in a
breeches buoy on the deck of *Revenge*.

In another experiment, made to determine if kites could
tow a target, they were rigged to a whaler. The procedure
'was found to be safe and easy, though not efficient as
regards speed', 4kts being the maximum.[20]

Another attempt to locate mines was made by Cody on
3 September, but failed in weather described by Usborne

as 'dull, misty, overcast, rain, continuous drizzle and
occasional heavy showers'. A similar try the next day
failed for the same reason plus problems with the kites,
which despite Cody's tinkering continued to display
instability. A two-week hiatus ensued, during which Cody
returned to Farnborough to continue his aeroplane work.
He was still absent during the first two days when trials
resumed on 28 September. That day saw a brief flight
from *Recruit* and then the entire apparatus was transferred, for reasons unknown, to HMS *Grafton*, an old cruiser
attached to *Excellent*. Two kites were slightly damaged
by coming down in the water.

The next day was devoted to a test of the time required
to get kites into the air. Usborne's report on this seems to
be the only source for such information: 'From "everything stowed" to "ready to fly", 21 minutes. From this
position, time taken to get up a flight, rig carrier kite and
basket, all ready to send a man up, 30 minutes. This time
could be improved on with more drill.' Even 30 min,
however, was not much longer than a seaplane carrier of
the First World War required to get an aircraft aloft.

Cody boarded *Grafton* on 30 September, a day that saw
several very successful flights, under as many as six lifters
– two by Usborne and three by '1 Petty Officer, specially
trained'. One of Usborne's flights was the highest, 1200ft,
from which altitude he could see the Isle of Wight at a
distance of 20 miles.

Everything had been transferred back to *Recruit* by 1
October and still another attempt to detect mines was
made that day. With Usborne at 1000ft under four lifters,
the destroyer steamed at 18kts (for a 'total' wind of 24 to
26kts) 'right over the places where the two lines of mines
were laid' but 'nothing was visible under water and
nothing could be seen of the mines.'

Usborne gloomily concluded that 'In the muddy condition of the water in and near the Solent it is certain that
nothing can be seen under water, whatever the height.'

The next day Cody was lofted under six lifters 'to
photograph Portsmouth Harbour and surrounding objects
from the kite steaming down Solent'. The photographs
were taken successfully but 'Nothing was visible under
water.'

On 5 October: 'It was attempted to ascertain to what
extent submarines were visible from a kite.' However,
'The weather was very foggy . . . and the officer in charge
of submarines did not consider it safe to dive' (earlier,
Cody had found he could see the upper works of a
semi-submerged submarine, but not its underwater portion).

On 6 and 7 October: 'It was intended to make a rapid
reconnaissance of the fortified ports of the South Coast of
England from Dartmouth to Dover [and] by means of
photographs and observations from the kites, ascertaining
their contents.' The project was foiled by thick channel
fogs in which the kites were lost to view from the
destroyer when 1000ft up.

This was the end. Usborne's final report, also signed by
Captain Tupper, writes *finis*: 'This completes Mr Cody's
time at Whale Island, and with the exception of the
experiments with magnezium [*sic*] lights, which will be
carried out without him [and of which no record seems to
exist], completes this series of experiments.'

Cody standing in a breeches buoy on the quarterdeck of the Revenge, *probably on 2 September 1908.* (RAE Museum)

The Sequel

The 1908 trials had demonstrated the potential value of aerial observation but had also shown that the kite was more subject to the whims of nature at sea, where winds are usually more continuous but frequently change velocity and direction more drastically and quickly, than on land. Kite handling proved a tricky business that could be performed routinely only by crews given thorough training – something repeatedly emphasised by Tupper and Usborne.

That point was stressed again by Tupper in a highly favourable report on the trials sent to the Admiralty on 22 October. He urged purchase of kites and their equipment for use by cruisers, asserting that destroyers were less suitable because of their cramped quarterdecks and extreme motion at high speed, and recommended more experiments by *Excellent*.

Tupper's points were strongly supported in a covering letter by the admiral superintending at Portsmouth, Admiral (later Admiral of the Fleet Sir) Arthur D Fanshawe, who urged that 'complete [kite] outfits should

Kite going aloft from the quarterdeck of the Revenge *on 2 September 1908 in a test which substituted a breeches buoy for the basket. The destroyer* Recruit *is in the background.* (RAE Museum)

Nothing more transpired. Cody had no association with the Navy, and very little with kites, after 1908, but turned his attention and talent to the development of his aeroplanes. He was killed in the crash of one of them on 7 August 1913.

The American Experience

Although the maritime man-lifter was dead in the Royal Navy after 1908, it saw two resurgences elsewhere three years later. The first was an experiment by the United States Navy conducted aboard the armoured cruiser *Pennsylvania*, the vessel on which Eugene Ely had made the first shipboard landing and the second take-off of an aeroplane on 18 January 1911.[23] The kites were man-lifters devised by Samuel F Perkins, another of the great turn-of-the-century kite exponents.

The experiment was authorized by the Secretary of the Navy but it is unclear when or by whom it was initiated; it may have been at the behest of Rear Admiral Chauncey Thomas, Commander in Chief of the Pacific Fleet.

The Perkins kites, although based on the Hargrave principle and somewhat resembling Cody's, were more of a combination of the box kite and the single-surface type. Perkins called them 'airplane kites'. His control and tethering systems were similar to Cody's but more complicated and, because his kites were of smaller dimensions, more of them were required to loft comparable weights.[24] Those who went up under them were suspended not in baskets but on unprotected saddle-like slings.

The *Pennsylvania* embarked Perkins and his kites (reportedly twenty units) at Tiburon, California, on San Francisco Bay, and then steamed to the Santa Barbara Channel off the Southern California coast, where the experiment was conducted on 24 January. A day or two earlier the kite system had been tested by lofting a 160lb sandbag and Perkins may also have made an ascent.

One participant in the test has described the kites and their launching technique as follows:

> First there were sent up 2 pilot kites, 9ft by 9ft, each on a separate line about 500ft long . . . The pilot kite lines were attached to a secondary line of 1in manila to which were attached 4 to 6 secondary kites, 6ft by 6ft. The secondary line was attached in turn to the main line of 2in manila to which were tied the lifting kites, 9ft by 9ft, and 5 to 10 in number.
>
> The height above the water was increased . . . by leading the kite line through a block at the after rim of the lower main top, and paying out the line from the bight on deck. The bight was then eased

be supplied to a [battle] cruiser of the *Invincible* type and a scout for further tests'.[21]

Admiralty officials ultimately turned deaf ears to these recommendations. They deplored the fact that destroyers were not deemed suitable for kites, that vessels capable of 25kts were needed (perhaps a misunderstanding of Usborne's report that 25kts could be achieved through a combination of natural and artificial wind) and that mines and submarines could not normally be detected in British coastal waters. The possibility that smoke would obscure the kite observer's view was theorized (although Usborne had found it did not) and also that the angle of vision over land features was too limited from the air.

Some of these objections were valid but others were misguided. There seems to have been an element of prejudgment, with, as Percy Walker has opined, less focus given to the potential usefulness of kites at sea than to the technical problems associated with them. He suggests also that cost (with a set of kites priced at £1000) may have been a factor.

Whatever the reason for refusal to adopt the man-lifting kite for the Royal Navy, it came in a letter of 24 December from the Admiralty to Fanshawe stating that, 'in view of the difficulties and risks at present attaching to the use of these kites . . . it is premature to supply them to sea-going ships, but HMS *Excellent* should be directed to keep in touch with any further developments in kites and kite-flying.'[22]

A kite and its observer under tow by Recruit. *The direction in which smoke from the funnels is blowing indicates the ship is steaming at an angle to the wind, a practice found necessary to permit unimpeded air flow.* (RAE Museum)

off by a line thrown over it with both ends on deck. In hauling in, the operation was reversed, the bight of the kite line being hauled down to the deck and taken to the after winch for heaving in.[25]

As *Pennsylvania* steamed at speeds reported as 13 to 20kts on the 24th, the first man to go aloft was the cruiser's assistant engineering officer, Lieutenant John Rodgers,[26] seated in a bosun's chair and fitted with a fire control telephone line. At a height of 400ft as estimated from deck, he communicated with the ship, reporting course changes as he observed them and taking photographs.

Later in the day a second ascent was made, by Ensign (later Captain) A M Charlton. Since he weighed 20lbs less than Rodgers, it was hoped he could rise to perhaps 1000ft but in light wind he reached only 200ft. He, too, took photographs. As the wind continued to fall, no more man-lifting flights were attempted but a sandbag was lofted successfully and flew well even as the ship made a 16 point turn at 13kts.

Reactions to this one-day experiment and the conclusions drawn from it are reported variously. *Pennsylvania*'s commanding officer, Captain (later Rear Admiral) Charles F Pond, who had become a convert to all things aeronautical as a result of the Ely experiment, is said to have believed it was 'perfectly feasible to send a man up to a height of 500 or 600ft, provided there was a steady breeze of at least 13kts; either a natural breeze or one resultant of the wind and ship's speed',[27] thus echoing Tupper's opinion of eight years earlier.

Rear Admiral Thomas drew the conclusion that 'the line of kites could be used as an aero-towline to which could be attached or suspended an aero-target, at which gun pointers could practice in aiming and in actual firing,'[28] an early realization that anti-aircraft fire would probably soon become important. Individual Perkins kites were indeed used later as AA targets.

Another officer aboard *Pennsylvania* that day, the future Admiral and Chief of Naval Operations William H Standley, writing many years later, reported an adverse reaction to the man-lifters:

> I do not know what the official report of the tests said, but I do know that Lt Rodgers and all the other officers taking part in the test considered the box kite method of hoisting a spotter aloft as wholly impracticable. No further tests with [man-lifting] kites were ever made.[29]

So vanished the man-lifter in the USN.

Cody about to be lifted from the quarterdeck of the Revenge. (RAE Museum)

The destroyer Recruit, *which was employed in the 1908 trials of the Cody kite.* (John Robert's collection)

The French Experience

The French Navy had been a leader in the use of balloons but in 1904 disbanded its aeronautical branch because of the hazards (which in 1902 included a fatal accident) involved in their use at sea, especially the ever-present danger presented by hydrogen. However, as the range of naval ordnance became so great that the fall of shot could not be observed adequately (or even observed at all) from a control top, the value of extending the range of vision by use of aerial devices became obvious.

The man-lifting kite offered an attractive alternative to the balloon, incorporating its advantages without its perils. The idea was therefore tested in 1911, employing a system developed during 1904–7 by an army engineer officer and balloonist, Capitaine (later Colonel) Jacques Theodore Saccony.[30]

Saccony's kites were remarkably similar to Cody's, including the wing-like extensions, employed almost identical baskets and the same pilot-lifter technique for launching. A train of them was embarked aboard the armoured cruiser *Edgar Quinet* at Toulon in August 1911 for initial tests. Supervised by Saccony, as many as twenty man-lifting flights were made, up to altitudes of 1500ft. Following this, a naval lieutenant, a sous-officier and four matelots were trained in kite operation and assigned to the cruiser for seagoing trials in the Strait of Bonifacio (between Corsica and Sardinia).

Several successful ascents were made, under three to five lifters, with the observer linked to the cruiser by telephone. In calm weather, a man could be raised to ̄984ft (300m) with the vessel steaming at 18kts. With ̄... kite train could be assembled and launched ... down in 10min, with the line either ... handled by forty matelots ̄.[31]

Despite these successful demonstrations, kites were not adopted by the Navy. Although the Saccony man-lifter was employed briefly on the Western Front during the First World War, its maritime counterpart went into the same limbo as those of Schreiber, Cody and Perkins.

The Kites Come Down

Various factors prevented the man-lifting kite from entering the naval arsenal. The first and most basic was its dependence on a minimum wind velocity in order to go aloft, something that could not be guaranteed under operational conditions. This handicap might have been accepted, however, but for the rise of aeronautical rivals to the man-lifter. The first was the kite balloon, also developed during the 1890s. Its elongated shape combined with a series of stabilizing fins and vents made it a far steadier and more reliable observation platform than the spherical balloon. It did not depend on favourable winds to ascend, while on the other hand it could function in winds too strong for a spherical balloon to withstand.

The kite balloon's size and bulk denied it the kite's advantage of disassembled carriage aboard conventional warships unless it were carried deflated, which required stowage of potentially dangerous hydrogen for inflation. However, experience in the First World War proved that shipboard carriage was not necessary; an unmanned balloon could be towed aloft by a vessel for days on end, needing to be reeled down only for the observer to enter and leave the basket.

Two even great rivals to the kite had appeared by 1911. The airship had been fairly well perfected and the aeroplane, although still young, was improving by leaps and bounds. The kite (as well as the balloon) were tied as intimately to the ships that towed them as a tail is to a dog, thus necessarily limiting their field of observation, but the independent mobility of the aeroplane and the airship permitted extending range of vision by scores or even hundreds of miles. Initially, both were handicapped by lack of air-to-surface communication, guaranteed to the kite or balloon by telegraph or telephone line, but the development of aerial W/T was eventually to solve this problem.

By 1911, the aeroplane, especially its seaplane version, seemed to offer great new possibilities for reconnaissance and spotting at sea. There were some straws in the wind that year. US Navy experiments showed that both wheeled aeroplanes and seaplanes were potentially capable of functioning from warships and the French Navy began conversion of the former torpedo-boat carrier *Foudre* (which had operated balloons in turn-of-the-century naval exercises) into a seaplane carrier.

The man-lifting kite, even as it was reaching its apogee, came into the field just too late. Unmanned kites were to serve a number of maritime purposes during and between the World Wars but the man-lifter turned out to be another blind alley down which naval aviation briefly strayed.

Notes

[1] For a general history of the kite, see Clive Hart, *Kites: An Historical Survey* Frederick A Praeger (New York 1967).

[2] Military standards or banners of the windsock type had existed in Europe for centuries, but it is uncertain whether the flat-surface kite was introduced from Asia or originated indigenously.

[3] Cochrane, Lord Thomas (10th Earl of Dundonald), *The Autobiography of a Seaman* Richard Bentley (London 1860), Vol I, p201.

[4] See Donn Draeger, *Ninjutsu: The Art of Invisibility* Arizona Books/Publishers (Phoenix, Ariz 1980).

[5] See Hart, *op cit*.

[6] Baden-Powell was an important figure in early British aeronautics but is less remembered today than his brother, Robert, founder of the Boy Scouts.

[7] Quoted in C F Snowden Gamble, *The Air Weapon: Being Some Account of the Growth of British Military Aeronautics From the Beginnings in the Year 1783 Until the End of the Year 1929* Oxford University Press (London 1931), p78.

[8] For a survey of naval use of balloons, see R D Layman and Stephen McLaughlin, 'The Shipboard Balloon – The Beginnings of Naval Aeronautics', *Warship 1992* Conway Maritime Press (London 1992).

[9] Bolshev is credited with introducing the balloon into Russian naval service. During the Russo-Japanese War he supervised the conversion of the former German liner *Lahn* into the world's first sea-going balloon ship, renamed *Russ*.

[10] These tests are described in reports of 28 July and 24 August 1903 (old style) by Captain V A Semkovskii, acting chief of the Imperial Navy's Aeronautical Section. I am indebted to the late Edgar Meos for copies.

[11] The various aspects of Cody's real and supposed career are summarized in the subtitle of Arthur Gould Lee's biography of him, *The Flying Cathedral: The Story of Samuel Franklin Cody, Texan Cowboy, Bronco-Buster, Frontiersman, Circus Sharpshooter, Horse Track Racer, Showman, Barnstorme* *Man-Carrying Kite Inventor and Pioneer British* A Methuen & Co (London 1965). Recent resea·

A photograph taken by Lt John Rogers during his kite ascent from the Pennsylvania. *(author's collection)*

unpublished) by Jean Roberts suggests that much that has been written so far about Cody's early life is, at the least, only partially correct. Samuel Franklin Cody has often been, and continues to be, confused with William Frederick Cody, whose famous sobriquet 'Buffalo Bill' was bestowed for his prowess in helping to hunt the North American bison to near-extinction. Although they were not related, they bore a striking physical resemblance to each other, enhanced by the fact that both affected Western American frontier-style apparel. Their careers were also remarkably similar: both were expert horsemen and marksmen, both were 'wild west' showmen with touring troupes and both acted on the stage. Samuel Franklin was at least twenty-one years younger than William Frederick and it has been suggested that Samuel Franklin, who did not begin his show business career until after William Frederick's was established, deliberately adopted the other's trappings for the sake of publicity. In another coincidence, Jean Roberts' findings show that Samuel Franklin was born (with the original surname

The armoured cruiser Pittsburgh (ex Pennsylvania) *was employed in several early aeronautical experiments, including the use of kites at sea. (Marius Bar)*

Cowdery) in Davenport, Iowa, located in the same county (Scott) in which William Frederick was born.

[12] For a survey of Cody's work with kites, see Percy B Walker, *Early Aviation at Farnborough, Vol I, Balloons, Kites and Airships* Macdonald & Co (London 1971).

[13] *Ibid*, p107.

[14] Quoted, *ibid*, p135.

[15] Unless otherwise noted, this and all subsequent quotations are from Air 1/669/17/122/792 or Adm 116/466B, Public Record Office. I am indebted to Jean Roberts for the loan of copies of these documents and for other assistance without which this article could not have been written.

[16] This interesting idea was never tried out. Hart, in *Kites, op cit*, states that German submarines of the First World War used man-lifting kites for observation while surfaced but I have found no source confirming this assertion. A few German submarines of the Second World War operated the man-lifting Focke-Achgelis FA300, which, although having some kite-like features, was more of an unpowered rotary-wing aircraft.

[17] Although this officer's full name never appears on these or other documents relating to the tests, he was Lieutenant Neville F Usborne. He later became a member of the inspectorate appointed to supervise construction of the RN's first, ill-fated rigid airship and joined the Royal Naval Air Service when it was organized in 1914. With the rank of wing commander he was in charge of the Kingsnorth Royal Naval Air Station at the start of the First World War. He helped develop the small Submarine Scout 'blimp' in 1915 and was killed in the crash of an experimenal combination airship/ aeroplane in early 1916.

[18] The reports are contained in Air 1/669/17/122/792.

[19] Usborne identifies the destroyer as *Rake* but I have been unable to find a vessel of that name in RN service.

[20] In November 1903 Cody had crossed the English Channel from Calais to Dover in a small boat towed by kites (an earlier attempt in the opposite direction had failed). Being at the mercy of the wind, he had to take a round-about course and the cruise took 13hrs. His first-person description of it, appearing in the *Daily Mail*, was reprinted in the *S F Cody Kite Society Newsletter* Vol I, No 1, January 1991. For an account of both ventures, see Harald Penrose, *British Aviation: The Pioneer Years 1903–1914* Putnam (London 1967) pp46–48.

21 Quoted in Walker, *op cit*, p156. The last of the three-ship *Invincible* class had been completed only two days before Fanshawe's letter. They were at this time designated as armoured cruisers. The officially designated 'scouts' afloat in 1908 were the eight vessels of the *Sentinel*, *Forward*, *Adventure* and *Pathfinder* classes, small, fast cruisers designed to work with destroyers.

22 Quoted in Walker, *op cit*, p158.

23 *Pennsylvania*, renamed *Pittsburgh* in 1912, was very active in USN aeronautical experiments in early 1911. The month after the Ely and Perkins episodes she received a seaplane (piloted by aviation pioneer Glenn Curtiss), which alighted alongside, was hoisted aboard and then placed back in the water for a return flight – another 'first' in aeronaval history.

24 Perkins' kites, while more cumbersome than Cody's, were equally successful but have received far less attention although they were used for exhibitions of man-lifting at fairs and other public gatherings until at least 1930. Hart, *op cit*, makes no mention of them at all.

25 Captain A M Charlton, 'Man-Lifting Kites in the Navy'. *United States Naval Institute Proceedings*, Vol LXIV No 428, October 1938.

26 Rodgers was soon to become USN Naval Aviator No 2 and an important and influential figure in USN aviation until his death in an aeroplane crash in 1926.

27 Charlton, *op cit*.

28 *Ibid*.

29 Admiral William H Standley, 'Naval Aviation, an Evolution of Naval Gunfire', *United States Naval Institute Proceedings*, Vol LXXVIII No 589. I have been unable to locate any official record or report of the experiment, and there are many contradictions in published material. I have therefore relied mainly on Charlton, who as an active participant is probably more reliable than a spectator such as Standley. Perkins' son, also named Samuel, gives a greatly different account (Samuel Perkins, 'Man in the Sky', *Yankee*, September 1969). He states that Rodgers lost wind lift when he was 450ft (*sic*) up and fell briefly into the water before it was regained.

30 Saccony also contributed to the development of aerial photography. He figured importantly in organization and operations of the French army balloon corps in the First World War and later was active in the administration of French civil aviation. For a summary of his career, see Charles Christienne and Pierre Lissarrague, *A History of French Military Aviation* Smithsonian Institution Press (Washington 1986).

31 These tests are described in *La Aérienne*, 10 September 1911, and *L'Illustration*, 5 July 1913. I am grateful to Edward L Sterne for additional information.

THE BALTIC DREADNOUGHTS

The *Sevastopol* Class

Russia's first dreadnoughts, the *Sevastopol*[1] class, have been criticised on any number of points, from structural weakness to poor armour protection. In this article, Stephen McLaughlin argues that these criticisms have been based on a fundamentally mistaken assumption regarding their intended role.

The Russo-Japanese War had been a disaster for Imperial Russia in every way; not only had her army and navy been defeated in the Far East but the obvious incapacity of the government had inspired revolutionary unrest in the cities and peasant disorders in the countryside. Before 1905 ended, the Black Sea port of Odessa had been gutted by violence in the streets, an uprising in a working-class district of Moscow had required a bombardment by artillery and the use of Guards' regiments in its suppression; a general strike had crippled the economy; unrest in the Baltic provinces had been brutally put down, and thousands of Russian subjects faced summary justice at the hands of army tribunals. Attempting to pacify the anti-government movement, Tsar Nikolai II, on the advice of Count S Iu Witte, issued a manifesto in October 1905 creating a parliament, the State Duma.

No institution had been more severely tried by war and revolution than the Imperial Navy. When Port Arthur surrendered in January 1905 the Navy lost many of its best ships and by May 1905 virtually all its remaining effective ships had been destroyed or captured at the Battle of Tsushima. Moreover, the Navy's injuries were not limited to matters of matériel. In June a mutiny had broken out on the Black Sea battleship *Kniaz Potemkin Tavricheskii*, sailors had rioted at Kronstadt and Libau and a rebellion, led by Lieutenant Petr Petrovich Shmidt, ended in a miniature naval battle within the harbour of Sevastopol, when the loyal battleship *Rostislav* and shore batteries pummelled the revolutionary cruiser *Ochakov* into submission.

It was clear to educated Russians of every political persuasion that things were desperately wrong with the [Imp]erial Navy. The new State Duma and the press called [for reform?] and as a result various measures were taken. [...] Grand Duke Aleksei Aleksandro-[vich ...]nd man, Admiral Fedor [... M]inister, long

empty, was filled by Admiral Aleksei Alekseevich Birilev, an energetic man with a pugnacious reputation. A new body, the Naval General Staff, was created to co-ordinate the drafting of war plans with construction programmes.

Even as revolution swept through the country and its own lower decks, the Imperial Navy began to take stock of its material resources. The Black Sea Fleet, racked by revolution but untouched by war, was more or less intact. The situation in the Baltic, however, was bleak; one pre-dreadnought, the *Slava*, had been completed too late to sail with Admiral Zenovii Petrovich Rozhdestvenskii's Second Pacific Squadron, while another, the French-built *Tsesarevich*, was limping back to Kronstadt after her release from internment in Kiaochow. There were also two semi-dreadnoughts, *Imperator Pavel I* and *Andrei Pervozvannyi*, under construction and six more ships of the same class (or possibly of a new type armed with four 12in and twelve 10in guns) were projected.[2] However, in December 1905 the government, faced with the tremendous economic dislocations of war and revolution, cut 38,000,000 rubles (£3,800,000) from the Navy's budget, most of which came from the new construction programme. This put an end to the projected ships and left the Baltic Fleet, now faced with the rapidly growing power of the German *Hochseeflotte*, with a grand total of two battleships in hand and two under construction.

Lessons of the Russo-Japanese War

Deprived of money for new construction the Imperial Navy turned its attention to digesting the lessons of the war, one of the most important of which concerned the effectiveness of torpedo attacks. The war had opened with a surprise torpedo-boat attack on the Russian squadron anchored in the roadstead outside Port Arthur on the night of 25–26 January/8–9 February 1904.[3] Ten Japanese torpedo-boats took part in the attack, firing a total of

eighteen torpedoes; the first eight were fired from a range of 600m, yet only three hit the moored and unprepared ships, damaging the battleships *Retvizan* and *Tsesarevich* and the cruiser *Pallada*. There were no other hits and all three ships were repaired at Port Arthur in spite of the lack of a drydock large enough to accommodate them.

Later battles gave similar results. During the abortive Russian sortie on 10/23 June 1904, and again after the Battle of the Yellow Sea on 27 July/10 August, the Japanese had launched torpedo attacks as the Russian squadron retreated to Port Arthur. In both cases, none of the torpedoes found a target.

Again, at the Battle of Tsushima on 14/27 May 1905, Admiral Togo Heihachiro withdrew his heavy ships at nightfall, leaving his torpedo-boats to finish off the many damaged Russian ships. The torpedo-boats and destroyers found it difficult to carry home their attacks in spite of the crippling damage sustained by many of the Russian ships. In fact, during the war only 17 of the 370 torpedoes fired by the Japanese had hit their targets, a success rate of only 4.59 per cent.[4]

The meaning of all this was clear: torpedo attacks were nowhere near as effective as prewar advocates of torpedo boats had maintained, especially against ships that were alert and free to manoeuvre. This lesson was reinforced by the Baltic Fleet's summer manoeuvres in 1908. Energetic efforts were made to improve torpedo tactics in the Imperial Navy, including the development of salvo-firing devices, but, despite these developments, the Navy concluded that light craft armed with torpedoes could not be relied upon to form an effective maritime defence.

Another lesson concerned the effects of shellfire on ships. At the Battle of the Yellow Sea and, to a far greater degree, at Tsushima the unprotected upperworks of the

Andrei Pervozvannyi, circa 1912–1913, showing the changes to the design following the Russo-Japanese War. The midships 8in turrets have been replaced by three 8in guns in casemates on either side; the 75mm anti-torpedo boat guns have been replaced by 120mm guns and their location shifted from hull embrasures to the superstructure above the 8in casemates, leaving the hull almost completely unpierced. It was originally intended to fit the Sevastopol class with cage masts similar to those shown here. (Boris Drashpil Collection of the US Naval Historical Center)

Russian battleships had been wrecked by the contact-fused high-explosive shells used by the Japanese; bridge-work was demolished, masts destroyed and funnels cut up by splinters. Worse, the unarmoured areas of the ships' hulls had been riddled by shell hits – even near misses would pepper the ships with splinters. These innumerable holes became a serious problem as ships settled from flooding, bringing more and more holes below the waterline. Also contributing to this damage-control nightmare were the many ports and scuttles, whose 'watertight' lids had been blown off or distorted by near-by shell hits.

In comparison, the effects of armour-piercing shells had seemed small; Admiral Rozhdestvenskii, in an interview with a French reporter a few months after Tsushima, stated that 'None of our ironclads were pierced by the shells but the repeated shock of the projectiles bursting against them disjointed their steel plates.'[5] The Admiral's judgement has been confirmed by susbsequent investigations, which indicate that no armour thicker than 6in was successfully penetrated during the war.[6]

Yet another lesson was the effectiveness of mines in narrow waters: one Russian battleship and a cruiser had been sunk by mines, while the Japanese had similarly lost two battleships in a single day. Finally, the Russians noted the value of speed – the faster Japanese fleet had been able to out-manoeuvre Rozhdestvenskii continually at Tsushima.

A report by a special commission summed up the lessons of the war, as they applied to potential future battleship construction, and came to three main conclusions:[7]

1. Long fighting ranges of up to 70 cables (14,000 yds) meant that medium-calibre guns were useless and it was the 12in gun that counted.
2. To keep a ship afloat in battle, it was necessary to provide a completely armoured hull, even if this meant a general reduction in armour thickness.
3. High speed was very important.

Some of these lessons could be applied immediately to the two battleships under construction. As originally designed in 1903, the *Imperator Pavel I* and *Andrei Pervozvannyi* were broadly similar to the preceding *Borodino* class. The only substantial change had been an increase of the intermediate battery from twelve 6in to twelve 8in, a reflection of the general trend of the time.[8] Work on these ships was halted after Tsushima and a major redesign carried out, a process that went through seventeen variants and was not completed until November 1906. The superstructures were reduced, the midship 8in turrets were replaced by casement guns, the calibre of the anti-torpedo battery was increased from 75mm to 120mm and moved from hull casemates to the superstructure, and the entire hull provided with armour protection; in fact, there were no openings in the hull at all – scuttles were done away with and all ventilation of the interior spaces was via vertical vents.

However, not even these thoroughgoing changes could alter the basic limitations of a design conceived before the war – especially in view of the debut of the *Dreadnought* in 1906. What the Imperial Navy really wanted was an entirely new design, an all-big-gun battleship built to suit Russian experiences and conditions. A sketch design of such a battleship was prepared and accepted on 27 July/9 August 1907. It featured a uniform main battery (apparently of 12in guns), a speed of 20kts, and a 254mm belt. However, nothing further seems to have been done with this design.

Ships from Vickers

The Imperial Navy was also apparently interested in acquiring foreign-built ships. In mid–1906 rumours circulated that the Russians had ordered a battleship from a Clydeside shipbuilder and, throughout the remainder of that year and well into 1907, there were reports of the imminent laying-down of Russian battleships, usually described as 20,000–21,000 ton, 21kt, turbine-driven ships with ten 12in guns. The various reports, and the alleged characteristics of the ships, are summarized in Table 1.

To what extent these rumours represented real Russian plans is difficult to judge. It is certain, however, that the Imperial Navy did want to order ships from foreign shipyards, where they could be built more cheaply and quickly than in Russian yards. By 1907 the Navy was certainly negotiating with the British firm of Vickers, which was then in the process of completing the powerful armoured cruiser *Riurik* for Russia (interestingly enough, at the time Vickers insisted on describing *Riurik* as a 'battleship'). In this year Vickers did design a 22,000-ton battleship with a speed of 21¼kts for the Imperial Navy,[9] but details have not yet come to light. However, it is possible, that a reference in the 1908 edition of *Jane's*

Table 1: REPORTS OF RUSSIAN BATTLESHIP CONSTRUCTION

Source	page	No of ships	Displacement	Speed	Armament
Times 13 Aug 1906	8	?	20,000	21	?
Times 29 Oct 1906	5	2	21,000	?	?
Times 7 Nov 1906	5	2	21,800	21	10 × 12in
Times 5 Mar 1907	17	2	21,800	21	10 × 12in
USNIP No 2 1907	872	1	22,000+	?	10 × 12in
M-R May 1907	685	1	21,800	21	10 × 12in
Times 8 Aug 1907	3	2	19,970	21	10 × 12in
Times 11 Sep 1907	6	4	21,000	?	?
Times 2 Oct 1907	8	2	25,000	?	10 × 12in
					6 × 8in
USNIP No 4 1907	1525	2?	19,900	21	10 × 12in
Jane's 1908	310	2	21,500	21	10 × 12in
					20 × 4.7in

Notes:

Jane's	*Jane's Fighting Ships*
M-R	*Marine-Rundschau*
Times	London *Times*
USNIP	*United States Naval Institute Proceedings*

Fighting Ships to 'Copies of the *Dreadnought* with armour over [the] entire hull' has its origin in this project. In addition to providing the design itself, Vickers undertook to supervise the construction of the ships in Russian yards. The deal was reportedly worth £400,000 to Vickers.

The Navy's contacts with Vickers inspired protests in the Russian press and in August 1907 the newspaper *Rus'* published an article, purportedly by a naval officer who had attended the trials of the *Riurik*, complaining about both the ship and her builders. Then came a series of articles in *Novoe Vremia* accusing the Naval Ministry 'of corruption and possible treason in its highest ranks in the construction of the cruiser *Riurik*'[10] (the charge of treason being based on the belief that Russian naval secrets had been revealed to Vickers in the course of the ship's construction).

These newspaper attacks led in turn to questions in the State Duma about the *Riurik* and the use of foreign shipbuilders in general. In November representatives of leading Russian firms lent their weight to the protests when they petitioned the prime minister to prevent any new Russian battleships being built outside Russia. The Naval Ministry issued a press release attempting to justify the Vickers proposal but by now the matter was clearly too sensitive for the Navy to handle by itself. The whole question was therefore laid before the Council of Ministers, which quickly decided (in typical bureaucratic fashion) to form a special commission to determine just how the Navy should go about obtaining new warships. However, to quiet further protests, it was stipulated at the outset that any new ships would have to be built in Russia using Russian materials. The end result of this process was an international design competition that ultimately led to the *Sevastopol* class dreadnoughts. Before describing this competition, however, it is necessary to outline Russia's strategic situation and the war plans that were being developed in conjunction with the new battleship design.

Geography, Strategy and War Plans

Russian naval planning in the Baltic was dominated by one consideration: the location of St Petersburg at the head of the Gulf of Finland. In the age of sail, the capital had been defended by a series of naval forts centred on Kotlin Island, site of the great naval base of Kronstadt, but, in an era of fast steam-driven ships and long-range guns, Kronstadt and its forts could no longer provide a complete defence. In the eyes of Russian naval planners, the capital city was an increasingly tempting target for naval bombardment or even amphibious assault – a possibility that seemed especially threatening given the weak state of the Baltic Fleet after the Russo-Japanese War.

The most important strategic role of the Baltic Fleet was therefore to defend the capital. That defence did not

Gangut *at Petrograd during the First World War, probably soon after completion. Note that she has the searchlight abaft the funnel which was, apparently, later removed. Note also that there is no rangefinder on the after turret.* (Boris Drashpil Collection of the US Naval Historical Center)

have to be permanent: The Army needed about two weeks to mobilize St Petersburg's defences; after that, the city would be relatively secure. However, until then it would be vulnerable to a naval *coup de main* that would certainly disrupt the Army's mobilization plans and might even force Russia to submit to an unfavourable peace.

As for whom the Navy had to defend against, that question was easily answered. The system of treaties and understandings between the great powers divided Europe into two blocs: Russia, France and (probably) Great Britain on one side, Germany, Austria-Hungary and (perhaps) Italy on the other. This system was completed in 1907 when Russia and Great Britain settled their long-standing conflict over influence in Persia. Germany, then, was the most probable enemy, perhaps with Sweden allied to it.

This new understanding with the world's greatest maritime power brought little comfort to Russian naval planners. The only entrances to the Baltic were the narrow and winding Belts between Denmark and Sweden, which could easily be rendered impassable for surface ships in wartime. Germany's *Hochseeflotte*, on the other hand, could be shuttled quickly and secretly between the North Sea and the Baltic through the Kaiser-Wilhelm (known today as the Kiel) canal, so the Russians had to anticipate withstanding the full force of an increasingly powerful enemy without significant assistance from their allies.

Planning for this difficult military situation was entrusted to the Naval General Staff (*Morskoi general'nyi shtab* or MGSh), which had been established in April 1906. Its first chief was Captain 1st Rank (later Rear-Admiral) Lev Alekseevich Brusilov, brother of the general who was to achieve such fame in 1916. Before the Russo-Japanese War, Brusilov had headed the Naval Operations Commission of the Admiralty, where he had been planning for a Baltic war. He was therefore able to pick up where he had left off, although with far fewer ships. Illness forced his retirement in 1908 (he died soon after) and his place was taken by Rear-Admiral Andrei Avgustovich Ebergardt, a very able officer who was to command the Black Sea Fleet with considerable distinction during the first two years of the First World War.

The General Staff's first war plans, worked out in 1907–1908, fully reflected the unfavourable naval situation:[11] the Baltic Fleet had only two pre-dreadnought battleships, with two more under construction, while the German Navy had twenty pre-dreadnoughts in commission by 1908 and nine dreadnought battleships and battlecruisers under construction. Obviously, a general engagement with the Germans could only end in the destruction of the Russian squadron.

The available light forces also offered little comfort and cruiser forces were especially weak. There were considerable numbers of destroyers and torpedo-boats available or under construction but the Naval General Staff did not place much faith in their ability to deter a powerful battleship force because, as we have seen, they had given a disappointing performance during the Russo-Japanese War.

The 1907–1908 plan therefore called for the laying of minefields north and south of Hogland (Sursaari) Island in the middle of the Gulf of Finland; torpedo-boats and submarines based in the Skerries (the rocks and islets that are strung along the rugged Finnish coast) would be used to whittle down an advancing German fleet before it reached the Hogland position and the battleships would engage only after the Germans had reached this point; they would stay behind the minefields and use their heavy guns to keep the enemy from sweeping clear channels through the minefields. It was hoped that this strategy would delay the Germans for twelve to fourteen days, giving the Army time to mobilize enough troops to defend the capital. Later plans elaborated on the basic concept of a 'mine-artillery position', pushing the defensive minefields out to the mouth of the Gulf of Finland and adding coast artillery on the flanks, but all followed the same basic scheme, a mine barrier defended by light forces and backed up by battleships.

This is the plan that moulded the General Staff's characteristics for new warships. There were clearly a number of tactical consequences of this scheme. First, the defence of the minefields would place a premium on long-range gunnery: if the Russian battleships could shell the enemy's minesweepers while staying out of range of its battleships, the enemy would be unable to close to decisive ranges. Radius of action was clearly a secondary consideration, as was habitability; the ships would spend most of their time in harbour, waiting for the enemy attack, and war would in any case be sudden, sharp and brief.

The Design Competition

The initial basis for design competition was a set of military characteristics worked out by the General Staff in April 1907.[12] In October 1907, the Navy Technical Committee (*Morskoi tekhnicheskii komitet* or MTK) began determining the desired technical features of a new battleship design, a process that was not completed until the end of the year. When the characteristics were first being formulated the main battery was to be disposed in twin turrets but, at some later point, this was changed to triple turrets, which allowed the entire battery to fire on either broadside. Because it regarded end-on fire as of minimal importance, the General Staff strongly endorsed what became known as the 'linear arrangement' of the main battery, that is, the placement of all the turrets on the same level along the centreline of the ship.

On 22 December 1907/3 January 1908 the Naval Ministry issued invitations to tender a design to six Russian and twenty-one foreign firms; proposals were due by 28 February/12 March 1908. The invitations called for a ship with a speed of 21.5kts and armed with 12in guns in triple turrets and sixteen 120mm guns in casemates.[13]

This competition excited a great deal of interest among shipbuilders; given the state of the Baltic Fleet, it was believed that the resulting contract would be the first of many. In February 1908 both the president and vice-president of the American Bethlehem Steel Company sailed to St Petersburg to press their case. Other firms involved included the Baltic Works, the Putilov Works and the Nevskii Works in Russia; Vickers Sons and

Maxim, Cammell Laird & Co and Armstrong in Great Britain; Stabilimento Tecnico and Ansaldo, Armstrong and Co in Italy; La Seyne and Le Havre in France; A G Vulcan, Stettin and Blohm und Voss in Germany. Fifty-one designs were submitted by the contending companies.

Ten designs were selected for further study, only one of which was Russian. There followed a long process of negotiation and requests for alternative designs and modifications; some companies dropped out of the race, believing, as one contemporary observer put it, that changes were made 'less from military needs than from a desire to acquire up-to-date information'.[14] What was actually happening (inevitably, one suspects) was that, after reviewing the designs submitted, the General Staff and the Technical Committee wanted to combine the best features from each. Thus the General Staff wanted to increase the speed, to rearrange the armour for greater protection and the machinery for greater survivability; it was also interested in substituting 102mm guns for the specified 120mm, in using diesel motors as cruising engines and in small-tube boilers. The Technical Committee, on the other hand, was so impressed by the structural arrangements of the design submitted by the Baltic Works that it wanted to see the same principles applied to other designs.[15]

Two photographs of Poltava *at speed, probably taken during her trials in December 1914. The range-finders on the first and fourth turrets are just visible, but the rangefinder atop the bridge has apparently not yet been fitted. Notice how deeply her bow is digging in, especially in the second photograph.* (Boris Drashpil Collection of the US Naval Historical Center)

In addition there was a conflict brewing between the Technical Committee and the General Staff. The former had long dominated Russian warship design but its views on ship design tended to be based on technical and financial, rather than tactical or strategic, considerations. Aleksandr Vasilevich Kolchak, at that time one of the young reform-minded officers on the General Staff, described the results in these terms: 'The building of ships had been going along without any plan, depending on the credits allotted for the purpose; at that, it sometimes reached such a point of absurdity that the kind of vessels built corresponded not to what was needed but to the amount allotted'.[16] The General Staff, on the other hand, saw ship designs as an extension of its war plans and desired ships whose characteristics did not depend solely on the amount of money available.

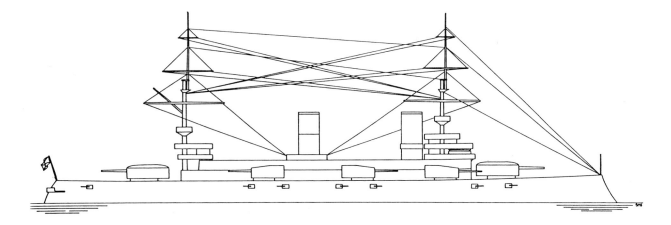

General appearance of the Andrei Pervozvannyi *as originally designed. Note the hull embrasures for the 75mm anti-torpedo boat battery, the extensive superstructures and the massive rig – all features that would be changed after the Russo-Japanese War.* (Author)

The Naval Technical Committee had a long history and was staffed by officers of imposing rank. The Naval General Staff was a new body and its leaders were relatively junior flag officers; its first head, L A Brusilov, was apparently still a captain at the time of his appointment. The bureaucratic position of the General Staff was not helped by the fact that Naval Minister, Admiral A A Birilev, had distrusted the new organization, while his successor, Admiral Ivan Mikhailovich Dikov, was 'indifferent to its work'.[17]

Given these circumstances, it is hardly surprising that the Technical Committee had its way in selecting the winning design. At a conference chaired by Admiral Dikov on 18/31 July 1908, the choice was narrowed to two designs: that from Blohm und Voss, favoured by the Technical Committee, and one submitted by the Italian naval architect Colonel Vittorio Cuniberti, championed by the General Staff. The German design apparently featured relatively modest characteristics: 20,000 tons, a speed of 21.25kts, a main battery of 12in guns and a crew of 800. The Cuniberti design was never described in the press but it was probably very similar to his *Danti Alighieri* and presumably featured a higher speed than the German design.[18]

The final decision came on 9/22 August 1908, when the Blohm und Voss design was selected. The General Staff's choice, the Cuniberti design, was rejected on a technicality: its secondary battery was mounted in turrets, not in casemates as set forth in the competition's specifications.[19]

Although Kaiser Wilhelm II sent a telegram congratulating Blohm und Voss, the matter was far from settled. The selection of a German design set off a small storm of protest in political circles. The idea of having a Russian battleship built by a German firm did not sit well with Russia's politicians, while France, Russia's closest ally, also voiced concern over the choice. Nevertheless, the Blohm und Voss drawings were finally purchased in August 1908.

It is likely, however, that the purchase of a foreign design was by this time more a matter of form than of actual interest. Throughout the competition there had been a strong interest in the design offered by the Baltic Works. It had been eliminated from the final selection process chiefly because it featured superimposed main battery turrets, rather than the linear arrangement favoured by the General Staff. The design was therefore reworked to incorporate a linear arrangement of turrets and, on 17 November/1 December 1908, the Naval Minister approved the construction of ships built to the modified Baltic Works design.[20]

Fighting for Finance

Even as the Naval Ministry was sorting out the results of the design competition, a tremendous political fight was shaping up over whether battleships should be built at all. Tsar Nikolai II believed that Russia's position as a great power rested, at least in part, on a strong battlefleet and commanded his prime minister, P A Stolypin (who was appointed by the Tsar, and was responsible to him alone), to press for their construction. In this Stolypin did his best, despite personal misgivings, but the State Duma refused to finance them. Even the generally pro-government Octobrist party, believing that the Naval Ministry and shipyards were so riddled with corruption and inefficiency that any credits voted for major construction projects would be largely wasted, rejected the proposal. The president of the Navy League, S V Rukhlov, stated that it would be 'a criminal policy to construct huge, expensive armoured battleships and cruisers at a time when Russia possessed no adequately furnished ports, no disciplined crews and no trained officers,'[21] while a newspaper subventioned by the Naval Ministry, the *Kotlin*, commented on the 'irregularities' of the ministry.[22] Various announcements by the government of plans to inspect naval bases and reorganize the Navy failed to impress the critics, and the Duma persisted in refusing to vote funds. The situation became so serious that, in January 1908, the Tsar threatened to dissolve the Duma unless it voted funds for battleship construction – by no means an idle gesture, since he had already dismissed the two preceding Dumas.[23]

The Army also opposed the building of expensive battleships, which it saw as a dangerous rival to its own plans for expansion. It argued that a coast defence fleet of light vessels would be a more effective (and, of course, cheaper) form of protection for Russia's Baltic coast.[24] This idea had the support of some naval officers; Captain 1st Rank Leonid Fedorovich Dobrotvorskii, commander of the cruiser *Oleg* at the Battle of Tsushima, argued for 'the necessity of building exclusively unarmoured ships, such as light cruisers, destroyers and, especially, submarines.'[25] Even Admiral Rozhdestvenskii, commander of the fleet that had been destroyed at the Battle of Tsushima, came out against the construction of battleships, although his reasoning (that Russian battleship construction would be seen by the Japanese as a threat and lead to an immediate attack on the Russian Far East) was uniquely eccentric.

Foreign observers also lent their voice to this line of reasoning; the French statesman Jean-Louis de Lanessan, a former Minister of Marine, said that 'France has no interest in Russia spending money on a fleet which she could not send out of the Baltic, even if she were strong, and which would be destroyed in the Baltic if it were not at least equal to the German fleet.' De Lanessan concluded that 'it would be a mistake to urge Russia to build ships which would be absolutely useless to her'.[26]

However, the government had an ally in the Council of the Empire (the upper house of the legislature, which was composed of senior officials, retired military officers and representatives of the hierarchies of the church and universities) which approved the battleship construction scheme. Meetings between representatives of the Duma and Council failed to reconcile the two, which meant there was no agreed budget for the Navy. This actually worked to the government's advantage, as the budget laws stipulated that under such circumstances it could choose which budget (the Duma's or the Council's) it wanted. The government opted for the budget approved by the Council, thus gaining funds to begin construction of the battleships but, unless the Duma voted credits for them in following years, there would be an annual repetition of the painful budget wrangling.[27]

That the ships *were* financed by the Duma in succeeding years was due in a large measure to the crisis that erupted when Austria-Hungary annexed Bosnia-Herzegovina in October 1908. When Russia made threatening noises in support of Serbian aspirations to those territories, Germany, Austria's ally, presented what amounted to an ultimatum to Russia. The Russians knew they were not ready for war and were forced to back down in March 1909. The sense of national humiliation was profound, and the Duma became far more amenable to voting credits for the armed services. Thus the battleships, begun against the expressed wishes of the Duma, were continued thanks to the Duma's support.

Construction and Characteristics

All four ships of the class were laid down on the same day, 3/16 June 1909. The ceremony included religious rites and a 'stirring speech' by Admiral Ivan Konstantinovich

Grigorovich, the Deputy Naval Minister.[28] The characteristics of the ships as designed are given in Table 2.[29]

The original design submitted by the Baltic Works was the work of Ivan Grigorovich Bubnov, who had done considerable research into the structure of ships. His design incorporated some novel structural arrangements which attracted favourable comments from the Technical Committee; among other things, he used longitudinal (rather than the standard transverse) deck frames, which increased the longitudinal strength of the hull, and splinter bulkheads set 3.66m (12ft) from the outer hull.[30]

The design had impressed the chairman of the Technical Committee, Aleksei Nikolaevich Krylov, who had also done extensive work on the mathematics of hull stresses and strength, and the final design would seem to have incorporated much of Krylov's own thinking on the structure of ships. High-tensile steel was used throughout the hull and the scantlings were relatively light in comparison to those of foreign battleships. Their dimensions were mathematically derived, rather than based on those of preceding ships, as was the general practice abroad, and Krylov may have used a mechanical computer he had constructed in 1904 in determining the hull stresses and the consequent sizes of the structural members. Detail design work and general technical consulting services were provided by the British firm of John Brown, Clydebank.

Table 2: *DESIGN PARTICULARS OF THE SEVASTOPOL CLASS*

Displacement:	23,000 tons normal
Dimensions:	590ft 6in wl, 594ft 6in oa × 87ft 3in × 27ft 4in (180.0m wl, 181.2m oa × 26.6m × 8.32m)
Machinery:	4 shaft Parsons turbines, 25 Yarrow boilers, 42,000shp = 23kts. Normal oil fuel supply 200 tons, coal 816 tons
Armour:	225mm (8.9in) main belt; 125mm (4.9in) forward/aft belts; 125mm (4.9in) upper belt (citadel); 75mm (2.95in) upper belt (forward); 50/37.5mm (1.97/1.48in) splinter bulkhead; 37.5mm (1.48in) upper deck; 25/19mm (0.98/0.75in) middle deck; 12mm (0.47in) lower deck; 203mm (8.0in) turret faces; 203mm (8.0in) turret sides; 305mm (12.0in) turret backs; 76mm (3.0in) turret roofs; 150mm (5.9in) barbettes; 254mm (10in) conning tower sides; 100mm (4.9in) conning tower roofs; 76mm (3.0in) conning tower floors; 22mm (0.87in) funnel uptakes
Armament:	Twelve 12in (305mm)/52 (4×3; 100rpg); sixteen 4.7in (120mm)/50 (16×1; 250rpg); eight 75mm (8×1; 52rpg); four 47mm (4×1; 200rpg); four 63.5mm AA (4×1; 300rpg); four 18in (457mm) underwater torpedo tubes (3 spares per tube)
Complement:	N/A (1126 as completed)

Table 3: *CONSTRUCTION OF* SEVASTOPOL *CLASS*

Name:	Builder:	Laid down:	Launched:	Completed:
Gangut	Admiralty (St Pet)	16 Jun 1909	7 Oct 1911	29 Dec 1914
Petropavlosk	Baltic Works (St Pet)	16 Jun 1909	9 Sep 1911	23 Dec 1914
Poltava	Admiralty (St Pet)	16 Jun 1909	10 Jul 1911	17 Dec 1914
Sevastopol	Baltic Works (St Pet)	16 Jun 1909	27 Jun 1911	17 Nov 1914

Note: *All dates given according to the New Style.*

The mathematically derived hull structure apparently led to concerns about the hull strength and construction was halted for a time in the summer of 1910, while changes were made. Another delay was caused by the exclusive use of Russian-manufactured materials for the ships, in accordance with the decision of the Council of Ministers and the wishes of the Duma. Production of the requisite high-tensile steel was slow; the first batches did not meet test specifications and had to be replaced.

The overall layout of the final design bore a superficial resemblance to Cuniberti's *Dante Alighieri* and the ships have often been described as a modified version of the design Cuniberti had submitted during the competition. In fact, the linear arrangement of turrets had been preferred by the General Staff before the design competition had begun; whether this was an outgrowth of Russian

Sevastopol *class general arrangement. This drawing, based on drawings published in the Russian magazine* Sudostroenie, *shows several features that were not included in the ships as completed – for example, the booms on the funnels and the guns atop the first and fourth turrets. The numerous circular objects in the plan view are ventilators, made necessary by the lack of scuttles in the hull. Some elements of the superstructure remain obscure in both published drawings and photographs.* (Author)

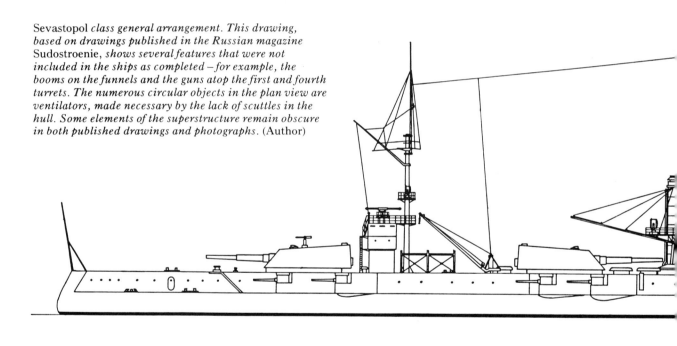

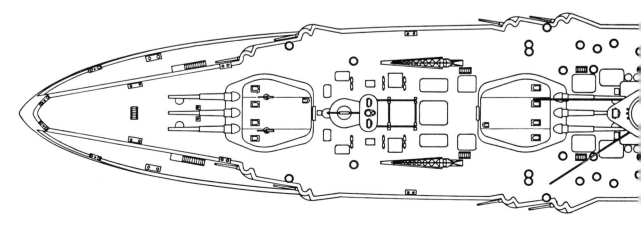

experience (which strongly indicated that broadside fire was far more important than end-on fire) or based on early reports of the Italian design (which was not laid down until June 1909, the same month as the Russian ships) is impossible to say.

In addition to its discounting the value of end-on fire, the General Staff may have seen long-range fire-control advantages as, with all the turrets on the same level, there would be no need to allow for differing turret heights in calibrating the guns.[31] It is also possible that the full advantages of the superimposed arrangement may not have been realized at the time; contemporary British ships with superimposed turrets obtained no increase in end-on fire, as the upper turrets could not fire over the lower turrets without concussing the men in the latter's sighting ports.

Unlike the Italian design, there was no raised forecastle and the secondary guns were mounted exclusively in casemates. A more subtle, but very important, difference was the lack of any scuttles in the ships' sides, with the

exception of a few along the middle deck, which resulted from the fact that the ships' hulls were completely armoured above the waterline except for a small section of the middle deck, aft.

General Features The starting point for the hull form was that of the *Andrei Pervozvannyi* class with the displacement increased to 21,000 tons. More than twenty hull forms were tested before the final scheme, very narrow forward and very full aft, was selected. Model tests indicated that a 23,000-ton ship would need 23,000shp for a speed of 21.75kts and 45,000shp for 24kts[32] – this in spite of the fact that the bow incorporated a reinforced icebreaker stem which reduced the overall hydrodynamic efficiency. The relative lack of buoyancy forward, and the lack of a forecastle deck, caused the ships to bury their bows in rough seas, which on occasion interfered with the operation of both the forward casemates and the foremost turret. There were two rudders, both on the centreline, the after one being the larger.

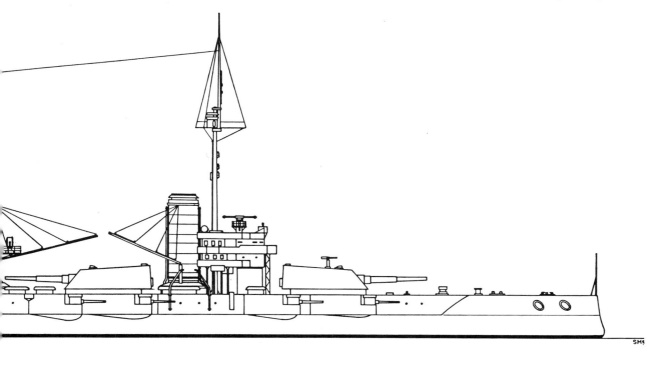

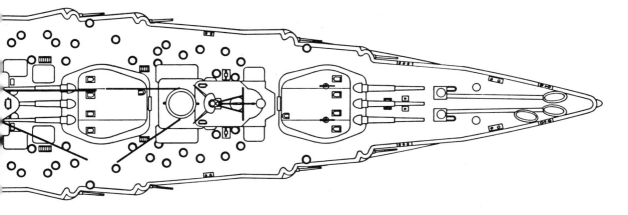

Inboard profile of the Sevastopol *class*. (Author)
Key:　1 Boiler Rooms
　　　2 Machinery Rooms

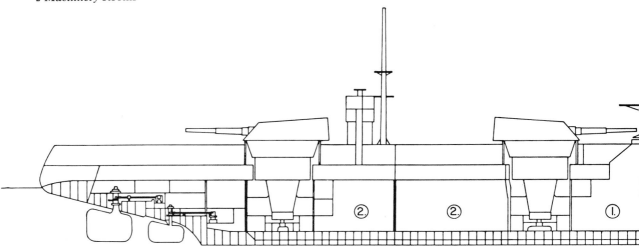

Superstructures were reduced to an absolute minimum – there was ·little above the weather deck apart from the main battery turrets, the fore and aft conning towers and the funnels. The ships were originally to carry cage masts, as had been fitted on the *Andrei Pervozvannyi* class, which were intended to provide a more battleworthy support for signal arrangements, these having been greatly hampered at Tsushima by the destruction of masts and yards. However, problems with vibration and the belief that they would provide an enemy with excellent reference points for range finding, led to their replacement in the *Sevastopol* class by simple pole masts. This decision may have been made easier by the development of short-range wireless for tactical communications.[33]

Armour and Protection The armour plate was made by the Izhora Works (*Izhorskii zavod*). The total weight devoted to armour is given by one unofficial source as 6750 tons, or 29.35 per cent of the design displacement.[34] The protection scheme was very different from that of the battleships of other nations.[35] The main belt, 225mm (8.85in) thick, tapering to 150mm (5.9in) at the lower edge, extended from the forward to the after barbette, a total length of 116.5m (64.72 per cent of the waterline length). It measured 5.06m (16ft 7in) vertically, of which 1.73m (5ft 8in) was below the waterline. In comparison, the 11in belt of the contemporary British *Colossus* class extended from 2ft 9in above to 5ft 6in below the load waterline, a total height of 8ft 3in. The *Colossus* also had an 8in upper belt, but the total height of both belts was still less than that of the Russian ships.

On the waterline forward and aft the armour thinned to 125–75mm (4.9–3in) and continued to the extremities of the ship. Above the main belt, a 125mm (4.9in) upper belt, 2.73m (8ft 11in) high, protected the sides of the ship to upper deck level, from the forward to the aftermost casemate. Forward of this the upper hull was protected by 75mm (3in) armour right to the stem. The only un-

armoured portion of the hull side was on the main deck abaft the after barbette; according to one contemporary source, it had originally been planned to armour this section also but weight problems prevented it.[36]

On each side of the ship, 3.4m (11ft 2in) inboard of the outer hull and extending from the forward to the after barbette, was a splinter bulkhead 37.5mm (1.48in) thick between the upper and middle decks and 50mm (1.97in) thick between the middle and lower decks. From the lower deck it sloped downwards to meet the lower edge of the armour belt; the thickness on the slopes being 25mm (0.98in). The citadel was closed forward by 100mm (3.94in) thick transverse bulkheads which ran from the hull side to the barbettes. There were also 25mm (0.98in) screens between the casemates.

The upper deck was protected by plating 37.5mm (1.48in) thick, while the main deck was 25mm (0.98in) thick from the hull sides to the splinter bulkhead and 19mm (0.75in) thick between these bulkheads. The lower deck was 12mm (0.47in) thick.

The turrets had 203mm (8in) face and side plates, and 76mm (3in) roofs. The turret backs were 305mm (12in), a thickness determined by the need to balance the turret rather than by considerations of protection.[37] The barbettes were 150mm (5.9in) above the upper deck and 75mm (2.95in) below it. The forward and after barbettes were 125mm (4.92in) thick where they formed part of the transverse bulkheads. The two conning towers were protected identically, with 254mm (10in) sides, 150mm (5.9in) roofs and 76mm (3in) floors. The funnel uptakes were protected by 22mm (0.87in) plating.

Underwater protection consisted of a 4ft deep double bottom and a single, mild-steel bulkhead about 11ft inboard of the outer hull. Coal was apparently used to fill the side compartments, at least abreast the boiler rooms.

Armament The main battery consisted of twelve 12in (305mm) guns in four triple turrets, all on the centreline

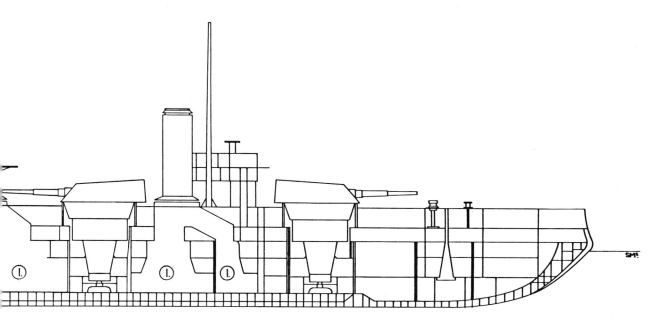

and all at the same height above the waterline. There had been a separate design competition for the turrets, with firms such as Vickers, Krupp and Schneider participating. The winning company was the Metallicheskii Works (*Metallicheskii zavod*).[38]

The guns and mountings were manufactured by the Obukhov Works (*Obukhovskii zavod*), a long-established plant famous for its excellent artillery pieces. By western measure (length of bore), the guns were 50.56 calibres long; by Russian measure, which covers the overall length of the piece, they were 52.13 calibres long. Their particulars were as follows.[39]

Model:	M1910/M1914
Weight (including breach mech):	51.03 tonnes (51.85 tonnes)
Projectile Weight:	1038lb (470.9kg) AP 714.3lb (324kg) HE (see below)
Propellant Charge:	346lb (157kg)
Muzzle Velocity:	2500f/s (762m/s)
Range:	26,925yds/25°

There is some disagreement about the shell weight; one source gives it as 447kg (983.4lbs) for high-explosive shells, while another gives the weight of a full broadside as 6250kg, or 520.8kg per gun; yet the same source gives the individual shell weight as 426kg![40] These variations may represent confusions between high-explosive and armour-piercing shells, as well as differences between shells used at different times.

The mountings had electro-hydraulic training and elevating gear and provided for a rate of fire of 1.67 rounds/minute, but at elevations greater than 13 degrees the rate of fire decreased to one round per minute. The rotating weight of each turret, including armour, was 720 tons. Magazine capacity totalled 1200 rounds.[41]

Even using the lightest shell weight cited for these ships (426kg), their main battery could fire a heavier broadside than any German dreadnought until the 15in-gunned *Bayern* class, and the *Sevastopol* class outranged even these superdreadnoughts, as shown in Table 4:[42]

The secondary armament consisted of sixteen 120mm (4.7in)/50 calibre guns mounted in casemates. They had a maximum elevation of 20 degrees which gave a maximum range of 14,450m (15,800yds), and fired a 22.9kg (50.5lb) shell at a maximum rate of eight rounds per minute.[43]

The original design also included eight 75mm guns and four 47mm guns (apparently to be mounted atop the turrets), and four 63.5mm (2.5in) AA guns with a maximum elevation of 80 degrees. By the time the ships were completed in late 1914, however, there was a

Table 4: *DREADNOUGHT ARMAMENTS, COMPARATIVE DATA*

Class	*Completed*	*Broadside*	*Weight* (kg)	*Range* (yds)
Sevastopol	1914–1915	12 × 12in	5,112	26,925
Nassau	1909–1910	8 × 11in	2,440	20,670
Helgoland	1911–1912	8 × 12in	3,240	22,310
Kaiser	1912–1913	10 × 12in	4,050	22,310
König	1914	10 × 12in	4,050	22,310
Bayern	1916	8 × 15in	6,000	25,370

Sketches showing the armouring of the hull surface (top) and decks and bulkheads (bottom). All figures in millimetres. The location and depth of the fore and aft 100mm bulkheads, and the extent and thickness of any deck protection fore and aft of the citadel, remain uncertain. (Author)

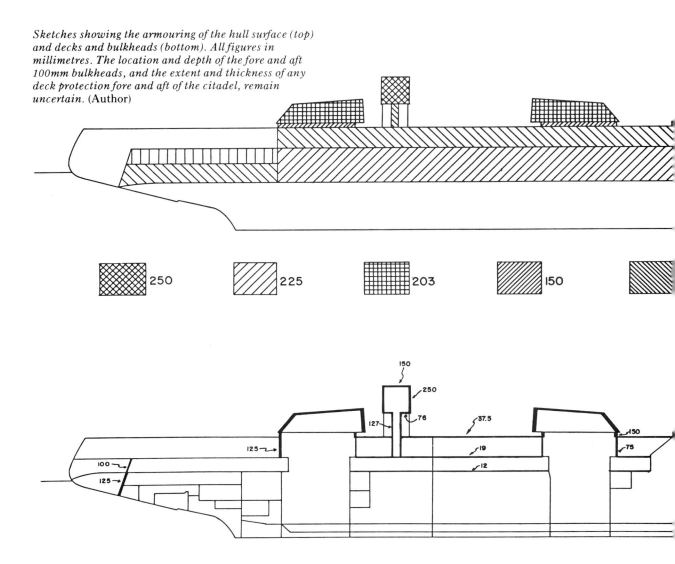

shortage of light artillery; *Sevastopol* and *Poltava* therefore entered service with two 75mm guns, while *Petropavlovsk* and *Gangut* had two 63.5mm guns. These alterations allowed for an increase in the 120mm ammunition stowage, from the designed 250 rounds per gun to 300rpg.[44] The ships were also fitted with four, underwater 450mm (17.7in) torpedo tubes, two on each side, for which they carried twelve reserve torpedoes.

Machinery The *Sevastopol* class ships were designed to achieve an unusually high speed for their day: 23kts. To this end they had a four-shaft power plant of 42,000shp. The Parsons turbines were designed by John Brown and Co and were manufactured by the Baltic Works (*Baltiiskii zavod* for *Sevastopol* and *Petropavlovsk*), and by the Franco-Russian Works (*Franko-Russkii zavod* for *Gangut* and *Poltava*). The machinery compartments were located between the third and fourth turrets, with the turbines for the two centre shafts in one compartment and those of the wing shafts in outboard compartments.[45]

There were twenty-five Yarrow small-tube boilers, with a working pressure of 17.6kg/cm² (250lb/in²), fitted for both coal- and oil-burning. The seven firerooms were arranged in four watertight compartments, the two forward compartments between the first and second turrets, the other two between the second and third turrets. At the time small-tube boilers were commonly used in destroyers, but not in capital ships; they were lighter and smaller than large-tube boilers of the same output but required more frequent and careful maintenance.

On trials the ships achieved their designed speed without forcing, in spite of increases over the designed displacement: *Poltava*'s normal displacement as completed was about 24,000 tons, that of *Sevastopol* 24,300 tons and *Gangut* 24,946 tons. *Poltava* ran trials on 21 November/4 December 1914, and by forcing the machinery achieved 52,000shp and a speed of 24.3kts.[46]

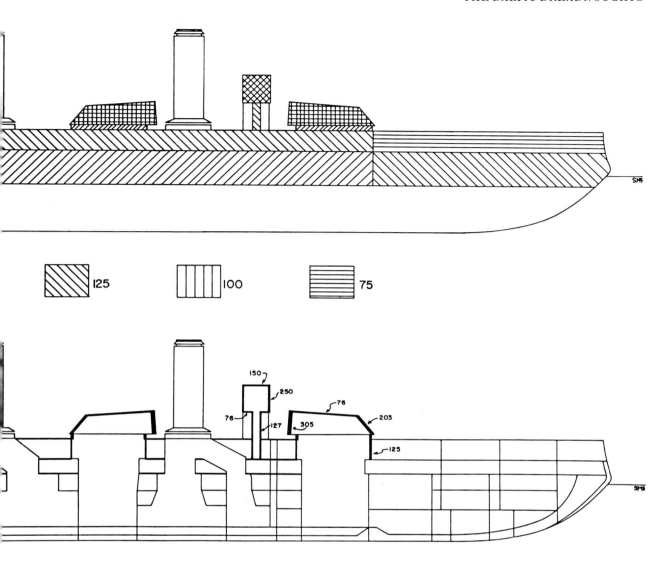

Criticism of the Design

Soon after they were laid down, the *Sevastopol* class ships were subjected to a variety of criticisms; criticisms that have been repeated over the decades until, today, they are accepted as common knowledge. Although the contemporary Russian press was critical of the design (the newspaper *Birzhevie Vedomosti* seems to have been especially outspoken) the most lasting damage to their reputation was done by a detailed description published in the British journal *Engineering* in 1910.[47] This description was based on a report from an unnamed 'correspondent in St Petersburg'. Given the general accuracy of the description and the accompanying drawings, it is possible that this 'correspondent' was one of the engineers from John Brown. Many of the points he raised have appeared in later works, sometimes almost verbatim.

The correspondent began by criticising the Russian Naval Ministry's process of selecting a design and then went on to tackle the specific features of the ships. Some

of his points, such as his preference for twin over triple turrets, can be dismissed as dictated by the prejudices of the era and have not reappeared in subsequent works. However, others have had a more persistent existence.

For example, there is the business of the arrangement of the secondary battery; the correspondent believed that 'the blast from three 12in guns will in all probability render the 4.7in casemates uninhabitable, thus making it impossible to use both the main and secondary batteries at the same time.' Furthermore, 'The casemate openings, always a weak point, are, because of their position relative to the big guns here, high-explosion shell traps to lead projectiles into the proximity of the barbettes.'

Recent writers have echoed these points. For example, Siegfried Breyer says:

Mounting the MCG [Medium Calibre Guns] immediately below the HG [Heavy Gun] turrets may be described as particularly unfortunate because both presumably interfered with each other in action. In addition, the MCG gun ports at these important and particularly sensitive places acted as dangerous shell-catchers.[48]

Donald W Mitchell writes 'the 4.7in guns were adjudged to be too close to the big guns to be kept in action,'[49] while Przemyslaw Budzbon comments that 'Positioning of the 120mm battery was not so successful as the casemates had been arranged immediately below the 12in muzzles'.[50] Most recently, Anthony J Watts has written: 'The casemates for these weapons [the 4.7in guns] were sited immediately beneath the muzzles of the 12in guns, and were thus to a large degree unserviceable when the main guns were firing broadsides'.[51]

There is an underlying assumption here that the main and secondary guns would be used at the same time. We have seen, however, that these ships were intended to defend the mine-artillery position by engaging at long ranges – in which case the secondaries do not come into the picture at all. The idea that the casemates were 'shell-traps' is peculiar, as they were as well-protected as other portions of the hull at that level, and therefore offered shells no better path to the interior of the ship, unless one counts on the shell actually passing through the 4.7in gunports.

A similar repetition occurs in descriptions of the armour protection of the ships. The correspondent noted that ' . . . the main belt armour protecting the machinery and the magazines is only 8.8in in thickness, which is not at all calculated to withstand the fire of the large-calibre guns being fitted to war vessels now about to be laid down.'

The correspondent then describes the internal armour bulkhead and asks: 'Would the weight put into these bulkheads not have been much more effective if used for thickening the outside armour?'

Following this lead, Mitchell writes that 'an overall weakness lay in substandard armor protection . . . The side armor was held to be too thin to keep out heavy shells,' Anthony Preston that ' . . . the novel arrangement of armour gave no measure of protection against long-range fire,'[52] and Jürg Meister, ' . . . their protection was noticeably weaker [than foreign contemporaries].'[53]

The only author who gives some explanation for the apparent weakness of the armour scheme is Hugh Lyon, who writes:

> Their armour was not as well arranged [as that of the *Dante Alighieri*]. This last was spread thinly over a large area of the hull to deal with the threat from quick-firing guns revealed by the Russo–Japanese War, but gave little protection against longer range fire now being adopted by other navies. Curiously, the Russian 12in (305mm) 52cal gun was extremely accurate at long range.[54]

The idea that the armour scheme was intended to protect the ships against a 'hail of fire' from intermediate and medium calibre guns may be dismissed immediately. If the Russian designers stood in such awe of the 'hail of fire' of relatively light guns, *why were no such guns included in the design of these ships?*

It was not the rapid-firing gun that the Russian

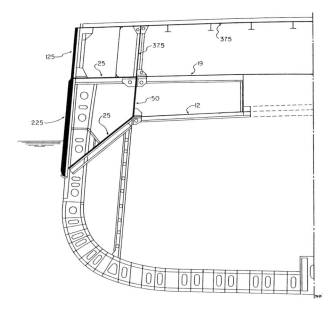

Cross section of the hull in way of the midship boiler rooms, showing armour thickness in millimetres. (Author)

designers feared, it was the high-explosive shell. The correspondent complained that 'It would seem that the idea was to protect every part of the above-water portion of the vessel with armour, irrespective of its thickness, so long as it could be termed armour' – *and in fact that was precisely the point.* At Tsushima, the Japanese high-explosive shells had demolished upperworks (hence they were reduced to a minimum in the *Sevastopol* class) and had displaced armour plating but their worst effects were on the unarmoured portions of the hulls of the Russian battleships, which were riddled with innumerable holes from shells and splinters. The extensive side armour of the *Sevastopol* class, while perhaps unable to keep out armour-piercing shells, *would* prevent the shattering effect of high-explosive shells and the riddling by splinters, thereby preserving the buoyancy of the ship. This same consideration led to the suppression of all but a few scuttles and those that were permitted were limited to the uppermost hull deck.

As for the relatively thin belt, this probably evolved out of a couple of considerations. First, as noted earlier, there is evidence that no armour thicker than 6in was successfully penetrated during the Russo-Japanese War. This seems remarkable, especially when compared to the impressive penetration figures often given for artillery pieces in contemporary sources, but these figures were derived from unrealistic tests that featured 'normal' shell impacts – that is, the shells struck at right angles to the armour plates, the most favourable angle for penetration. The reality, of course, is that shells fall at an angle, which increases the effective thickness of armour; also, ships will most likely not be steaming on exactly parallel courses, so the target angle will also tend to increase the effective thickness of vertical armour (although not of deck armour). Thus, in contrast to foreign designers using *theoretical* penetration data in establishing armour thicknesses, the Russian designers, with data from real engagements, may have considered the 8.86in belt more than adequate, especially given the long ranges at which these ships were intended to fight.

The inner armour bulkhead was probably intended to contain the damage from armour-piercing shell hits that did penetrate the side armour.[55] Penetrating the hull armour would both slow the shell down and activate its delayed-action fuse. The shell would detonate inside the ship but the splinter bulkhead would prevent the damage from being too extensive.

The deck protection followed the same principles. The relatively heavy 1.48in upper deck would activate the fuse of a plunging shell and the splinters from the explosion would be stopped by the 0.98in main deck or the 0.47in lower deck.

Next comes the matter of the structure of the ships; to quote the correspondent again:

> In order to keep the weight of the hull and fittings as small as possible, it was decided by the Russian authorities that high-tensile steel should be used, it being apparently considered that on account of the greater tensile strength of this material it would be possible to reduce the scantlings throughout. This again, of course, is an error, because, in many parts of the structure, stiffness has to be obtained where longitudinal strength does not enter very much into the question. The idea of weakness is borne out by the fact that in order to get the necessary longitudinal strength the beams of the upper deck have been placed longitudinally, so as to be taken into the strength calculation.

Again, this point has been raised by more recent writers. Anthony Preston speaks of 'Krilov's inexplicable insistence on high-tensile steel (normally only required for destroyers)' while Jürg Meister brings up the question of hull strength by noting that the *Sevastopol* class ships 'lacked constructional strength . . . the hull could not withstand a full broadside.'

Certainly, questions were raised about the strength of these ships' hulls in the summer of 1910, when construction was halted, but, after some corrections were made, there is nothing to indicate that they suffered from weak construction. The fact that three of them survived until the Second World War (despite periods of great neglect) and two of them continued to serve well into the 1950s indicates that there was nothing fundamentally wrong with their structure.

In many ways they foreshadowed the treaty-limited warships built in the 1920s and 1930s; in the latter high-tensile steel and longitudinal framing were also extensively used. The Russian designers in 1909 were trying to do exactly what everyone else did not have to do until a couple of decades later: cram the most payload (armour, guns, speed) into a design whose absolute size was constrained by external factors. One obvious way of doing this was to reduce the structural weights as much as possible.

A rarely published shot of Petropavlovsk. *Note how the overweight condition of the complete ship has submerged her ice-breaker bow, giving it the appearance of a ram.* (Boris Drashpil Collection of the US Naval Historical Center)

The Oktjabrskaya Revolutsiya (*ex* Gangut) *in 1935, with Marat (ex* Petropavlovsk) *in the background*. (Boris Drashpil Collection of the US Naval Historical Center)

The final major criticism of the correspondent concerned the machinery: 'the mechanical department of the Marine Technical Committee in St Petersburg were desirous of having water-tube boilers of the large-tube type for the vessels but, on account of the necessity of keeping the weight of the machinery installation as small as possible, the advice of these experts was over-ridden, with the result that it was decided to fit water-tube boilers of the small-tube type.'

The correspondent further complained about 'the unnecessarily high speed of 23 knots.' Thus also Preston, who maintains that 'the extra weight devoted to machinery produced no increase in speed or endurance [compared to the *Dante Alighieri*]' while Breyer holds that by giving the ships a speed 'well above average for those days' other aspects of the design were hopelessly compromised.

These complaints about the speed can be answered by referring to the Russian strategic and tactical situation. In the first place, the Naval General Staff's plan called for basing the battleships at harbours some distance from the defensive minefields; when warned of the approach of an enemy force, they would have to get to the minefields as quickly as possible, hence speed was a strategic necessity. Once there, they would have to manoeuvre so as to use their long-range guns to the best possible advantage; their 23kt speed gave them a 2–3kt advantage over their German contemporaries, sufficient to select the range or (if the mine defences failed) to get away.

As for the use of small-tube boilers, it demonstrates nothing more than the fact that the Russian Navy was in some ways more open to innovations than the Royal Navy, which did not adopt small-tube boilers for capital ships until the *Hood*, despite almost overwhelming evidence of their advantages over large-tube boilers.[56] Their only disadvantage was the need for more careful and frequent maintenance, and even on this score there is nothing to indicate that they caused any unusual difficulties for either the Russian or Soviet operators of the *Sevastopol* class ships.

The correspondent also raised a number of points that have not been picked up by subsequent writers, among them the close spacing of the twin rudders and the adverse hydrodynamic effects of the icebreaker stem. Curiously, one of the correspondent's major criticisms, the weakness

of the underwater protection scheme, has not been repeated. Overall, he believed the ships to be 'a hybrid design, which discloses many serious inefficiencies from the fighting point of view'. Others have agreed with this assessment; Jürg Meister, for example, writes that 'The final result was a far from happy combination,' while Siegfried Breyer called the ships 'a compromise type between battleship and battle cruiser which, however, did not turn out particularly successful. While the strongest possible armament was fitted, adequate protection was dispensed with.'

A few issues were not raised by the 'correspondent in St Petersburg', but have since become common points of criticism. Chief among these is the ships' habitability, or lack thereof. Many editions of *Jane's Fighting Ships*, for example, carried the note that these ships were 'Said to be most unhealthy, insanitary and badly ventilated,'[57] an evaluation repeated by several subsequent writers; thus Breyer: 'they were regarded as highly uncomfortable, difficult to ventilate and insanitary,' Meister 'they were poorly ventilated,' and Preston, 'the reported lack of efficient ventilation would have decreased their efficiency.'

The correspondent concluded by noting that the Russians would have been far better off if they had accepted a design from 'any of the big warship-building countries, arranged, of course, to meet Russian conditions . . .' while 'the ships designed and built there will be obsolete before they are in a fighting condition' due to the long building times of Russian yards.

Certainly having ships built in Russian yards meant long construction times, and both the Imperial Navy and the Russian government were well aware of this fact. The decision to rely on Russian manufacturers, while it no doubt delayed Russia's acquisition of dreadnoughts and drove up their cost, was in the long run the right choice. How else were the industries necessary for future naval construction to be fostered? There were bound to be problems in building such ships but the only way to overcome them was to go ahead and find out what they were. Lessons were clearly being learned; it took five and a half years to complete the *Sevastopol* class ships, but less than four to complete the first two *Imperatritsa Mariia* class ships for the Black Sea Fleet (the third ship was delayed by wartime reallocations of resources and the fourth was never completed for the same reason).

In one area, however, the justice of the 'St Petersburg correspondent's' criticisms must be admitted; the underwater protection of the ships was dangerously weak.

There was only one torpedo bulkhead aside from the upward extension of the double bottom.[58] Since the Russo-Japanese War had made the dangers of underwater weapons, especially mines, abundantly clear, it would appear that this weakness was the result of a deliberate choice on the part of the designers. One possible explanation is that other qualities were considered so much more essential that the underwater protection had to be sacrificed to obtain them. Another is that the ships may not have been expected to be exposed to underwater attack. These explanations may in fact be linked, as a successful mine defence – relying in large measure on the gunnery and speed of the *Sevastopol* class ships – would mean that they would operate almost exclusively behind their own minefields, and would therefore be safe from enemy mines and torpedo craft.

In reality, of course, the minefields were not an absolutely impenetrable barrier. During the First World War U-boats did on occasion get through the mine defences and to these the *Sevastopol* class ships would have been vulnerable. During the First World War the Russian naval command clearly recognized this flaw and, except for a few brief forays, these ships were not allowed to venture outside the protected waters of the Gulf of Finland.

Conclusions

Certainly, the *Sevastopol* ships were far from perfect but they were an intelligent design based on a reasonable scheme of national defence. The Naval General Staff, however, could not reveal the mine-artillery rationale behind the *Sevastopol* design without likewise revealing their plan of maritime defence. Thus the ships had to be sold to the Duma as conventional battleships – at a time when most of the members of the Duma considered battleships nothing more than expensive symbols of national prestige. The impression that these battleships were simply vehicles for national glory was reinforced by the fact that the Tsar wanted them for precisely that reason; in the era of 'navalism', he wanted a big navy of big ships.

The *Sevastopol* class were part of a very rational scheme of naval defence. They were not designed to slug it out with the *Hochseeflotte* – that way lay madness and destruction. By defending the defensive minefields they could have prevented, or at least significantly delayed, any naval attack upon the heart of the empire, St Petersburg. This is what they were intended to do but, because most writers have assumed that these ships were classic sea-control battleships, they have been subjected to a great deal of unwarranted criticism. The features of their design that have been most criticised stem directly from the Naval General Staff's war plans, and from Russian experiences in the Russo-Japanese War that went unnoticed or were misunderstood by foreign observers. There is no more fitting judgement on this class than that which appeared in the 1919 edition of *Jane's Fighting Ships*: 'The design of these ships has been very severely criticised but, although abnormal in many details, they may have proved quite successful in service.[59]

Notes

1 These ships are usually referred to as the *Gangut* class in the west but Russian and Soviet sources uniformly call them the *Sevastopol* class. Dates throughout are given in the form Old Style/New Style; the Russian calendar was thirteen days behind that of the west until it was revised by the Bolsheviks in 1918.

2 Siegfried Breyer, *Soviet Warship Development. Vol I: 1917–1937*, Conway Maritime Press (London, 1992), p32; L Koromal'di, 'Tusimskii boii bronirovanie korablei' (The Battle of Tsushima and the Armour of Ships), *Morskoi Sbornik*, Vol XXXIII, No 3 (March 1906), pp205–232.

3 For the war in general see the *Official History (Naval and Military) of the Russo-Japanese War* (Historical Section, Committee of Imperial Defence), 3 vols, HMSO (London, 1910–20). For Tsushima, the best recent account is N J M Campbell, 'The Battle of Tsu-Shima', *Warship*, Vol II, Conway Maritime Press (London, 1978).

4 Arthur J Marder, *From the Dreadnought to Scapa Flow, Vol 1, 1904–1914*, Oxford University Press (London, 1961), p329.

5 London *Times*, 17 November 1905, p5.

6 Keith McBride, 'After the Dreadnought', *Warship 1992*, Conway Maritime Press (London, 1992), p99. This point was also raised in Great Britain, where some argued that the Russo-Japanese War 'showed that armour could not be pierced and that its thickness could thus be reduced', P A Towle, 'The Effect of the Russo-Japanese War on British Naval Policy', *Mariner's Mirror*, Vol LX, No 4 (November 1974), p383–4. Towle raises the possibility that this information led to the *Dreadnought*'s relatively thin belt.

7 I I Chernikov, 'Lineniyi korabli tipa Sevastopol' (Battleships of the *Sevastopol* Class), *Sudostroenie*, No 2, 1986, pp60 and 62.

8 Information on the *Andrei Pervozannyi* class is based on N N Afonin, 'Lineniyi korabl' Respublika' (Battleship *Respublika*), *Sudostroenie*, No 11, 1987, pp64–67.

9 *The Naval Annual, 1909*) J Griffin and Co (London, 1909), p29.

10 Ben-Cion Pinchuk, *The Octobrists in the Third Duma, 1907–1912*, University of Washington Press (Seattle, 1974), p71.

11 The discussion of Russian naval war plans that follows is based on N B Pavlovich (editor), *The Fleet in the First World War, Vol I: Operations of the Russian Fleet*, Ministry of Defence (Moscow, 1964). English translation published by Amerind Publishing Co Pvt Ltd (New Delhi, 1979), pp45–67.

12 The following paragraph is based on Chernikov, 'Lineniyi korabli tipa Sevastopol', *op cit*, pp62–3.

13 *Conway's All the World's Battleships*, Conway Maritime Press (London, 1987), p135; Chernikov, 'Lineniyi korabli tipa Sevastopol', *op cit*, p62; Pavlovich, *The Fleet in the First World War, op cit*, p46.

14 'The Present State of the Russian Navy', *The Engineer*, Vol CIX, No 2823 (4 February 1910), p110.

15 Chernikov, 'Lineniyi korabli tipa Sevastopol', *op cit*, p63.

16 *The Testimony of Kolchak and Other Siberian Materials*, edited by Elena Varneck and H H Fisher (translated by Elena Varneck), Hoover War Library Publications, No 10, Stanford University Press (Stanford, 1935), p20.

17 Birilev: Pavlovich, *The Fleet in the First World War, op cit*, p21; René Greger, *The Russian Fleet 1914–1917*, Ian Allan

[ ] (London, 1972), p9; Dikov: *Testimony of Kolchak, op cit*, p22.

[18] London *Times*, 1 August 1908, p7; 24 August 1908, p4.

[19] London *Times*, 24 August 1908, p4; *Conway's All the World's Battleships, op cit*, p135.

[20] Chernikov, 'Lineniyi korabli tipa Sevastopol', *op cit*, p63.

[21] London *Times*, 7 January 1908, p3.

[22] *The Naval Annual, 1911*, J Griffin and Co (London, 1911), p35.

[23] London *Times*, 20 March 1908, p7; 23 March 1908, p6; 3 June 1908, p9; 4 June 1908, p7; 8 June 1908, p4; 24 January 1908, p7.

[24] Evan Mawdsley, *Russian Revolution and the Baltic Fleet: War and Politics, February 1917–April 1918*, The Macmillan Press Ltd (London, 1978), p85.

[25] London *Times*, 7 January 1908, p3.

[26] London *Times*, 9 April 1908, p5.

[27] London *Times*, 29 June 1908, p8; 6 July 1908, p7; 22 July 1908, p9; 3 August 1908, p8. See also Geoffrey A Hosking, *The Russian Constitutional Experiment: Government and Duma, 1907–1914*, Cambridge University Press (Cambridge, 1973), pp77–78.

[28] *United States Naval Insitute Proceedings*, Vol XXXV, No 3 (September 1909), pp976–977.

[29] *Conway's All the World's Battleships, op cit*, p135; Chernikov, 'Lineniyi korabli tipa Sevastopol', *op cit*, p64.

[30] Chernikov, 'Lineniyi korabli tipa Sevastopol', *op cit*, p63.

[31] As was argued by T G Owens (later Sir George Thurston) in a paper presented to the Institution of Naval Architects in 1914; see the *Transactions* of that society, Vol LVI, pp1–32, especially p9.

[32] Chernikov, 'Lineniyi korabl' Respublika', *op cit*, p63.

[33] Afonin. 'Lineniyi korabi Respublika' *op cit*, p67. The vibration problem with cage masts is frequently noted in published works; see, for example, Siegfried Breyer, *Battleships and Battlecruisers, 1905–1970, op cit*, p392 and *Conway's All the World's Battleships, op cit*, p136. Alfonin, however, mentions only the belief that the cage masts provided too good an aiming point for enemy range-finding. The use of short-range wireless for tactical communications was well advanced in the Black Sea Fleet; presumably the same equipment was available in the Baltic Fleet.

[34] *The Naval Annual, 1910*, J Griffin and Co (London, 1910), p44; *The Naval Annual, 1911, op cit*, p36 – quoting an article from *Birzhevie Vedomosti*.

[35] The description of the armour layout is taken largely from Chernikov, 'Lineniyi korabli tipa Sevastopol', *op cit*, p64, and a sketch from an Imperial Navy manual reproduced in Edward C Fisher Jr, 'Battleships of the Imperial Russian Navy, Part 5', *Warship International*, Vol VI, No 3 (Summer 1969), p207.

[36] 'The New Russian Battleships', *Engineering*, Vol LXXXIX, No 2316 (20 May 1910), pp652–654.

[37] The turret face plates are sometimes credited with 305mm armour but this is, apparently, based on sources that simply list the maximum thickness of turret armour without specifying which part of the turret was so protected. See for example K G Chetverykin, 'Lineniyi korabl' Poltava' (Bat-

[ ] tleship Poltava), *Sudostroenie*, 1982, No 4 (April). pp52–54.

[38] Chetverykin, 'Lineniyi korabl' Poltava', *op cit*, p52. John Campbell, *Naval Weapons of World War Two*, Naval Institute Press (Annapolis, 1985), p359, states that the turrets were designed by the Coventry Ordnance Works.

[39] Campbell, *Naval Weapons of World War Two, op cit*, p358.

[40] Chetverykin, 'Lineniyi korabl' Poltava', *op cit*, p52; Chernikov, 'lineniyi korabli tipa Sevastopol', *op cit*, p64.

[41] Campbell, *Naval Weapons of World War Two, op cit*, p359; Chernikov, 'Lineniyi korabli tipa Sevastopol', *op cit*, p63; Rolf Erikson, 'Soviet Battleships, Part 1', *Warship International*, Vol IX, No 4 (1972), p420.

[42] German ship broadsides and ranges are based on the shell weights and gun ranges given in Breyer, *Battleships and Battlecruisers, 1905–1970, op cit*, p257.

[43] Campbell, *Naval Weapons of World War Two, op cit*, p257.

[44] Chernikov, 'Lineniyi korabli tipa Sevastopol', *op cit*, p64.

[45] Chetverykin, 'Lineniyi korabl' Poltava', *op cit*, p53; Christian de Saint Hubert and Boris Drashpil, 'Main Shipyards, Engine Builders and Manufacturers of Guns and Armour Plate in the Saint Petersburg Area Up to 1917', *Warship International*, Vol XXII, No 4 (1985), pp346 and 350.

[46] Chetverykin, 'Lineniyi korabl' Poltava', *op cit*, p53; Chernikov, 'Lineniyi korabli tipa Sevastopol'. *op cit*, p64.

[47] 'The New Russian Battleships', *op cit*.

[48] This, and all subsequent quotes attributed to Siegfried Breyer, are from his *Battleships and Battlecruisers, 1905–1970*, Doubleday and Co Inc (Garden City, NY, 1973), pp393 and 396. Breyer repeats many of his criticisms in his more recent *Soviet Warship Development, Vol I: 1917–1937*, Conway Maritime Press Ltd (London, 1992), pp33–35.

[49] Quotes attributed to Donald W Mitchell are from his *A History of Russian and Soviet Sea Power*, Macmillan Publishing Co Inc (New York, 1974), p278.

[50] *Conway's All the World's Battleships, op cit*, p135.

[51] Anthony J Watts, *The Imperial Russian Navy*, Arms and Armour Press (London, 1990), p58.

[52] This, and subsequent quotes attributed to Anthony Preston, are from his *Battleships of World War I*, Galahad Books (New York, 1977), p215.

[53] This, and subsequent quotes attributed to Jürg Meister, are from his *Soviet Warships of the Second World War*, Arco Publishing Co Inc (New York, 1977), p15.

[54] Hugh Lyon, *The Encyclopedia of the World's Warships*, Salamander Books Ltd (London, 1978), p193.

[55] This argument follows Norman Friedmann, 'Re: The Czarist Dreadnoughts', in *Warship International*, Vol IX, No 2 (1972), pp107–09; see also the same author's *Battleship Design and Development 1905–1945*, Mayflower Books (New York, 1978), pp63–64 and the diagram on p75.

[56] Alan Raven and John Roberts, *British Battleships of World War Two*, Naval Institute Press (Annapolis, 1976), pp69–70.

[57] *Jane's Fighting Ships*, editions from 1920 to 1952–3.

[58] As shown by a sketch in F V Migacheva and I H Migachev 'Vydaiushchiisia russkii uchenyi–korablestpoitel' I G Bubnov' (The outstanding Russian Academic–Shipbuilder I G Bubnov), *Sudostroenie*, 1972, No 1 (January), p45.

[59] *Jane's Fighting Ships*, 1919, p556.

'THE HATBOX'

HMS *Argus*

HMS *Argus* was the world's first true 'Flat Top' aircraft carrier and, had the First World War continued a little longer than it did, might well have become a very famous ship, as the first to launch a torpedo air-strike against an enemy fleet. Keith McBride describes her origins, the evolution of the flight deck arrangement and her subsequent lengthy career, which lasted until almost the end of the Second World War.

In the very early days of aviation, it seemed logical that heavier-than-air craft flying over water should have floats to take off from and to 'land'[1] on water, and to keep them from sinking. For a long time, the difference in performance between 'landplanes' and 'seaplanes' or 'flying boats' was not very great. Though demonstrations of flying off or onto ships' decks were made as early as 1909–10, the usual technique for operating aircraft at sea in 1914–15 was for the ship to stop and hoist out a seaplane, which would, if all went well, take off from the water and land back on it. This depended very much on weather conditions; almost a flat calm was needed so as not to break up the fragile wood and canvas seaplanes, on the other hand an absolute calm also presented problems; seaplanes often failed to 'unstick'

The Argus *completing; the fore end of the flight deck is not yet plated. Note the many, precarious painting stages hung from the ship's side.* (IWM)

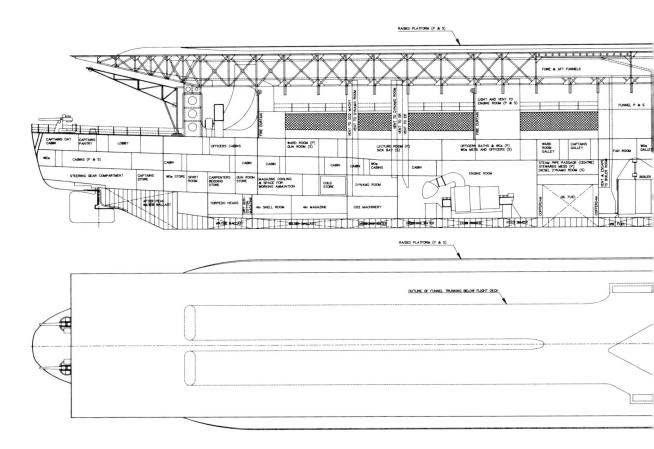

General arrangement of Argus *based on official drawings dated 9 August 1917 and held by the National Maritime Museum. Note the sided superstructures and cranes and the raised platform along each side of the flight deck, none of which appeared in the completed ship. On the original drawings the superstructure carries the legend 'Arrangement of bridges and masts to be specially considered.'* (Drawn by John Roberts)

under such conditions. In addition, this method of aircraft operation could be dangerous when submarines were about.

A partial solution had already been tried in the shape of shipboard launching ramps or decks but some thinkers had already conceived of a true sea-going mobile aerodrome. Commodore Sueter of the infant Royal Naval Air Service suggested the idea to the shipbuilding firm of

The Argus *in dazzle paint; probably on trials in 1918.* (IWM)

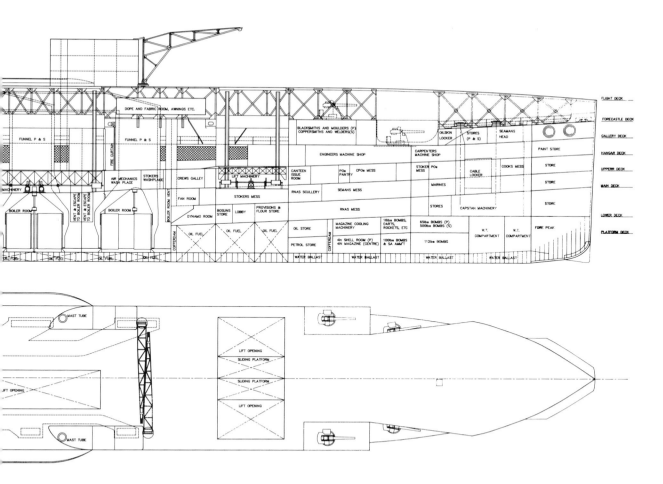

William Beardmore, of Dalmuir NB – as they proudly styled themselves. They put proposals to Eustace Tennyson d'Eyncourt, the Admiralty's Director of Naval Construction, in late 1912. The Beardmore proposal was for a ship of 15,000 tons, with a speed of 15kts. Side-by-side funnels were to be fitted, as in a '90s battleship, each funnel rising from a separate superstructure 220ft long, with a gap 50ft wide along the centre line providing a take-off deck or alley. The forecastle and quarterdeck were to be left as clear as possible, for take-off and landing purposes. The armament was to be six or eight 4in guns, mounted singly on steps on the two superstructures.

The aircraft outfit was to be six fully assembled machines, carried in the forepart of the superstructures, with roofs over them extending inboard from the side. Four more aircraft were to be carried dismantled in the

The Argus *laying an anti-submarine smoke screen during her trials.* (IWM)

The Argus *soon after completion, probably off the shores of her native Scotland. Note that the starboard dazzle pattern differs from that of the port side.* (CMP)

forward hold and could be brought up by cranes. The ship was also to act as a parent for destroyers and submarines; there was a natural wish to bring all these new-fangled 'unconventional' devices under a common command and control organization and a powerful radio installation was to be provided for this purpose. The very large fuel

An early aerial view of Argus, *probably at Rosyth. Note the long, narrow after lift (amidships) and the forward lift with its roller platforms, which were pushed inboard to cover the sides of the lift opening. A touch-down ramp for aircraft was placed between the lifts and covered with gym mats. In the background a* Royal Sovereign *class battleship represents the old order of sea power.* (IWM)

supply, 5500 tons, was intended partly for use by her flock.

The Admiralty's first efforts towards an aircraft-carrying ship were on 'hoist out and in' lines. HMS *Ark Royal*,[2] included in the 1914–15 programme, was a half-completed merchant ship, fitted with cranes (falsely said to have been 'lifted' from Barry Docks) and facilities for repair and maintenance of seaplanes. She was far too slow to keep up with the fleet and to do this, or to carry seaplanes on fast offensive missions, there was a choice between Atlantic liners, cross-Channel packets or converted cruisers, none of which were plentiful. The old cruiser *Hermes* had been converted but was now being converted back. At the outbreak of war, the old but fast liner *Campania* was bought from the breakers for £32,500 and fitted with a flying-off deck forward.

Several cross-Channel packets, the first being the *Empress*, *Engadine* and *Riviera*, were also converted. They had speeds of around 20kts, rather limited radii of action and were lively in a seaway; passengers preferred a swift and seasick voyage to a slow and comfortable one which delayed their arrival in the sun or the mountains. Aircraft had to be hoisted out and in. The Admiralty doubted these ships' structural strength, though this may have been unfair. The weakness of 'hoisting out and in' was emphasised on one attempted air strike, when the only seaplane to 'unstick' promptly ran into a destroyer's radio aerial.

The *Campania* was fast enough and big enough to push through heavy seas without difficulty but her twenty-one-year career on the 'Atlantic Ferry' had taken its toll and her engines and watertight integrity were doubtful. A back-up and potential replacement was urgently needed. A series of alterations made her capable of flying off seaplanes, whose wheeled take-off gear was jettisoned on becoming airborne, but they had to come down onto or into the water, which could easily be fatal.

Conte Rosso

The idea of a landing-on deck aft was born very early. It was later tried in the second conversion of HMS *Furious*

but she was still in the design stage. A new ship of similar dimensions would take from fifteen to eighteen months to build. What the Admiralty needed was a large, fast, reliable ship, which was immediately available for conversion into an aircraft carrier. Among the few suitable hulls on hand were two partly completed liners, which had been building in Britain for Italian shipping lines and whose construction had been suspended at the outbreak of war.

One was No 519 at Beardmore's Dalmuir yard, which had been ordered by the Lloyd Sabaudo line, all of whose ships were named after the various Counts of Savoy, as the *Conte Rosso*. She was designed for a trial speed at half load of 19.5kts, which would give 18kts sea speed at full load; the propelling machinery was Parsons compound reaction turbines on four shafts, with low pressure ahead and astern turbines on the inner shafts, while the 'outers' were driven by one high and one intermediate pressure turbine. The steam was to be supplied at 185psi by five double and four single-ended coal-fired boilers. There were three turbine-driven dynamos of about 100kw/110 volts capacity and one emergency dynamo of 18kw driven by an oil engine. As a liner, she would have had a crew of 372, with 208 first, 309 second and 74 third-class passengers, plus 2009 emigrants. She was in frame; 6700 tons of steel had been worked in or fabricated but she was a long way from being launched.

The rival candidate, *Giulio Cesare*, was being built by Swan Hunter on the Tyne, as their No 967 and was longer and broader but of shallower draught. She was in a more advanced state, but her machinery was less so. Proposals to complete her were made but she seemed unpromising to the Admiralty. Potential aircraft capacity of the two ships was much the same, as was their speed, and the machinery question seems to have decided the Admiralty's

choice, which was made on 20 September 1916 and was to be implemented as soon as possible.

Archibald Campbell, Beardmore's General Manager, had had plans prepared for turning the *Conte Rosso* into a giant torpedo-proof refrigerated freighter for the River Plate run, reducing the number of boilers and adjusting the pitch and area of the screws to give a full-load speed of 15kts. He mentioned this to d'Eyncourt, the DNC, in early May 1916 but the latter felt her potential value as an aircraft carrier to be far greater. It seems likely that memories of Beardmore's 1912 proposal suggested that firm as the ideal partner in designing and building a new kind of ship at the very edge of 'the state of the art'. Evidently d'Eyncourt gave a provisional go-ahead to Beardmore to start design work on converting the *Conte Rosso*; they put forward proposals on 20 June. The Air Department of the Admiralty preferred the *Giulio Cesare*, and had hopes of using both ships, but in September the Board of Admiralty decided on the Beardmore ship.

Conversion

There were two choices for placing the bridge and navigation facilities; either to cut the flying deck off short of the bow and place the bridge below its forward end, which would give a good view ahead and abeam but not in other directions, or to have islands on each side, as in the 1912 project, joined by a gantry-type bridge high enough for aircraft to pass underneath. The latter was

A Sopwith 2F1 Camel making an approach to Argus's *flight deck. Note the fore-and-aft, 54-wire, early arrester system.* (IWM)

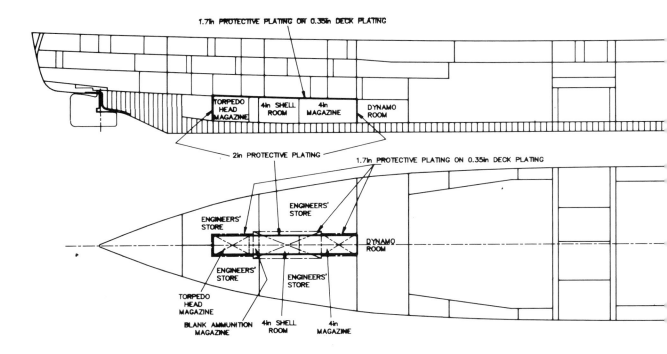

Arrangement of protective plating fitted to the magazines of Argus. (Drawn by John Roberts)

chosen. At first the plan followed the 1912 project closely, with twin-sided superstructures, each side having its own funnels, flanking a landing and take-off deck, now only 44ft minimum width, between them. The layout anticipated the whale factory ships of the twenties and later, which also had the problem of embarking very large objects. As compared with the 1912 project, speed was much higher, in an effort to enable the carrier to work with the fleet. The air group was increased from the ten of 1912 to twenty-four; twelve for scouting, six anti-Zeppelin and six torpedo carriers ('Raiding Machines', ie bombers, were not thought of great importance to the fleet). A very large internal hangar, 330ft x 68ft (48ft clear) x 25.5ft (20ft clear) was provided for the aircraft. A change was made from coal to oil firing; the *Campania*'s aircraft had suffered severely from the effects of coal dust and had to be disembarked before coaling ship.

Boiler power was increased from five double-ended and four single-ended as a liner (five and two as a freighter) to six and six, which, with oil firing, delivered 21,376shp for 20.506kts at 15,266 tons on the contractor's trials in September 1918. It was noticed that the *Argus* took a long time to raise steam, had to be pressed to the limit to attain full speed and, unlike most ships with cylindrical boilers, needed frequent boiler cleaning. The Admiralty would have liked 25kts speed, which was obtained in the new *Hermes*, but a fairly adequate carrier was needed as soon as possible and the *Argus* was just about fast enough; 'the best is always the enemy of the good'.

There were many problems to be solved, notably the storage of large quantities of petrol (US 'Avgas'). Bulk storage was rejected as experience suggested that a pipe system would leak.[3] It was decided to use ordinary 2–(=2.4 US) gallon tins, stored as if they were ammunition. The storage compartment was forward and surrounded by voids, the fuel being brought up in a lift with a fire barrier (probably a moveable flap) in the shaft. A man was to ride in the lift. Large numbers of fire extinguishers and sand boxes were to be strategically placed; possibly the thought was that a petrol fire would have to be put out quickly if it was to be put out at all. The hangar was divided into four by fire curtains, with another placed at the after end between the hangar and the quarterdeck.

The armament initially proposed was two low-angle and four high-angle 4in, though there were proposals later for four 6in plus two 4in AA, or for 5.5in guns. At all times there was a problem in finding space for the guns. A Committee of the Admiralty Air Department noted that aircraft were developing so rapidly that it was difficult to state the sizes and weights which might have to be accommodated – a problem which still baffles designers.

Magazines for the ship and her aircraft were placed fore and aft on the platform deck; the after one was enclosed in a box protected by 0.35in plating and 1.7in protective plating but forward there was a protective deck only. Storage was provided for 520, 550, 100, 112 and 230lb bombs and a bomb lift was provided. Torpedoes were stored in the hangar. It was decided to fit a Type II Wireless Telegraphy set, as for most big ships, and a seaplane set as well. The rudder was operated by a Brown's Patent steam tiller, which puffed out steam and made weird noises, but functioned well.

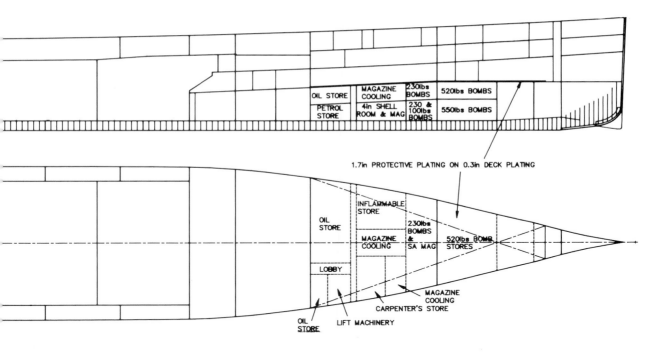

1.7in PROTECTIVE PLATING ON 0.3in DECK PLATING

Superstructure

The main items to be installed were, however, the 'flying-off' and 'flying-on' decks, the outlets for boiler smoke and the navigational facilities. For a considerable time the 1912 layout, with side-by-side funnels and superstructure, was retained. The bridge, which at first was literally a bridge joining the superstructures, grew into a rectangular platform high above the flying decks so that aircraft would have to land almost literally into a tunnel.[4] A safety net was to be rigged between the two islands to stop overshooting aircraft. The disturbed airflow likely to be caused by the twin islands had worried those in the Admiralty who had considered the 1912 project; they felt that an expert pilot might cope but not average ones. The idea of a complete flight deck seems to have arisen from the concept of a flying-on deck aft and a flying-off deck forward, linked by trackways so that aircraft which had landed and were still serviceable could taxi forward ready to fly-off. The *Furious* was so equipped in her third guise, though her funnel still arose on the centreline.

The situation was complicated by the fact that the Air Department had been assigned its own naval architect[5] and had its own ideas on the subject. It particularly favoured six small funnels, three on each side, whereas the DNC staff were coming round to the idea of leading the furnace smoke and gasses off through horizontal ducts discharging at the stern. During 1916, the National Physical Laboratory carried out wind tunnel tests (already in use for aircraft) on various funnel, duct and superstructure arrangements, and these proved remarkably accurate. The aviators would have preferred internal combustion engines, and no funnels whatever, but diesels of the necessary power did not yet exist and would, in any case, produce a substantial output of fumes.

There was an 'option of difficulties' in that the ideal arrangement of ducts for aircraft operation involved bending and constricting the boiler uptakes, which was bad from the marine engineering point of view. It was at first thought that ducts were only feasible in low powered ships and even then fans had to be fitted to cool the gases. The ducts were of course hot, which was bad for the crew and for aircraft made of wood and 'doped' fabric and fuelled by hand.

One noticeable change from 1912 was that the flight deck was much higher out of water. This may have resulted from the constraints of the original liner design but it provided space for the hangar and protected aircraft from spray while taking off or landing. At one time, cross-deck take-offs by the lightweight aircraft of the day were contemplated! The ship was launched on 2 December 1917; construction was hampered by shortage of skilled personnel and the demands of other construction.

The twin islands were actually made and were lying on the quay ready for installation when, in April 1918, Rear Admiral Phillimore, Admiral Commanding Aircraft Carriers, visited Dalmuir with his aviation advisers. As a result of trials with the *Furious* and her new flying-on deck[6] he considered an absolutely clear deck necessary; otherwise the air currents created made landings almost impossible. His recommendations were accepted and *Argus* was completed with a flush flight deck and, instead of funnels, horizontal smoke ducts. They ran between the flight deck and the hangar roof and were surrounded by casings through which cool air was blown by fans. Other, 117in diameter, fans helped the smoke on its way. Normally it emerged right aft but in harbour, in a following wind or when operating aircraft, it was deflected by dampers through openings on the quarters. The system was complex but it worked. The two aircraft cranes were shifted from near the bridge to the low stern

A Sopwith 1½ Ship Strutter taking off from Argus. *This is probably Bell Davis making a practice touch-and-go before his first deck landing on 1 October 1918. Note the steam jet, the arrester hooks under the Strutter's undercarriage and the angled struts which gave the aircraft its name.* (IWM)

and the space above this helped to disperse the smoke. Control positions were fitted on either side and, when no flying was in progress, a chart house rose from the centre line of the flight deck on a hydraulic ram. Two aircraft lifts were provided, the after one having flaps to fill the shaft.

Early Career

Argus was finally commissioned on 14 September 1918 and the first deck landing was made by Lieutenant-Colonel Richard Bell Davis RAF (ex-RNAS) in a Sopwith 'Ship Strutter' on 1 October. No arrester gear had been fitted by the builders, pending a decision as to type, but a 54-wire fore and aft set was borrowed from the *Furious* and the aircraft hooked onto it with a row of overlapping hooks fitted below the undercarriage axle. The aircraft of the day landed so slowly that the arrester gear was used mainly to prevent them from being blown overboard after stopping, rather than to slow them down.[7]

Although training by her squadron of Sopwith Cuckoo torpedo planes was begun, the Armistice came along before the hoped-for strike against the High Seas Fleet in its bases. Late in 1918, the Japanese Naval Attaché expressed interest in her and was supplied with drawings, which apparently influenced Japanese carrier design for many years. Similarly, the French Naval Attaché was supplied with drawings of the *Eagle*, which influenced the *Béarn*, for many years France's only carrier. Naval Constructor McBride, USN, who was on exchange with Stanley Goodall, RCNC, also received drawings.

In April 1919, the Grand Fleet, its work done, was dispersed and *Argus* became part of what was variously known as the Home or the Atlantic Fleet. For several years, she carried on normal peacetime exercises and cruises, receiving new types of aircraft from time to time. It was noticed that she handled beautifully at speed but, because of her great 'sail area', was tricky at low speeds. Thanks to the steam tiller, she was very agile and had a very small turning circle. Her 20kt speed was, as had been foreseen, not enough for a true fleet carrier and she had to maintain nearly full speed most of the time just to keep station. She proved an excellent seaboat.

On the debit side, her ducts got very sooty if the fans were not used and fastening the arrester gear to them caused leaks and rust. Because of the great amount of topweight added to the original liner hull, her metacentric height was too low for safety and, in 1925–26, she was fitted with a girdling to cure this. An accidental grounding led to calls for more compasses but the Admiralty said it was the fault of the captain and the navigator. The after

lift was permanently fixed in the up position in the early twenties.

Apart from her, and the *Furious* in her third guise, subsequent British fleet carrier designs incorporated funnels (horizontal in some cases) and islands offset to starboard, which suggests that the Royal Navy had decided against horizontal ducts. *Argus*'s curious appearance from sea level got her the nicknames of 'the Hatbox' or 'the Flatiron'. Evil men spread the story that the lookout at Gibraltar once reported 'A grey dismasted hulk, on fire aft, drifting towards the Straits from the West'.

With the great increase in aircraft weight in the late 1920s her value was further reduced[8] and from that period she was laid up; no money was available for a ship with such limitations. However, in 1927 her hull was surveyed and found good for another fifteen years. Having been completed before 9 December 1921, she counted as 'experimental' under the Washington Treaty so did not have to be scrapped.

New Purpose

The revival of international naval rivalry and tension in the 1930s gave her a new lease of life. In January 1936, just before the first big re-armament programme, it was proposed to fit her with the new athwartships arrester gear and with hangar fire sprays. In February, Admiral Henderson, the Controller, saw a way to save her sturdy

Bell Davis approaches in his 1½ Strutter for the first landing on Argus. *Note 'goofers', the ramp, which kept the arrester wires at their proper height, and the smoke from* Argus's *ducts.* (IWM)

hull, by refitting her as a Queen Bee tender. Queen Bees were radio-controlled DH82 Tiger Moth trainers, employed as AA targets.[9] Such a big ship was unnecessary for the task and *Argus* did not in fact operate them much but she was to fly off many another aircraft, despite her age. The flightdeck accelerator intended for her went into the new *Ark Royal* and for a time *Argus* had no armament whatever but, unlike her rough equivalent USS *Langley*, she retained a usable flight deck. Her old cylindrical boilers were replaced by six lighter, destroyer boilers, which further reduced her metacentric height and produced far more steam than her old turbines could normally use. Hence her speed remained much the same but her acceleration and braking became nearly as good as her cornering, which fooled many an Axis aviator. It was reckoned that one torpedo, mine or heavy bomb would sink her.

Aircraft Ferry

For the first few months of the Second World War she was in the Gulf of Toulon, where she could carry out deck landing training under almost peacetime conditions. On

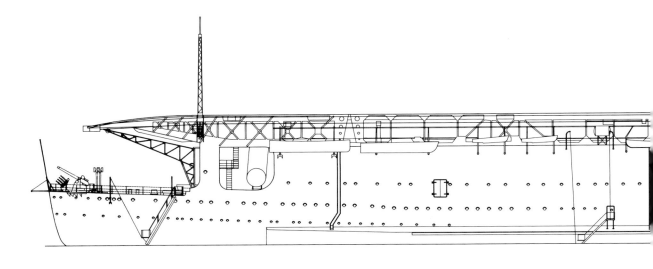

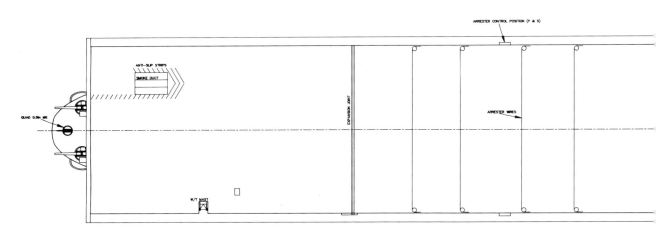

General arrangement of Argus *in 1940. She carries two, sided, quadruple 0.5in machine-gun mountings forward and one aft on the centre line of the quarterdeck together with two MKV 4in AA guns. All these weapons were added after the outbreak of war.* (Drawn by John Roberts)

the fall of France, by which time she carried two 4in and three of the almost useless Vickers quadruple 0.5in machine gun mountings, she was used to ferry aircraft from Britain to Malta and to West Africa, whence they could – usually – reach Egypt via the trans-Africa air route. Her first Malta operation succeeded but, on the second, the inexperienced and badly briefed pilots were almost all lost.

In December 1940, when ferrying aircraft to West Africa with the *Furious* as part of Convoy WS 5A, *Argus* sighted and tried to ram a U-boat. She reported it by radio, for which she was reprimanded. At dawn on Christmas Day, the convoy was attacked by the heavy cruiser *Admiral Hipper*. *Argus*'s chaplain had just come onto the quarterdeck to take the morning service when he saw some six or eight ships firing: 'Fortunately the wine had not yet been consecrated.'

The two carriers, whose hangars were full of crated aircraft, turned away under smoke, then turned into the wind and set off in pursuit. *Furious* flew off three Skua dive-bombers and kept them overhead until the enemy was located, while *Argus* flew her two Swordfish across to *Furious*, who had torpedoes available. In the meantime the cruisers *Berwick* and *Bonaventure* engaged the *Hipper*, hitting her twice for four hits on *Berwick*, and eventually everybody lost contact with everybody else. Two of the convoy were damaged but all reached port, though one independently routed British ship and one German blockade runner were destroyed.

Argus continued her ferry runs until August/September 1941, when she ferried two RAF Hurricane squadrons to north Russia. In November, she was with 'Force H' in the Western Mediterranean when the *Ark Royal* was sunk by a U-boat. Then came more Malta ferry operations, until June 1942, which proved to be the climax of *Argus*'s long career.

Malta was in desperate straits; fighters, all brought in by carrier, commanded the air over and close to the island but supplies were short and the heavy naval losses of the last few months reduced the available escorts. In mid-June 1942, the eleven-ship convoy 'Vigorous' sailed from

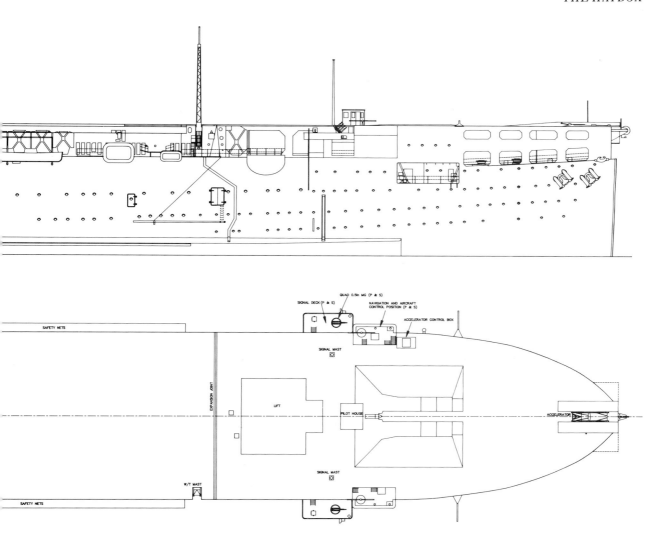

QUAD 0.5in MG (P & S)
SIGNAL DECK (P & S)
NAVIGATION AND AIRCRAFT
CONTROL POSITION (P & S)
ACCELERATOR CONTROL BOX
SAFETY NETS
SIGNAL MAST
EXPANSION JOINT
LIFT
PILOT HOUSE
ACCELERATOR
SIGNAL MAST
W/T MAST
SAFETY NETS

Alexandria, protected by large numbers of cruisers and destroyers, shore-based aircraft and submarines. From Gibraltar came the six-ship convoy 'Harpoon', escorted by the battleship *Malaya*, the carriers *Eagle* and *Argus*, three cruisers, seventeen destroyers, four minesweepers and four MLs. The Axis had naturally prepared a hot reception for both. 'Harpoon' was something of a shoestring effort; the *Malaya* had never been modernised, while the carriers had only the very slow Fulmars and early-model Sea Hurricanes, which could hardly keep up with the faster Axis aircraft and were armed with .303in guns, which had great difficulty in piercing their armour. By this time, *Argus*'s quadruple 0.5s had been replaced by thirteen Oerlikons; not many, but her most effective AA yet.

'Harpoon' passed Gibraltar on the night of 11/12 June and was shadowed from 0845 on 13 June, despite the efforts of the fighters; at most, the two carriers could keep four to six Hurricanes and two Fulmars in the air at any one time. 'Hurricanes made contact with one Ju88, probably killing the rear gunner, and destroyed one Cant Z1007.' Shadowing was resumed on the 14th: '0830. One Ju88 was badly damaged by Hurricanes who expended all ammunition. 0930 A BR88 shadower was badly damaged

in air combat with a Hurricane.' The big attacks came at 1112 to 1125, 1815 to 1835 and 2006 to 2032. In the first, fifteen to eighteen high-level bombers went for the carriers; *Argus* did some fancy dodging, while about thirty very determined Italian torpedo-bombers attacked the convoy from both sides. Five to seven aircraft were shot down, mostly by fighters, but they hit and sank the Dutch merchantman *Tanimbar* and damaged the cruiser *Liverpool*, which was 'out' for the rest of the war. The high-level and dive-bombers in the second big attack made a near miss on the *Eagle*, while the carrier fighters were only able to force four aircraft to jettison their bombs.

The last attack of the day included all three types of bomber, and a fighter escort which held off the carrier fighters, while anti-aircraft fire, as usual, proved a deterrent only. Fortunately, skilful evasive action foiled all the attackers. At dusk, with Malta-based fighters in contact, most of the escort turned back, leaving a light screen, Force 'X', to take the convoy on to Malta. Italian cruisers and destroyers had been reported leaving Palermo but, without the *Liverpool*, the convoy commander, Vice-Admiral Curteis, was unable to spare another cruiser to reinforce the screen.

Touchdown! 1 October 1918. (IWM)

The Argus *in the early 1920s. Three of her four 4in HA guns are visible, the starboard mounting forward, at the break of the forecastle, and the two on the quarterdeck. The shield of the low angle 4in is just visible, aft of the charterhouse and immediately below the flight deck. This view also gives a clear indication of the supporting structure to the flight deck and the boat stowage arrangements.* (CMP)

Force 'W', the main escort, remained west of Sicily until the 17th, when Force 'X' rejoined, having been heavily attacked by Italian cruisers and destroyers, by aircraft, and also having run into a minefield. Three more merchantmen and two destroyers were lost and only two merchant ships reached Malta. The other convoy, 'Vigorous', had to turn back after firing away most of its anti-aircraft ammunition. What the Italians called 'The Battle of Mid-June' had been a success for them, in spite of the best efforts of the carrier fighters and many others. *Eagle*'s sixteen Hurricanes and *Argus*'s six Fulmars were credited with shooting down thirteen Axis aircraft and

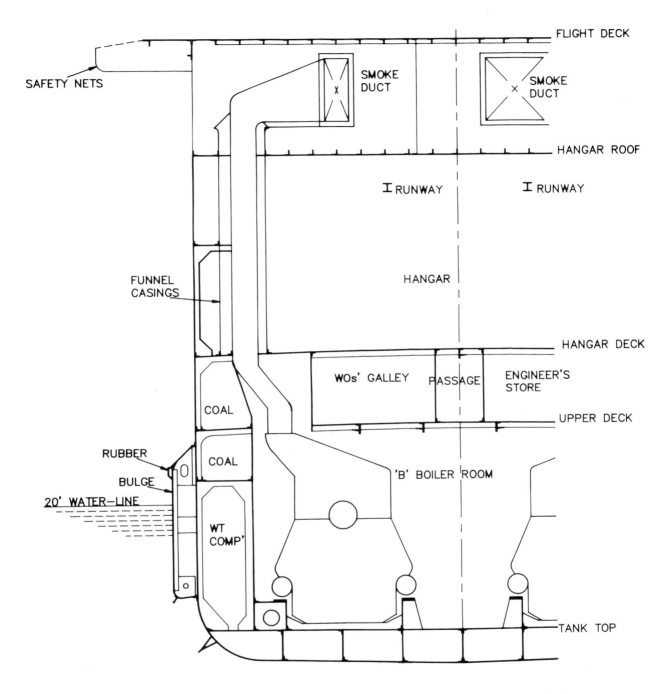

FLIGHT DECK

SAFETY NETS

SMOKE DUCT

SMOKE DUCT

HANGAR ROOF

⊥ RUNWAY   ⊥ RUNWAY

FUNNEL CASINGS

HANGAR

HANGAR DECK

WOs' GALLEY   PASSAGE   ENGINEER'S STORE

UPPER DECK

COAL

RUBBER

COAL

BULGE

'B' BOILER ROOM

20' WATER-LINE

WT COMP'

TANK TOP

Part midships section of Argus *in 1938 after her major refit and reboilering. Note the bulge, or girdling, which was added in 1925–26 to improve her stability.* (Drawn by John Roberts)

damaging eleven more during the battle, despite their inferior performance and armament. Three Hurricanes and four Fulmars were lost, at least two by friendly anti-aircraft fire.

The two shiploads of supplies delivered by 'Harpoon' were totally inadequate and a further Malta convoy, 'Pedestal', was planned for August. No less than three carriers, *Victorious*, *Indomitable* and *Eagle*, were assigned to provide cover, while a fourth, *Furious*, ferried in fighter reinforcements. *Argus*'s role was limited to ferrying spare aircraft to bring the other carriers up to strength before the vital convoy. After a Homeric struggle, in which *Eagle* was lost, five out of *Pedestal*'s fourteen merchant ships reached Malta, which was now safe for another three months.

HMS Argus *at anchor in the 1920s; note flying boats passing overhead.* (CMP)

The Argus *under way, in the 1920s with a Blackburn Dart flying overhead. The charterhouse is in the 'up' position and the port control position is clearly visible. The 4in low angle guns have been replaced with HA mountings giving her a total AA armament of six 4in. Note the resemblance to the escort carriers of twenty years later.* (CMP)

The Argus, Eagle *and* Indomitable *during Operation 'Berserk', the rehearsal for the* 'Pedestal' *convoy of August 1942.* (IWM)

Escort Carrier

In November, Operation 'Torch' occupied much of French North Africa, taking Rommel in the rear and making the re-opening of the Mediterranean sea route a matter of time. Practically every carrier in home waters, plus five American ones and a vast array of other ships, took part, including *Argus* and the new escort carriers *Avenger* and *Dasher*. After operating her aircraft against shore targets, *Argus* was attacked by Ju88s at dusk on 10 November and hit by one bomb, which killed four men; fortunately, aircraft torpedoes missed. After the success of the initial landings, *Argus* and *Avenger* sailed from Gibraltar at midnight of 14/15 November with a convoy of 'returned empties'. This was detected by German intelligence and within a few hours the convoy was warned that U-boats were shadowing. *Argus* was in position 22 and *Avenger*, astern of her, in position 23 in the centre column of the convoy when, at 0255, radar echoes were picked up on the port bow. The convoy made a 40° emergency turn to starboard but, at 0300, a salvo of torpedoes arrived from *U-155*, commanded by the 'ace'

The Argus *avoiding high-level bombing on 14 June 1942 during the 'Harpoon' Malta convoy. The aircraft on the flight deck is a Fulmar.* (IWM)

Table 1: *HMS* Argus, *Comparative data*

	1912 Project	Liner, Conte Rosso	Super Freighter	Argus 1916	Argus 1918	Argus 1938	Argus 1942
Length pp (ft):	430	535	535	535	535	535	535
Beam (ft):	82	68	83.5 (incl bulges)	68 (moulded)	68 (moulded)	74 (incl girdle), 75.75 (over fenders)	74 (incl girdle), 75.75 (over fenders)
Flight deck width (ft):	110/50	N/A	N/A	70	68	c79	c79
Flight deck length (ft):	450	N/A	N/A	565	549	c551	c551
Legend draught (ft-in):		22	28/26	21	21–1		
Legend displacement (tons):	15,000	15,350	11,000	14,500	14,450		
Full load displacement (tons):		17,750	12,000		15,775		
SHP:		14,000/ 16,000	12,000		20,000	29,824	
Speed (kts):	15	18sea/19.5 measured mile	15/16 at 26ft draught		20.5 (trials)	19.16	19.5
Endurance at full speed (miles/kts):		1000/18	6500/15–16	3840/20	3840/20		3900/19
Endurance at cruising speeds (miles/kts):				7000/15	7000/15		5000/16 6000/12
Fuel capacity (tons):	5500		4000	2300 (oil)	2000	2000	2000
Aircraft capacity:	10	N/A	N/A	24	24	15	15
Armament:	6–8 × 4in	N/A	N/A	4 × 6in, 4 × 4in AA	2 × 4in, 4 × 4in AA	none	2 × 4in, 13 × 20mm
Weights (tons):							
Hull:		9500	9650	9650	9650	9650	9650
Machinery:		2500	2350	2900	2900	2700	2700
Stores:			1000 incl RFW				
Complement:		372			495		
Passengers:	—	2600	—	—	—	—	—
Cost:				£660,500			

Lieutenant-Commander Adolf Piening. The USS *Almaack* (in position 11) and SS *Ettrick* (in position 21) were badly damaged (the latter sank several hours later) and *Avenger* blew up with great violence; the area was showered with pieces of wood from her flight deck and there were only twelve survivors.

Argus's repairs took a month, after which she resumed convoy work, but from February to May 1943 further repairs were needed. About this time she was disrated to an escort carrier. Large numbers of these, mostly American-built, were now coming into service and, having about the same aircraft capacity as *Argus*, the change was logical but it didn't please the ship's crew. From May to August 1943 she resumed deck-landing training duties. Like the *Furious*, the other surviving pre-war carrier, she was virtually worn out. In October 1943 she was 'to be regarded as at six months' notice for operational service' and on 27 January 1944 she was ordered to be paid off. However, deck landing training continued until 2217 on 27 September, when a Swordfish flew off, nearly twenty-six years after Bell Davis's 'Ship Strutter' had landed on.

In late 1944 it was proposed to fit her as an 'aircraft freighter' to carry sixty Hurricanes but this was not done (the Hurricane was also becoming obsolete.) For a time, like the old 'Wooden Walls' in their latter days, she served as an accommodation ship at Chatham but in March 1947, the world's first aircraft carrier was broken up at Inverkeithing, not far from Dalmuir, her birthplace.

Notes

[1] In France, they invented the words '*aterrisage*' and '*amérissage*' to cover whatever the intrepid aviator wanted to descend upon. English remains ambiguous; 'ditching' has its own specialised meaning.

[2] In 1588, Lord Howard said of the first *Ark Royal*: 'I think her the odd ship of the world for all proportions'; presumably the Admiralty remembered this, as well as Noah's early reconnaissance efforts.

[3] As USS *Lexington*'s did, with fatal results, on 8 May 1942.

Table 2: *AIRCRAFT TYPES OPERATED BY HMS ARGUS, 1918–1944*

Name	Manufacturer	Type	*When carried by* Argus
Ship 1½ Strutter	Sopwith	Reconnaissance/fighter	October 1918
Camel 2F1	Sopwith	Fighter	October 1918–1 April 1923
Panther	Parnall	Reconnaissance	? October 1918–1 April 1923
Pup	Sopwith	Fighter	October 1918–?
Cuckoo	Sopwith	Torpedo-bomber	October 1918–?
IIIC	Fairey	Reconnaissance seaplane	1919 (ferry only)
Puffin	Parnall	Amphibian	1921 (trials)
DH9 (or DH9A?)	De Havilland	Bomber	1921 (trials)
Walrus	Westland	Spotter/Reconnaissance	1921 (trials)
Viking	Vickers	Amphibian	1921 (trials)
Seagull	Supermarine	Reconnaissance amphibian	1921 (trials)
IIID	Fairey	Reconnaissance/general purpose	1921 (trials)
Sparrowhawk	Gloster	Fighter	1921 (trials)
Bison	Avro	Reconnaissance	1922–26
Nightjar	Nieuport	Fighter	1923–24
F2B ('Fighter')	Bristol	Fighter	1922 (ferry only)
Snipe	Sopwith	Fighter	1923–? (trials, found unsuitable)
Blackburn	Blackburn	Reconnaissance	1922 (trials), 1923–29
Flycatcher	Fairey	Fighter	1923–30
Plover	Parnall	Fighter	1923–?
Hanley	Handley	Page Torpedo bomber	1923? (trials?)
Dart	Blackburn	Torpedo bomber	1921 (trials)
Hedgehog	Hawker	Reconnaissance	1925 (trials)
Ferret	Fairey	Reconnaissance	1925 (trials)
Hendon	Handley Page	Torpedo-bomber	1925 (trials)
IIID	Fairey	Reconnaissance	1927–28
Peto	Parnall	Reconnaissance	1929 (ferried out for submarine *M2*)
Queen Bee	De Havilland	Radio-controlled target	1938–39
Swordfish	Fairey	Torpedo-bomber/Reconnaissance	1939?–44
Skua	Blackburn	Dive-bomber/fighter	1939–41
Sea Gladiator	Gloster	Fighter	1939?–40
Hurricane and Sea Hurricane	Hawker	Fighter	1940 (ferry) – 1942
Walrus	Supermarine	Reconnaissance	1939–?42
Fulmar	Fairey	Fighter/Reconnaissance	1940–42
Martlet/Wildcat	Grumman	Fighter	1941–?
Albacore	Fairey	Torpedo bomber/Reconnaissance	1941–?
Seafire	Supermarine	Fighter	1942–?44
Barracuda	Fairey	Torpedo bomber/Reconnaissance	1943–44 (deck landing training)
Hellcat	Grumman	Fighter	1943–44
Auster	Taylorcraft	Reconnaissance	1943

4   Some of the bolder aviators of the day were wont to fly aircraft through hangars, when the CO wasn't looking!

5   Lieutenant G Holmes, in peacetime Cunard's Assistant Naval Architect.

6   It is believed that only three successful landings were made.

7   Wheel brakes were not fitted to any aircraft before the late 1920s.

8   She was never able to operate the widely used Fairey IIIF and its descendants.

9   Of much lower performance than the attackers of 1939 onward; on one occasion King George VI watched the fleet banging away in vain at a Queen Bee. Some high ranking officer told the aircraft controller 'Dial *Spin*' and the aircraft duly span into the sea. The King was not fooled but his protests came too late and British naval AA fire remained a 'scarer' at best.

THE 2400-TONNES SERIES

The four-funnelled *contre-torpilleurs* of the prewar Marine Nationale

Writings about the French *contre-torpilleurs* of the interwar period have tended to focus either on the early *Jaguar* class or on the later *Le Fantasque*-type. In this article John Jordan argues that the backbone of the interwar *contre-torpilleur* was constituted by neither of these types, but by the eighteen ships of the four-funnelled *2400-tonnes* series.

Given the impact of the revolutionary *Jaguar*s on contemporary tactical thinking and the undisguised glamour of the later *contre-torpilleurs*, with their racy silhouette, powerful armament and unsurpassed capacity for sustained high speed, the lack of attention paid to the *2400-tonnes* series is perhaps unsurprising. However, not only was this series the most numerous of the prewar *contre-torpilleurs* but they bridged the technological gap between the early *Jaguar*s and the later ships of the *Le Fantasque* and *Mogador* classes. Laid down over a four-year period, between March 1927 and February 1931, they spanned four separate naval programmes and were officially divided into five sub-groups, each of which incorporated incremental improvements. The early types were built on the success of the *Jaguar* class and the later ships prepared the way for the *Le Fantasque* class. Yet these various sub-groups were bound together by their striking four-funnelled silhouette, which made it impossible to confuse them with other contemporary flotilla craft.

The Guépard–Valmy Sub-Group

The first three ships of this sub-group were ordered under the 1925 Naval Programme and, like their predecessors of the *Jaguar* class, were named after wild animals. The second batch of three ships, also intended to operate as a homogeneous three-ship division in accordance with the operational practice of the interwar Marine Nationale, was ordered under the 1926 Programme and received historical names beginning with the letter 'V'.

These first two batches were essentially identical in terms of appearance and characteristics and are, therefore, generally grouped together; indeed the last of the first batch, *Lion*, was laid down after *Valmy*, the first of

the second batch. The basic design, which was broadly adhered to for the later sub-groups, was drawn up by the new *Ingénieur Principal*, Antoine, who took up this post in 1923 and was to be responsible for successive classes of *contre-torpilleurs*.

The major weakness of the otherwise successful *Jaguar* type had been its artillery. The 130mm/40 Model 1919, developed in the immediate postwar period as the standard weapon for flotilla craft, had been fitted in both the *Jaguar* class and in the *torpilleurs* of the *Bourrasque* class. However, the Marine Nationale had for some years contemplated a larger calibre 140mm lightweight gun (and even the 155mm gun fitted in the postwar light cruisers of the 1922 Programme) for deployment aboard *contre-torpilleurs*. Such a weapon would not only have far greater hitting power than the 120mm guns which armed the latest destroyers belonging to France's major competitors but would enable a three-ship division of *contre-torpilleurs* to take on enemy light cruisers armed with 6in (152mm) guns on a more equitable basis.

For all the great expense of the *Jaguar*s, in terms of weaponry they carried only one additional 130mm gun compared to the *Bourrasque*s; an increase in calibre was clearly necessary if the new *contre-torpilleurs* were to punch their weight. Hence the decision to develop in parallel an improved 130mm (Model 1924) for the 1500-tonnes *torpilleurs* of the *L'Adroit* class, which followed on from the *Bourrasque*s, and a heavier 138.6mm gun (Model 1923) for the new *contre-torpilleurs*.

The 138.6mm Model 1923 The 138.6mm Model 1923 gun which armed the *Guépard–Valmy* sub-group shared many characteristics with its 130mm Model 1924 counterpart, being of autofretted construction with a traditional Welin screw breech. The height of the trunnion was reduced from 1.5m in the Model 1919 to 1.34m in the later

Table 1: *CONSTRUCTION DATA*

Name	Builder	Laid down	Launched	In service
1925 Programme				
Bison	Lorient	14 Mar 1927	29 Oct 1928	24 Oct 1930
Guépard	Lorient	14 Mar 1927	19 Apr 1928	Sep 1929
Lion	A Ch France	27 Jul 1927	5 Aug 1929	5 Feb 1931
1926 Programme				
Vauban	A Ch France	23 Mar 1929	1 Feb 1930	5 Feb 1931
Valmy	Penhoët	5 May 1929	19 May 1928	26 Jan 1930
Verdun	A Ch Loire	10 Aug 1927	4 Jul 1928	19 Apr 1930
1927 Programme				
Aigle	A Ch France	8 Oct 1928	19 Feb 1931	1 Nov 1932
Vautour	F Ch Méditerranée	21 Feb 1929	26 Aug 1930	25 Jan 1932
Albatros	A Ch Loire	30 Jan 1929	27 Jun 1930	1 Jun 1932
Gerfaut	A Ch de Bretagne	15 May 1929	14 Jun 1930	15 Mar 1932
1927 Programme (experimental type)				
Milan	Lorient	1 Dec 1930	13 Oct 1931	18 May 1934
Epervier	Lorient	1 Aug 1930	14 Aug 1931	18 May 1934
1928–29 Programme				
Vauquelin	A Ch France	13 Mar 1930	29 Mar 1931	28 Mar 1934
Kersaint	A Ch Loire	19 Sep 1930	14 Nov 1931	14 Jan 1934
Cassard	A Ch de Bretagne	12 Nov 1930	8 Nov 1931	7 Oct 1933
Tartu	A Ch Loire	29 Sep 1930	7 Dec 1931	8 Feb 1933
Maillé Brézé	Penhoët	19 Oct 1930	9 Nov 1931	24 Apr 1933
Chevalier Paul	F Ch Méditerranée	28 Feb 1931	21 Mar 1932	28 Apr 1934

guns, resulting in a slight reduction in maximum elevation (36 to 35 degrees). However, this failed to have the desired effect of facilitating loading at higher angles of elevation, and both guns were difficult to load above 15 degrees. The rate of fire was therefore no improvement on the *Jaguar* – five or six rounds per minute was the most achieved in practice.

There was also a slight reduction in maximum theoretical range as compared with the Model 1919, 18,200m

The contre-torpilleur Lion on 10 May 1936. The Thornycroft A/S mortars have been removed, and she has a new 5m stereoscopic rangefinder in a circular housing above the bridge, complemented by a 4m rangefinder aft. Twin Hotchkiss 13.2mm Model 1929 MG have been fitted at forecastle deck level abeam the bridge. Note the fore-and-aft searchlight arrangement, which proved unsuccessful and was modified in the later Vauquelin *class. (Marius Bar)*

being the figure generally accepted for the 138.6mm Model 1923. However, even this continued to be far in excess of the range at which fall of shot could be accurately observed using the single 3m base coincidence rangefinder located atop the bridge. Moreover, the relatively low muzzle-velocity of 725m/s of the short, 40 calibre gun meant a flight time of 17.6 seconds over 9000m, making it difficult to hit a fast-manoeuvring target of comparable size. The rangefinder problem would later be addressed but the performance defects of the 138.6mm Model 1923 would remain throughout the ships' service lives.

The official drawings of these ships, as designed, show the light gunshields initially fitted in the *Jaguar* and *Bourrasque* classes. All units were, however, completed with the more substantial gunshield fitted from about 1928.

Propulsion Machinery The other major difference between the *Guépard–Valmy* sub-group and the earlier *Jaguar* lay in the revised layout propulsion machinery. The *Jaguar* class had five boilers, each with a nominal rating of 10,000shp, the uptakes for the second/third and the fourth/fifth boilers being combined to give broad, flat-sided funnels. The turbines were housed in two separate machinery compartments abaft the boiler rooms. In the *2400-tonnes* type there were only four boilers, each rated at 16,000shp. The boilers were grouped in pairs in forward and after boiler rooms, each boiler room serving a turbine machinery room located immediately abaft it (see interior profile). This 'unit' arrangement of the machinery was far superior, from a damage control point of view, and was responsible for their distinctive appearance, with

Guépard in 1939, displaying the new tactical numbering system which marks her out as the lead-ship of the Third Division of Contre-Torpilleurs *(DCT). She has her after 4m rangefinder in a circular housing similar to that of the forward 5m model. Note the absence of 13.2mm Hotchkiss MG, which would subsequently be installed on a platform atop the munitions hoists forward of the bridge. (Marius Bar)*

four slim, raked funnels, disposed as two pairs with the forward bank of torpedo tubes between them.

The new-design vertical-tube boilers had a working pressure of 20kg/cm^2, slightly higher than the Du Temple boilers of the *Jaguar* class. The single-reduction turbine machinery (Zoelly in *Lion* and *Vauban*, Parsons in the other four units) comprised high-pressure, low-pressure and cruise turbines. The results of speed trials were even more impressive than those for the *Jaguar* class: all ships exceeded 40kts with 72–84,000shp at Washington displacement. In the eight-hour steam trial at full load displacement they achieved 35.5–37kts with 56–72,000shp and 37–38.5kts with 69–76,000shp in the ninth hour. Perhaps even more impressively, these high speeds continued to be achieved in service, with 35–36kts being sustained comfortably in formation, even at full load.

General Configuration The hull form of the *Guépard–Valmy* class was modelled on that of the *Jaguar*, being some 3m longer with corresponding increases in beam and draught. Transverse stability was later found to be inadequate and the ships rolled badly in any sort of sea; attempts were made to correct this in the later sub-groups, in part by reducing freeboard.

The tall square bridge structure of the *Jaguar* was retained, together with the light tripod foremast. The pole mainmast was similar to that of contemporary *torpilleurs*. The *Jaguar* class and the early *1500-tonnes* had their 75cm searchlight projectors mounted atop pedestals port and starboard at the after end of the bridge. In the *Guépard-Valmy* class and their successors, the four *rapaces*, they were repositioned fore and aft, the forward projector being located on a platform projecting from the forward side of the foremast and the after unit in a circular tub atop the after deckhouse. This arrangement, repeated in the last four units of the *1500-tonnes* type (1926 Programme), had certain advantages: superior coverage of the forward and after arcs close to the ship's axis, together with the possibility of using both searchlights on the beam. However, operation of the forward projector effectively blinded the occupants of the bridge, and this resulted in a further relocation of the projectors in later ships of the *2400-tonnes* series.

Armament The layout of the main armament was identical to that of the *Jaguar* class, with two 138.6mm guns superimposed forward of the bridge, a further two superimposed aft and the fifth gun immediately abaft the after funnel. Triple banks of torpedo-tubes were placed between and abaft the funnels. They accommodated the 550mm Model 1923D, a new high-performance torpedo 8.3m in length, with a 310kg TNT warhead and ranges of 13,000m at 35kts and 9000m at 39kts. The centre-line position of the tubes restricted training arcs to 30 degrees either side of the ship's beam, a constraint that would be addressed in the design of subsequent sub-groups.

Modifications to the AA armament followed the pattern established by the contemporary *torpilleurs* of the *1500-tonnes* type, the single 76mm Model 1922 HA gun being replaced by a single 37mm Model 1925, which fired a 0.725kg shell at a rate of 30rpm. Muzzle velocity was 840m/s and maximum practical range 5,000m. Two single 37mm were placed on either side of the midships deckhouse abeam of the third funnel, at upper deck level, and optical rangefinders were sited directly above them at the forward end of the deckhouse. The ammunition for these guns was stowed in a magazine abaft the after 138.6mm magazine (see interior profile).

The A/S armament was on a par with that of the *Jaguar* class. There were eight 200kg depth-charges in each of the tunnels beneath the quarterdeck aft, with a further eight reloads stowed in a magazine (see interior profile). Four Thornycroft Model 1928 trainable mortars, each with three 100mm charges, were initially fitted on the upper deck abeam the fore-funnel, the rails on which they were mounted being aligned with the ship's axis. The mortars were removed in 1932 in an effort to improve the ships' stability but two were subsequently restored during the Second World War.

Les rapaces

The following sub-group, named after birds of prey, was funded under the 1927 Programme. It was originally to have numbered six ships, to give two further homogeneous three-ship divisions. However, it was sub-

Table 2: Bison *AND* Valmy *Classes: Characteristics as designed*

Displacement:	2436 tonnes standard, 2690 tonnes normal, 3220 tonnes full load
Dimensions:	123.10m pp, 130.20m oa × 11.71m × 4.68m
Complement:	10 officers, 220 men
Machinery:	4 Yarrow vertical small-tube boilers, 20kg/cm^2 (215°C); 2-shaft Parsons (Zoelly in *Lion*, *Vauban*) geared steam turbines, 64,000shp = 35.5kts
Oil Fuel:	572 tonnes; 3450nm at 14.5kts
Armament:	5 × 138.6mm/40 Model 1923 semi-automatic guns in single mountings (140 rounds per gun); 4 single 37mm/50 Model 1925 (2400 rounds per gun); 6 tubes in two triple mountings Model 1928T for 550mm Model 1923D torpedoes; 2 racks each for eight 200kg depth-charges (+8 reloads in separate magazine); 4 Thornycroft mortars each for three 100kg depth-charges
Fire Control:	1 × 3m coincidence rangefinder; torpedo sights on bridge

sequently decided to allocate two of the hulls, *Milan* and *Epervier*, to experimental work with alternative advanced steam propulsion systems. In the event these two units, both constructed by Lorient Naval Dockyard, were laid down some 18 months after the other *rapaces*, and were the last units of the eighteen ship series to enter service, in May 1934. Because of the lengthy redesign work, they

Albatros on 16 January 1934, some 18 months after completion. The Thornycroft mortars have already been removed. The original 3m coincidence rangefinder can be seen atop the bridge. The 1m rangefinders for the 37mm AA can be just made out at the forward end of the midships deckhouse. (Marius Bar)

Bison as initially completed. The official drawings, on which the author's drawings are based, show the 138.6mm guns with the early half-gunshields, which were modified while the ships were building. The drawings also show two single machine guns of an indeterminate type mounted on the forecastle deck abeam the bridge structure but these were not fitted being eventually superseded by the twin Hotchkiss 13.2mm mounting. (Author)

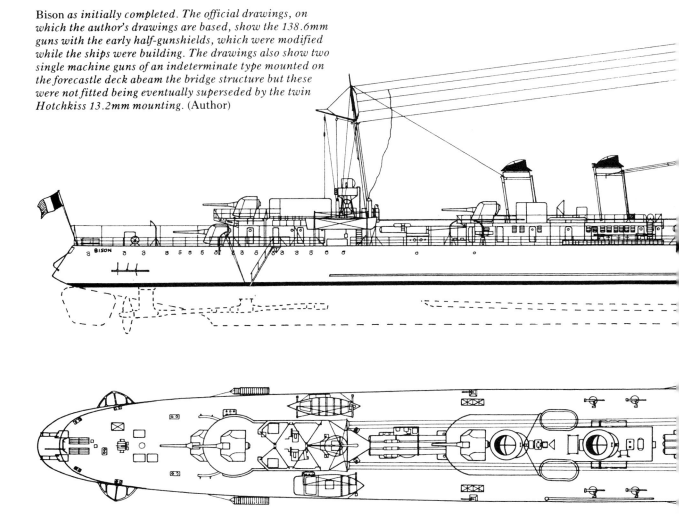

were to be completed with a hull and superstructure configuration identical to that of the last sub-group, the *Vauquelin* class.

Although *Aigle* and her three sisters were virtually identical in appearance to the earlier *Bison–Valmy* sub-group, there were a number of significant improvements in the design.

Armament The major advance lay in the performance of the 138.6mm/40 Model 1927, which replaced the less successful Model 1923, The Model 1927 was a scaled-down copy of the Krupp 15cm KL/45 lightweight gun mounted in the ex-German destroyer *S113* which, as the French *Amiral Sénès*, had been subjected to intensive gunnery trials during the early 1920s. The gun was a semi-automatic weapon with a horizontal sliding breech-block and an automatic spring-rammer. A significant reduction in the height of the trunnion (1.25m) and a consequent reduction in maximum elevation from 35 degrees down to 28 degrees was accepted in order to secure the higher rate of fire promised by the simpler

breech-mechanism. It was argued that even the reduced theoretical range of 16,700m was still 1700m outside the 15,000m range of the 120mm weapon which constituted the main armament of Italian destroyers and *esploratori*.

The end result was a two-fold improvement in the rate of fire from 5/6rpm to 12/15rpm per gun. Unfortunately, the bucket hoist system remained unmodified so the guns fired off shells at twice the rate they could be supplied from the forward and after magazines. The provision of additional ready-use racks during the mid-1930s was partially effective in tackling this problem but the ships could not have maintained their initial high rate of fire in a prolonged 'slugging match'.

Some improvements were made in fire control (the main artillery was telepointed both in elevation and azimuth) but the single 3m base rangefinder remained inadequate.

According to the official drawings, a single 76mm HA gun was to have been fitted in addition to the 37mm AA mountings at the forward end of the midships deckhouse, at the base of the third funnel. There is some dispute in reference sources as to whether this was the Model 1922 or

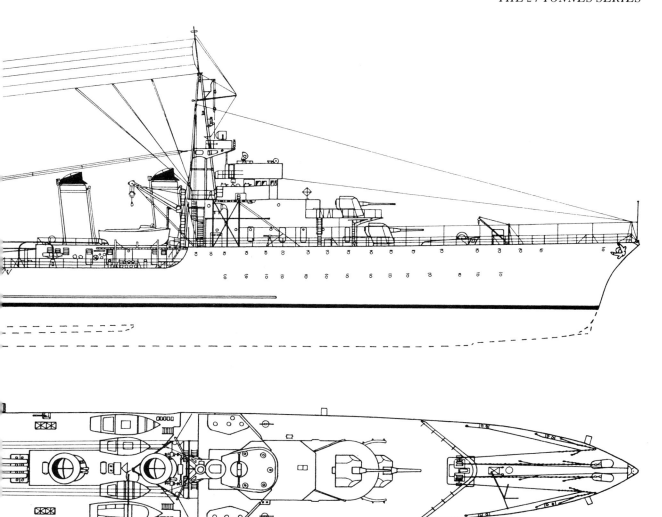

the Model 1927. However, it was probably the former, the guns having almost certainly been those removed from the *torpilleurs* of the *Bourrasque* class during the early 1930s to be replaced by two 37mm singles. Since this measure would have made twelve guns available, it may have been intended to fit them not only in the *rapaces* but in the last six ships of the series. However, sea trials in 1932 highlighted the need to reduce topweight in order to improve stability and the single 76mm was an early casualty.

The *rapaces* had the same arrangement of torpedo-tubes as the *Guépard–Valmy* sub-group and the A/S armament was unchanged. As with the preceding group, the four Thornycroft A/S mortars were quickly landed; two were subsequently replaced during the Second World War.

Hull and Propulsion Machinery The hull-form of the *rapaces*, although in appearance identical to that of the preceding sub-group, was shorter with a slight increase in beam and draught and a slight reduction in freeboard.

This resulted in greater transverse stability (GM was increased to 0.8m). On trials they demonstrated less heel on high-speed turns and proved capable of running at high speed in anything except a head sea. However, at lower speeds they continued to roll badly.

The bridge structure, which had been squared off with hard corners in the *Jaguar* and *Guépard–Valmy* types, was modified in the *rapaces*, which had a rounded front end to their navigation bridge. Overall the constructors estimated that some 50–60 tonnes were saved in the hull and accessories by careful redesign. The search for weight savings in hull and superstructures in order to improve overall performance would be taken further in the following sub-group, the *Vauquelin* class.

A new type of boiler developed by St Nazaire-Penhoët was fitted in this class and was to prove particularly successful. The four *rapaces* generally exceeded the speed trials performance of the *Guépard–Valmy* sub-group by one knot, the fastest being *Gerfaut* (the only ship of the group fitted with Rateau turbines), which made 41.3kts with 89,700shp at Washington displacement, 40kts with

Key: 1 Fwd 138.6mm magazine
      2 Fwd magazine hoists (P & S)
      3 Navigation bridge
      4 Main W/T office
      5 Secondary W/T office
      6 After magazine hoists (P & S)
      7 After 138.6mm magazine
      8 37mm magazine
      9. Depth charge magazine
     10 Emergency steering position
     11 Depth charge chutes

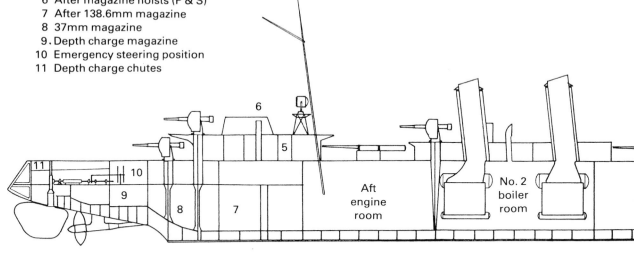

79,750shp on her eight-hour trial and 41.5kts with 83,450shp in the ninth hour. In service they could comfortably maintain 36–37kts in formation in favourable conditions.

Vautour on 7 April 1939. Her tactical number marks her out as the lead-ship of the 7th DCT, the three-ship division being completed by her sisters Gerfaut *(X72) and* Albatros *(X73).* Vautour *has the new stereoscopic rangefinders fore and aft, and 13.2mm Hotchkiss twin MG have been mounted forward of the bridge.* (Marius Bar)

The Vauquelin *Class*

The six units of the *Vauquelin* class were ordered under the 1928–29 Naval Programme. They incorporated a number of modifications to hull, superstructure and armament which distinguished them from their predecessors of the *Guépard–Valmy* and *Aigle* sub-groups.

The most striking external difference was the cutaway stern (*cul de poule*), adopted to enable these ships, and their successors of the *Le Fantasque* class, to operate as fast minelayers. Using their high speed to approach a hostile coastline at dusk (the Mediterranean coast of Italy and the Sicilian Narrows were clearly envisaged), they would off-load their fifty Bréguet 500kg mines and depart before daylight exposed them to air attack. The twin

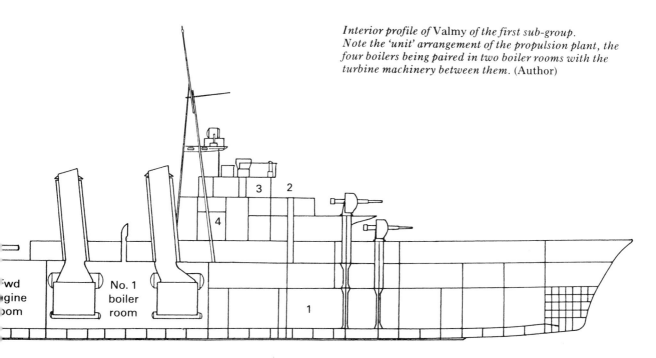

Interior profile of Valmy *of the first sub-group. Note the 'unit' arrangement of the propulsion plant, the four boilers being paired in two boiler rooms with the turbine machinery between them.* (Author)

minerails were installed on the quarterdeck directly above the depth-charge 'tunnels', with the result that A/S capabilities were unaffected.

The poor arcs of the centre-line mounted torpedo-tubes of the early *contre-torpilleurs* had long been a source of concern to certain French naval officers, who were concerned about the ships' ability to respond promptly to surface threats under conditions of low visibility. This concern was addressed in the *Vauquelin* class, in which the forward triple bank of torpedo-tubes was replaced by two twin mountings (Model 1928D) located close to the outer deck edge. These tubes were capable of being fired within 20 degrees of the ship's axis.

The position of the forward tubes precluded the mounting of Thornycroft A/S mortars on the upper deck,

Gerfaut *on 15 September 1941. The newly-built AA deckhouse aft houses a twin 37mm Model 1933 visible abaft the 4m rangefinder, which was retained in this group. Two of the original four single 37mm Model 1925 guns (visible abeam the third funnel) have been retained, and 13.2mm Hotchkiss twin MG have been fitted forward of the bridge. Two of the original four Thornycroft mortars have been restored beneath the boat-deck extension abeam the first pair of funnels. Note the revised radio aerial arrangements. The divisional tactical numbers were repainted in red with black highlighting following the outbreak of war in 1939.* (Marius Bar)

abeam the forward funnels. Instead, these ships had a single Thornycroft Model 1928 mortar mounted at upper deck level on either side of the fourth funnel, the rails running athwartships. In compensation, four additional 200kg depth-charges could be accommodated in each of the longer tunnels made possible from the revised configuration of the stern.

Other Modifications Important modifications were also made to the superstructures of these ships. The 75mm searchlight projectors, which had been mounted fore and aft in the earlier sub-groups, were relocated to a platform immediately forward of the third funnel. Remote power control was provided to enable them to be operated from the bridge.

The other modification was to the forward superstructures, which were completely rounded with no sharp corners. This feature not only had a streamlining effect which decreased wind resistance, but was intended to make it more difficult for enemy rangefinders to determine the angle of approach of the ships.

The *Vauquelin* class introduced welding to the construction of French flotilla craft, with a weight saving of about 30 tonnes. Further weight was saved by the extensive use of duralumin for superstructures; this measure was criticised in a post-trials report, however, because the lack of strength of this material, as compared with steel, made the ships more vulnerable to damage in heavy seas and in combat.

The propulsion plant was essentially the same as that of the *rapaces*, and gave similar results in speed trials. The sea-keeping qualities of the *Vauquelin* class were highly-

Epervier on 10 May 1936. She has the new 4m rangefinder aft, the pole mainmast being encased within the DCT; the 5m rangefinder has yet to be fitted atop the bridge. Note the revised arrangement of the searchlights and the rounded bridge structures. The only external difference between the experimental Epervier *and* Milan *and their near-sisters of the* Vauquelin *class is the position of the 7m boats; the davits for the port-side launch can be seen abeam the fourth funnel.* (Marius Bar)

Table 3: AIGLE *CLASS* (LES RAPACES):
CHARACTERISTICS AS DESIGNED

Displacement:	2441 tonnes standard, 2660 tonnes normal, 3140 tonnes full load
Dimensions:	122.40m pp, 128.50m oa × 11.84m × 4.97m
Complement:	(as *Bison*)
Machinery:	4 Penhoët vertical small-tube boilers, 20kg/cm^2 (215°C); 2-shaft Parsons (Rateau in *Gerfaut*) geared steam turbines, 64,000shp = 35.5kts
Oil Fuel:	580 tonnes; 3650nm at 18kts
Armament:	5 × 138.6mm/40 Model 1927 semi-automatic guns in single mountings (140 rounds per gun); 1 single 75mm/50 Model 1922 AA gun (removed shortly after completion); 4 single 37mm/50 Model 1925 (2400 rounds per gun); 6 tubes in two triple mountings Model 1928T for 550mm Model 1923D torpedoes; 2 racks each for eight 200kg depth-charges (+8 reloads in separate magazine); 4 Thornycroft mortars each for three 100kg depth-charges
Fire Control:	1 × 3m coincidence rangefinder; torpedo sights on bridge

regarded although, like the earlier ships, they had a tendency to roll badly at low speeds and when their fuel tanks were half-empty. The auxiliary machinery, traditionally a less-than-satisfactory feature of French flotilla craft, represented a major advance on the preceding sub-groups.

Table 4: MILAN *AND* VAUQUELIN *CLASSES:*
CHARACTERISTICS AS DESIGNED

Displacement:	(as *Aigle*)
Dimensions:	122.40m pp, 129.30m oa × 11.84m × 4.97m
Complement:	(as *Aigle*)
Machinery:	*Vauquelin* class: 4 Yarrow vertical small-tube boilers, 20kg/cm² (215°C); 2-shaft Parsons (Rateau in *Kersaint, Cassard*) geared steam turbines, 64,000shp = 36kts *Milan/Epervier*: 4 high-pressure super heated boilers (F C Méditerranée and Yarrow-Loire in *Milan*; Thornycroft Penhoët and du Temple-Normand in *Epervier*), 27kg/cm² (325°C); 2-shaft Parsons (*Milan*) or Rateau (*Epervier*) triple-reduction geared, steam turbines 68,000shp = 36kts
Oil Fuel:	585 tonnes; 5,000nm at 15kts
Armament:	5 × 138.6mm/40 Model 1927 semi-automatic guns in single mountings (140 rounds per gun); 4 single 37mm/50 Model 1925 (2400 rounds per gun); 2 twin 13.2mm Hotchkiss Model 1929 (not fitted until after completion); 7 tubes in one triple Model 1928T and 2 twin Model 1928D mountings for 550mm Model 1923D torpedoes; 2 racks each for twelve 200kg depth-charges (+8 reloads in separate magazine); 2 Thornycroft mortars each for three 100kg/250kg depth-charges (not in *Milan, Epervier*); twin rails for 50 Bréguet-type 500kg mines
Fire Control:	1 × 3m coincidence rangefinder; torpedo sights on bridge

Milan *and* Epervier

As completed these ships were identical to the *Vauquelin* class in every respect save two: the repositioning of the after boats on davits abeam the fourth funnel (with the consequent loss of the Thornycroft A/S mortars); and their propulsion machinery.

Both were fitted with a new type of superheated boiler derived from a model previously fitted in the seaplane carrier *Commandant Teste*. These boilers operated at the relatively high pressure of 27kg/cm² (325 degrees), as compared with 20kg/cm² (215 degrees) in the other ships of the series. In order to test a wide range of potential models the two trials vessels had boilers of different manufacture in their forward and after boiler rooms; *Milan* had boilers developed by Forges et Chantiers de la Méditerranée in the forward compartment, and Yarrow-Loire boilers in the after room; her sister-ship had Thornycroft-Penhoët boilers in the forward boiler room and Du Temple-Normand boilers (manufactured by Chantiers de Bretagne) aft.

Each of the two ships had triple-reduction turbines of different design. *Milan* had a Parsons combination comprising HP, MP, LP turbines working in series, with separate cruise and reverse turbines. *Epervier* had a set of turbines provided by Rateau which featured two cruise turbines. The cruise turbines were always on line, making for a rapid increase in speed when the other turbines were engaged.

The high-speed performance of the propulsion machinery installed in these two ships proved particularly successful and influenced the machinery installations of

An early photo of Cassard *on 6 October 1933. She has the original 3m rangefinder above the bridge and the Thornycroft Model 1928 A/S mortar is clearly visible at upper-deck level between the after funnels. Note the distinctive stern adopted in this class to facilitate minelaying and the beam torpedo-tubes forward. (Marius Bar)*

Vauquelin: *Profile and Plan Views*
Vauquelin, *the lead-ship of the final sub-group, as initially completed. Note the position of the single Thornycroft mortar at upper deck level between the after funnels, and the mine rails for fifty Bréguet 500kg mines on the quarterdeck. The official drawings show four single MG similar to those on the* Bison *drawings on the forecastle deck abeam the bridge structure. These were never fitted, being superseded by twin 13.2mm Hotchkiss mountings from the mid-1930s.* (Author)

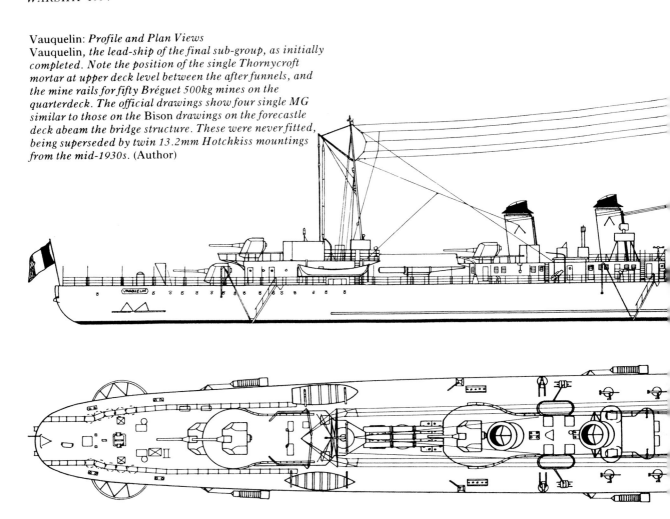

the later *contre-torpilleur* designs. Fuel consumption at high speed was relatively low: *Epervier* burned 26.3 tonnes per hour at 39.4kts as compared with figures of 27.4–31.5 tonnes per hour for the other ships of the *2400-tonnes* series. In contrast, fuel consumption at lower speeds remained high in comparison with contemporary foreign destroyers designed for prolonged operations at sea. The theoretical radius for these ships, calculated following trials as 2,750nm at 21kts, or 5,000nm at 15kts, proved illusory; their true operational radius was subsequently estimated to be half that figure, 2,500nm at 14.5kts.

The Missions of the Contre-Torpilleur

The year in which the last of the *2400-tonnes* series was completed, 1934, also saw the publication of an official document entitled *Instruction Particulière sur la Conduite des Forces Maritimes* in which the rôle of the *contre-torpilleur* was discussed and re-evaluated for the first time since the original proposals of 1922.

The missions of these ships were defined as follows:
1. General:
   to ensure security of command ('*sûreté de commandement*'); to threaten enemy sea lines of communication; to defend French sea lines of communication; and to contribute to attacks on the enemy's coastline and to coastal defence

2. Combat:
   to protect the flanks of the fleet (*mener le combat d'ailes*); and to fend off and destroy enemy light vessels and torpedo-boats, and simultaneously to support the attacks of friendly torpedo-boats.

These were missions formerly undertaken by 'scout' cruisers, which the *contre-torpilleur* effectively replaced in French tactical thinking. The primary differences between these ships and the scout cruisers built for the British, German and Italian fleets before and during the First World War were their exceptionally high speed, their relatively short radius of action and the total absence of armour.

The deliberate choice of high speed performance over

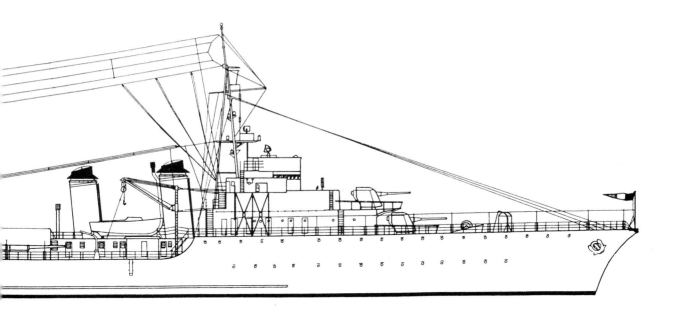

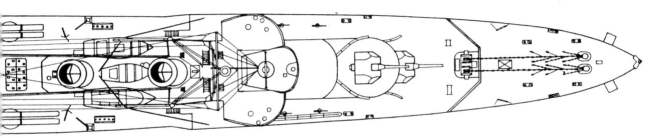

endurance reflected French tactical thinking regarding the likely pattern of naval combat in the constricted waters of the Western Mediterranean. The question of armour is more complex than it might at first appear (see David Brown's excellent article in *Warship 1992*).

When confronted with the problem of how to counter the *contre-torpilleur*, the Italians rejected the 'super-destroyer' path, opting instead for a new type of light cruiser with exceptionally high speed. These ships could not only catch and keep pace with the new French flotilla craft, but would outgun them in combat and have a greater capacity for absorbing punishment through the provision of armoured plating to sides, decks and turrets. Although successful in terms of hitting power (their eight 152mm guns outranged the French 138.6mm by some 3000m and fired a heavier shell) and speed performance, the *Condottieri* were protected by only light armour (20–24mm) which could easily be penetrated by the 40.6kg shell of the 138.6mm, which was capable of piercing 52mm of armour at 14,000m. Moreover, they had a displacement more than twice that of the *2400-tonnes*, were significantly more expensive to build and could, therefore, only be funded in small numbers. During the

period 1927–34, when the French built the eighteen ships of the *2400-tonnes* series, the Italians completed only six *Condottieri*. This failed to shake French faith in the *contre-torpilleur* type; whilst it was not envisaged that a solitary *contre-torpilleur* should engage an Italian cruiser in combat, it was considered that a well-trained division of three could engage a larger ship, even at longer ranges, on at least equal terms.

In order to ensure maximum effectiveness of the division as a fighting unit each was kept, as far as possible, completely homogeneous and the ships were trained to manoeuvre and fight in formation. Their fifteen guns could fire off between five and twelve broadsides every minute, and the use of special shells with colourants enabled each ship to spot its own fall of shot. At ranges of 9–13,000m the French 550mm torpedo would come into its own; the Model 1923D had greater weight and range than its Italian counterpart and, whereas a *Condottiere* could launch a maximum of two 533mm torpedoes on the broadside, a division of three *contre-torpilleurs* could launch broad salvos of up to fifteen to eighteen weapons.

Tartu *as she appeared in October 1941, when the photograph overleaf was taken.*
Note the restoration of the Thornycroft A/S mortar, at upper deck level between the after funnels, and the revised arrangement of the radio aerials following suppression of the pole mainmast. (Author)

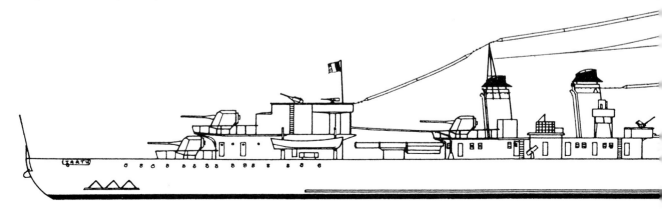

Prewar Modifications

Some of the modifications extended to the *2400-tonnes* series following completion were dictated by problems encountered on trials. The inadequacy of transverse stability in the first two groups has already been remarked upon. Disembarkation of the four Thornycroft mortars, together with the single 75mm HA gun of the *Aigle*

A stern quarter view of Kersaint *on 20 February 1936, with the new 4m rangefinder installed aft but the original 3m rangefinder still in place above the bridge. The Thornycroft A/S mortar has been removed. The photo gives an excellent view of the stern configuration, with the depth charge tunnels clearly visible beneath the minelaying rails.* (Marius Bar)

sub-group, helped to reduce topweight. However, these measures were quickly followed by others which aimed to correct more serious defects in the ships' capabilities (and which, ironically, restored much of the weight margin gained by suppressing the mortars and their loading trays).

The principal concerns of the Marine Nationale focused on the firing rate and accuracy of the main artillery. In this respect the provision of additional ready-use racks in the later sub-groups to compensate for the inadequate rate of replenishment from the bucket hoists constituted a 'patch-up' solution to a problem which could only be properly addressed in a revised design.

More fundamental was the decision, dating from June 1933, that fire-control arrangements in the *contre-torpilleurs* would have to be drastically revised, the single 3m rangefinder having proved totally inadequate at long range. It was proposed to exchange this for a 5m stereo-

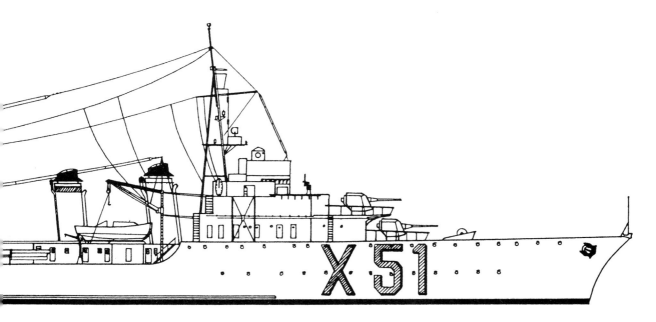

scopic model, currently under development, and to add a 4m rangefinder aft. The first two sub-groups were duly taken in hand for this modification in 1935, the 4m rangefinder being initially trialled aboard the *Gerfaut*. The after rangefinder which, like the 5m model, was in a circular housing, was located on a pedestal between the pole mainmast and 'X' mounting. The arrangement adopted for the later *Milan* and *Vauquelin* sub-groups differed in that the after rangefinder was incorporated in a more substantial DCT built around the pole mainmast itself. The new DCT, which became a model for later *contre-torpilleur* types, was trialled aboard *Milan* and *Epervier* in 1935, and was subsequently extended to the *Vauquelin* class, the entire rangefinder upgrade programme being completed in 1936.

The final prewar modification extended to these ships was the addition of twin Hotchkiss 13.2mm Model 1929

AA guns, initially at forecastle deck level, abeam the bridge structure, and subsequently on a platform above the forward 138.6mm hoists immediately forward of the bridge. Although some ships received these as early as 1934, they appear only as single MG mountings of an unspecified calibre on the official drawings and were clearly a relatively late addition.

Chevalier Paul on 19 July 1939, as the second ship in the 5th DCT; the other two units belonging to this division were Tartu *(X51) and* Vauquelin *(X53)* Chevalier Paul *has the new stereoscopic rangefinders fore and aft, and twin 13.2m Hotchkiss MG forward of the bridge.* (Marius Bar)

Wartime Modifications

The sequence of events at the beginning of the Second World War did not conform to French prewar military planning and the *2400-tonnes* series, together with the 'fleet submarines' of the *1500-tonnes* type, were arguably the major sufferers. The missions which were thrust upon them by force of circumstance differed fundamentally from those for which they were primarily designed.

With the late entry of the Italians into the war these ships were employed primarily to protect military, and even mercantile, convoys, tasks for which they were fundamentally unsuited. There were few opportunities for them to show off their high sustained speed and formidable surface strike capabilities. On the contrary, the wartime missions allotted to them were precisely those which highlighted their inadequacies: low endurance, insufficient AA guns (installed piecemeal and without effective HA fire control) and a total absence of A/S detection equipment.

Following the French capitulation in June 1940, studies were made which aimed to enhance the AA and A/S capabilities of the entire class. Some of the early ships had two of their original four Thornycroft A/S mortars replaced, at some cost to their already marginal stability.

Major refits began in April 1941 and some were still in progress in November 1942 when the French fleet was scuttled at Toulon. These modifications were not extended to *Lion* or *Vauban*, which were demilitarized at Toulon under the terms of the Armistice. *Bison* had been lost during the Norwegian campaign, as had *Maillé Brézé*, the victim of a torpedo explosion accident at Greenock.

AA and ASW Modifications

There were differences in the modifications extended to the various sub-groups. *Guépard*, *Valmy* and *Verdun* had a new AA platform constructed atop the after deckhouse for a twin 37mm Model 1933, flanked by two 1m rangefinders, and the original upper-deck 37mm Model 1925 guns were removed. The pole mainmast and the after 4m rangefinder for the main guns were suppressed, the radio aerials being strung between the foremast and outriggers on the fourth funnel. The twin 13.2mm Hotchkiss, which in 1939 had been located atop the munition hoists immediately forward of the bridge, were re-located to circular tubs at the forward end of the midships deckhouse and in their place were mounted single 13.2mm Browning MG.

In compensation for the additional topweight *Guépard* lost the forward bank of torpedo-tubes, and *Valmy* the after set; curiously, *Verdun* retained both sets. These modifications were carried out in 2/3-month refits from April to December 1941.

The *rapaces*, which had slightly superior stability, received a different arrangement. The new AA deckhouse aft incorporated the 4m rangefinder and two, of the original four, single 37mm Model 1925 were retained to complement the newly installed twin 37mm Model 1933. The 1m rangefinders were removed altogether. The twin 13.2mm Hotchkiss were initially retained forward of the bridge, with 13.2mm Browning singles being added in the bridge wings. However, a later photo of *Gerfaut* suggests that the final arrangement followed the pattern of the first sub-group. These modifications were carried out between mid-1941 and late 1942, *Aigle* being in refit when scuttled in November.

Tartu in her final configuration, 14 October 1941. The twin 37mm Model 1933 mounting is clearly visible in the centre of the new AA deckhouse, as is the starboard-side single 37mm Model 1925, mounted in the large circular gun-tub. The twin 13.2mm Hotchkiss MG have been relocated at the forward end of the midships deckhouse, and the starboard 13.2mm Browning MG is just visible forward of the bridge. Note the outriggers on the fourth funnel which have replaced the pole mainmast. The after 4m rangefinder has been suppressed. (Marius Bar)

The *Vauquelin* classes were to have received a more substantial AA outfit than the earlier ships. In *Cassard*, *Tartu* and *Vauquelin* the AA platform aft was significantly larger, with broad circular tubs extending from its forward end (see photo and drawing) to accommodate two of the original single 37mm Model 1925 in addition to the twin Model 1933. The upper deck 37mm Model 1925 were suppressed, as was the after 4m rangefinder. As in the earlier sub-groups, the twin 13.2mm Hotchkiss were re-located in tubs forward of the third funnel, and replaced by single 13.2mm Browning MG forward of the bridge. *Milan* as refitted is reported to have resembled the *rapaces Epervier* and *Vauquelin*.

Photographic evidence suggests that there were individual variations in the above arrangements and that some modifications were applied in a piecemeal fashion, depending on the availability of the new weapons. *Chevalier Paul* received the platform aft for the twin 37mm Model 1933 prior to her sinking off Syria in June 1941 but retained two single 37mm Model 1925 on her upper deck amidships; no 13.2mm Brownings were fitted. *Kersaint* had only a provisional outfit of three single 37mm Model 1925 plus two 13.2mm Browning MG on her new after deckhouse when scuttled at Toulon.

During this same period six of the later units were fitted with an Asdic Type 128 submarine detection system: *Gerfaut* and *Albatros* of the *rapaces*, together with all four surviving units of the *Vauquelin* class.

Conclusion

Although these wartime modifications illustrate an awareness on the part of the Marine Nationale of the ships'

fallibilities, it is questionable how effective they would have been if put to the test. Superior arcs of fire were obtained for the 37mm AA but the performance of the twin Model 1933 was little better than the single Model 1925 (it was essentially the same gun), and the primary weakness, the lack of effective HA fire-control arrangements, was not addressed. The 13.2mm Hotchkiss and Browning machine guns were too small in calibre and too few in number to provide an effective close range AA capability.

The addition of Asdic and the replacement of the Thornycroft mortars would have improved their anti-submarine capabilities in one-off encounters but did little to alleviate the fundamental unsuitability of these high-performance vessels to A/S escort duties, which required robust hull construction, good sea-keeping at lower speeds and high endurance. Like other French *contre-torpilleurs*, the *2400-tonnes* series suffered from being over-specialized for a conflict that in the event never materialized.

Sources

Henri Le Masson, *Histoire du torpilleur en France 1872–1940*, Académie de la Marine (Paris 1963).

Robert Dumas, 'Les contre-torpilleurs français type Guépard-Valmy', *Cols Bleus* (7 Jan 1989); 'Les contre-torpilleurs français de 2441tW', *Cols Bleus* (3 Feb 1990).

Official plans of *Bison*, *Valmy*, *Aigle* and *Vauquelin*, Centre d'Archives de l'Armement.

John Campbell, *Naval Weapons of World War Two,* Conway Maritime Press (London 1988).

ABDIEL CLASS

Fast minelayers at war

Richard N J Wright describes the origins, design and war service of the Royal Navy's fast minelayers, a group of ships in a class of their own which proved of greater value than expected and had a truly 'legendary' speed.

The *Abdiel* class fast minelayers of the 1938–39 Programme were not completed until well after the outbreak of hostilities, and wartime secrecy, three funnels and certain other factors contributed to their becoming renowned for a legendary speed of over 40kts; a legend that, curiously enough, was to continue long after peace had been declared. The writer joined HMS *Apollo* in the 1950s and well remembers studying the black-and-white painted revs-per-knot board displayed prominently on the compass platform; and the anti-climax at finding not 41 or 42kts, or even the long rumoured 45kts, but 33kts as the maximum speed shown. Another curious feature of *Apollo* in the 1950s was that her 'B' gundeck, which from the gunnery point of view is *the* primary gun position, was innocent of any gun whatsoever.

The British fast minelayers of the Second World War were in a class of their own and, being neither cruisers nor destroyers and not very abundant in numbers, appear to have eluded examination to any great degree in reference books; apart from acknowledgement that their sea speed was rather less than the 40kts commonly quoted. Half a century after they were laid down there are still to be found references to an originally planned 4.7in armament, while details of their subsidiary armament are varied and uncertain. Speeds over the measured mile are never quoted, which only tends to add to a slight air of continuing mystery. Thus the following brief examination of a fascinating, handsome, versatile and highly successful class of ships may help to set the record straight.

Development

British destroyers had been temporarily adapted and employed as fast minelayers during the First World War as the requirement evolved. An earlier *Abdiel* became a permanent minelayer conversion (80 mines) from a flotilla leader during building in 1915 and was retained so in service until the late 1920s. New construction for the

Abdiel *on trials in March 1941*. (IWM)

Manxman *during trials in July 1941. She carries quadruple 0.5in machine gun mountings in her bridge wings and the aerials for radar Types 286M (at the foremast head) and 285 (on the director).* (IWM)

Royal Navy during the 1930s comprised the minelaying destroyers *Esk* and *Express* (sixty mines), with the 'G', 'H' and 'I' classes of destroyer capable of rapid conversion, although only four ships of the 'I' class were actually used for minelaying during 1939–41.

British rearmament brought to the fore the desirability of having custom-built, high-speed minelayers if war with Germany was to come about. Experiments for such craft were carried out at Haslar early in 1937, resulting in a preliminary Staff Requirement for a ship capable of carrying 100 Mark XIV or Mark XV mines in the standard condition at a maximum speed of 40kts, giving 37–38kts in deep condition. Arrangements were to be available to carry an additional fifty mines, some reduction in speed being acceptable. The armament was to be primarily anti-aircraft, four 4in and one four-barrelled 2pdr pom-pom being suggested. A small silhouette was regarded as essential. Further features included taut wire measuring gear, Asdic and a small depth-charge armament.

Happily the threat of war reduced the time available for committees to cloud the issue. A tentative proposal to make the design more 'destroyer-like' by substituting two twin (and, relatively, extremely heavy) 4.7in weatherproof 'L' class destroyer mountings for the 4in AA, and another proposal to fit torpedo tubes, was rapidly discarded, emphasis being placed on the fact that ¼kt of speed would be lost with each 50 tons of additional weight. An extra twin 4in mounting was added in lieu. The design particulars had been finalised by mid 1938; details are given in Table 1.

Table 1: ABDIEL CLASS FAST MINELAYERS, DESIGN PARTICULARS, 1938

Displacement:	2650 tons standard, 3780 tons deep
Dimensions:	410ft (wl) × 40ft × 10ft (for), 12ft (aft) standard; 13ft (for), 15¼ft (aft) deep
Machinery:	4 Admiralty 3-drum boilers; 2-shaft Parsons geared steam turbines; 72,000shp = 39.75kts expected standard and about 36kts deep
Oil fuel:	700 tons
Endurance:	5500 (later amended to 5000) miles at 15kts
Armament:	156 MkXIV or MkXV mines (with possibility to increase to 162); 6 × 4in MkXVI guns on 3 twin MkXIX HA/LA mountings; 4 × 2pdr MkVIII pom-poms on one quadruple MkVII mounting*; 8 × 0.5in MG on two quadruple mountings; 4 × 0.303in Lewis guns on two twin mountings (to be fitted on upper deck); 6 depth charges (3 to be stowed on rail and 3 on stowage chocks)

* Sufficient ammunition stowage was to be provided for an 8-barrel pom-pom mounting 'which may be fitted at a later date'. It was also necessary to provide structural support sufficient for the heavier mounting.

Welshman *in Valetta harbour, Malta, in June 1942 disguised as a French* Léopard *class destroyer. The change in appearance was achieved simply by adding funnel caps and painting a dark triangular strip on the upper hull, amidships, to give the illusion of a forecastle break.* (IWM)

Contracts

Contracts for the first three ships of the class, which were to be named *Abdiel*, *Latona* and *Manxman*, were placed on 23 December 1938 as part of the 1938 building programme. (The previous *Latona* had been a First World War minelayer of the converted *Apollo* class of protected cruisers. It was *Latona*'s mines that had sunk the *Breslau* and damaged the *Goeben* during their disastrous sortie in 1918.) The contract for *Abdiel* went to Samuel White, which had just completed the two large, fast destroyers *Grom* and *Blyskawica* for the Polish Navy; she was subsequently appointed lead ship for the class. The contract for the fourth ship, *Welshman*, was placed early in the following year under the 1939 programme.

Details released in the press were, no doubt of necessity, somewhat sparse. 'No particulars of these ships have been published,' wrote a naval correspondent in December 1938, 'but it is expected that they will be high-speed vessels of considerably greater displacement than the small minelayers of the *Linnet* type completed this year'.

However, by March 1939 their details were quoted in the press as 'mentioned in the Navy Estimates as being of 2650 tons, with guns of 4in calibre.' (*The Observer* 26 March 1939). The 4.7in armament appears to have been a *Jane's Fighting Ships* invention: the edition for 1939 quoted 'Probably 4.7in', while the 1940 to 1944 editions gave '6–4.7in'. As no further details, plans or even photographs had been released by the 1943–44 edition this error is hardly surprising but it did mean that even by the fairly late date of *Abdiel*'s loss in 1943 she was inaccurately credited by the press, no doubt after checking with the reference book, with an armament of six 4.7in. (On the other hand, Weyer's *Taschenbuch der Kriegs Flotten*, 1943–4, correctly quoted six 10.2cm.)

'Snatched from Shipyards'

The completion of *Abdiel* was slightly delayed by the exigencies of war and delivery was postponed until 6

Table 2: *BUILDING DATA*

Name	Builder	Laid down	Launched	Completed
Abdiel	Samuel White	29 Mar 1939	23 Apr 1940	15 Apr 1941
Latona	Thornycroft	4 Apr 1939	20 Aug 1940	4 May 1941
Manxman	Alex. Stephen	24 Mar 1939	5 Sep 1940	20 Jun 1941
Welshman	Hawthorn Leslie	8 Jun 1939	4 Sep 1940	25 Aug 1941
Apollo	Hawthorn Leslie	10 Oct 1941	5 Apr 1943	12 Feb 1944
Ariadne	Alex. Stephen	15 Nov 1941	16 Feb 1943	9 Oct 1943

March 1941. Under normal circumstances she would have been subjected to a rigorous schedule of First-of-Class Trials, obviously particularly important in the case of a completely new type of warship. On the other hand, in the dark days of 1941 conditions were no longer normal and the potentialities of this new class of ship were under active scrutiny from all quarters.

War damage and losses had put a premium on escorts and the remaining minelaying destroyers of the 20th Flotilla were returned to their destroyer duties forthwith while, in March 1941, *Abdiel* was dispatched to lay nearly 300 mines off Brest. The General Manager of White's reported of *Abdiel* that 'two trials had been arranged on separate occasions and each had been cancelled owing to the vessel being ordered by the Admiralty on special missions.' Come April *Abdiel* was hot-footing it for the cut-off island of Malta with stores and by May she was supplying both Suda Bay and Tobruk. In her first three months of life her mining deck had been used for mines, stores and troops; and she had more than proved her worth.

Meanwhile, the next of class, *Latona*, was having her mining hatches measured up for 2pdr anti-tank guns. She left immediately after completion in May for Alexandria, via the Cape, and thereafter was employed almost exclusively on high-speed supply runs to besieged Tobruk.

The point to be made here is that both these ships, as the Admiralty put it, 'were sent off on urgent service with practically no sea trials'. There appear to be no records of the measured mile runs for *Abdiel*, while *Latona*'s full power trial was carried out on passage and speed calculated by land fixes and estimated tidal stream. Thus there was an air of uncertainty about their true speed from the very beginning and this uncertainty needed to be perpetuated.

Close Range Armament

Photos show that the first four ships of the class were completed with the multiple 0.5in guns mounted on either side of the bridge. About September 1941 it was authorized for these to be replaced by two single 20mm, while a further five single 20mm were to be mounted, one between the searchlights, two port and starboard just forward of the pom-pom, and two port and starboard on the superstructure right aft, a total of seven 20mm in all (and making full use of the convenient spare capacity in the pompom magazine). It is probable that *Latona* was lost before these guns were fitted.

Repeats

The two repeats of the class, *Apollo* and *Ariadne*, might be thought to be replacements for war losses. However, *Apollo* was actually laid down a fortnight before the first fast minelayer was sunk. The Admiralty had noted with some approval, 'It is quite obvious, from the way these ships have been snatched from the builder's yards, that they fill a very important gap in the naval service for which they were *not* designed', and had decided to increase numbers accordingly. The commanding officer of *Abdiel* – under frequent air attack in the Mediterranean – had recommended the fitting of a second multiple pompom in place of the twin 4in on 'B' deck and the removal of the pompom director 'which only slows up performance'. Endurance for the two new ships was to be increased, the searchlights were to go and they were to be made more suitable for tropical operations. By September 1941 the revised details for the repeats had been finalised and are given in Table 3.

Abdiel in Admiralty disruptive camouflage, March 1943. She carries radar Types 291, 285 and 282 and mounts seven single 20mm Oerlikons. (IWM)

Ariadne *as completed, September 1943.* (IWM)

Table 3: *REVISED DATA FOR* APOLLO *AND* ARIADNE, *1941*

Displacement:	2810 tons standard, 3960 tons deep
Draught:	Increased by 6in
Oil fuel:	880 tons (95% capacity)
Endurance:	5800 miles at 15kts
Speed:	39.25kts (max) standard, about 33.75kts deep
Gun armament:	4 × 4in MkXVI guns on two twin MkXIX mountings in 'A' and 'Y' positions; 6 × 40mm Bofors on three twin MkIV mountings; 7 × 20mm on single mountings

Apollo *as completed in February 1944; like* Ariadne *she differs from the earlier ships of the class in having the mainmast close-up against the third funnel. She mounts a close range AA armament of six twin 20mm mountings and two twin 40mm mountings. Note the lantern of radar Type 272 on the foremast.* (IWM)

An aerial view of Apollo *in 1953 with her mainmast shifted aft. Her armament has not changed since 1945 except that the two twin 40mm Hazemeyer mountings have been replaced by simpler twin 40mm Mk V mountings.* (IWM)

Employment 1941–1945

Latona: sailed immediately after completion in May 1941 via the Cape to Alexandria, where she arrived in June. She was employed thereafter almost exclusively in the supply of Tobruk and was scuttled on 25 October 1941 after severe damage inflicted by enemy aircraft off Bardia. She had no opportunity during her short career to lay any mines.

Manxman: In July 1941, a month after completion, she was in the Mediterranean, operating as an AA escort for a Gibraltar–Malta convoy and as a troop carrier. In August she was disguised as the French destroyer *Léopard* in order to lay a minefield off Leghorn; the operation, which began and ended at the mine depot in Milford Haven, occupied a total of two weeks. After this she operated in home waters, laying minefields from Norway to the Bay of Biscay. In 1942 she was transferred to the Indian Ocean to relieve *Abdiel*, returning to the Mediterranean in October. On 1 December she was torpedoed by a U-boat and disabled. She was laid up at Gibraltar for some months before being towed back to the UK for repairs which were completed in early 1945. She sailed for the Far East in June, arriving in Australia at the conclusion of hostilities. During her first eighteen months of operations she laid just over 3000 mines.

Welshman: From completion in August 1941 she was operating in home waters with *Manxman*. In February 1942 she was transferred, temporarily, to the Dover Command as a reinforcement to the forces preparing for a Channel breakout by the German fleet. For the remainder of the year (apart from a short refit, and action damage repairs) she was in the Mediterranean, employed primari-

ly running urgently needed supplies to Malta. On one such occasion she adopted the *Léopard* disguise first used by *Manxman*. She was torpedoed and sunk by a U-boat on 1 February 1943 while on return passage from Malta to Alexandria. During her eighteen months of operations she laid over 3000 mines, slightly more than *Manxman*.

Abdiel: From May 1941 she was employed in the eastern Mediterranean on operations which included the evacuation of Crete, the relief of Tobruk and minelaying in Greek waters. In January 1942 she joined the Eastern Fleet in the Indian Ocean until relieved by *Manxman* in the latter half of the year, when she returned to home waters. Subsequent operations included intensive minelaying on enemy supply routes between Sicily and Tunisia early in 1943, operating from a temporary mine depot at Algiers maintained by HMS *Adventure* from the UK. Later on she was present at the Sicilian landings. On 9 September, after transporting 400 troops to Taranto, she swung over a mine in the harbour and sank with heavy loss of life. During her two and a half years of life she had laid just over 2000 mines.

With the loss of *Latona*, *Welshman* and *Abdiel*, and with *Manxman* under repair, fast minelayer operations came to a brief halt. However, the replacements, with remarkable prescience, were already on the horizon. *Ariadne* was completed exactly one month after *Abdiel*'s loss and *Apollo* early in 1944.

Ariadne: After two months in home waters she operated during December 1943 in the Mediterranean. In January she sailed for the USA and, after passing through the Panama Canal in February 1944, was temporarily transferred to the US 7th Fleet, one of only two HM ships to be so employed (*Victorious* was loaned to the USN in the

Manxman in 1944. Most of her radar aerials have been deleted from this photograph by the wartime censor. (CMP)

Pacific for six months in 1943). In the latter half of the year she was attached to the Australian Navy for training and experience. She subsequently took part in the Leyte operations as an assault troop carrier. In January 1945 she was recalled to the UK to assist *Apollo* laying barrier minefields. In May 1945, on completion of the European war, she and her sister ship conveyed the Norwegian royal family on their return to Oslo. She then sailed again for the Far East, where she arrived in August at the end of hostilities. During her wartime service she laid over 1000 mines.

Apollo: From completion until the end of 1944 she operated exclusively in home waters, initially laying defensive minefields off Normandy. She made her debut to the press when General Eisenhower and Admiral Ramsay inspected the invasion beaches from her on 7 June. Later minelaying operations included vast anti-submarine fields south of Ireland and, in April 1945, a deep field off the Kola Inlet. After conveying the Norwegian royal family in May, she sailed to the Far East with the recently repaired *Manxman*, ahead of their sister ship. In just over a year she had laid the greatest number of mines for the class, just over 8500.

Later Close Range Armament

Both *Apollo* and *Ariadne* had been designed to carry three twin 40mm Hazemeyer mountings of the type introduced into the RN at the end of 1942. In the event, demand obviously outstripped the supply and both ships were temporarily fitted with a twin 20mm mounting on 'B' deck, mounted slightly forward of the 40mm pedestal in order to secure improved arcs of fire. At the same time the original single 20mm were replaced with twin 20mm mountings, two in the bridge wings, two abreast the second and third funnels and one mounting on the superstructure aft, making a secondary armament of four 40mm and twelve 20mm.

Ariadne finished the war with three US twin 40mm in place of the original 40mm Hazemeyer mountings. While precise details are lacking it seems likely that these were fitted in the US early in 1944, not only to enhance her AA capability against Japanese aircraft but to obviate any maintenance problems that might have arisen with the Hazemeyer mountings while she was serving with the 7th Fleet (*Victorious* had had US 40mm quads added to her armament at Pearl Harbor). Both *Ariadne* and *Apollo* had

their twin 20mm armament (five and six mountings respectively) converted to single 40mm 'boffins' at Sydney at the end of the war. Furthermore, at some time in 1945 *Apollo*'s forward AA capability, which was less than *Ariadne*'s, was enhanced by the addition of two single 20mm in sponsons port and starboard just forward of the bridge. The final count in August 1945 was *Ariadne* eleven 40mm, *Apollo* ten 40mm and two 20mm.

Manxman emerged from refit early in 1945 with her armament little changed, except that four twin 20mm had replaced the original seven single 20mm, in positions in the bridge wings, and between the second and third funnels. Her 20mm were not updated to 'boffins', possibly because she had to be taken in hand at Melbourne for repairs on arrival in Australia, or because she was beginning to suffer stability problems.

Speed Trials

The ships covers show no full power trial details for *Abdiel*, and those for *Latona* are unofficial and carried out on passage. Nevertheless, comparison of the listed sea trials for the class reveals considerable uniformity. Assuming the original estimate of ¼kt loss of speed for each 50 tons added was correct, projecting the tonnages back to the standard displacement of 2650/2810 tons (ie without fuel or reserve feed water) does give a rule of thumb figure for speed in the 'standard condition' neatly within the 39¼–40¼kt bracket. Details of trials are given in Table 4.

Post War Employment

Following the cessation of hostilities in August 1945, *Manxman*, *Apollo* and *Ariadne* came into their own once more as high-speed transports, ferrying repatriated prisoners of war between Tokyo, Shanghai, Hong Kong and Singapore until the task was completed at the end of the year.

In 1946 consideration was given to converting the ships to LSIs, a role already explored by *Ariadne*. The scheme was intended to cause the minimum disturbance to the minelaying equipment but involved the removal of 30ft of minerail (reducing capacity by forty-two mines), the mining cranes, the 25ft motorboat and its davits and the

Table 4: TRIAL DATA

Ship	Date	Displacement (tons)	Mines carried	shp	Speed (kts)
Latona	7 May 1941	3340	unknown	72,560	35.7 est
Manxman	20 Jun 1941	3450	24	72,970	35.59
Welshman	25 Aug 1941	3300	50	71,950	36.08
Ariadne	9 Oct 1943	3692	none	69,258*	34.73
Apollo	10 Feb 1944	3715	18	71,000	35.8

Considered a defective low reading and that full power was achieved.

after twin 4in mounting and its ammunition. In their place would be six LCAs and their crews, and 200 troops. However, nothing came of this scheme.

On return from the Far East *Ariadne* went into reserve and was never employed again; she was broken up in the 1960s. For a decade during the 1950s both *Apollo* and *Manxman* found niches in the Home and Mediterranean Fleets respectively as NATO minelayers, with a peacetime role laying exercise minefields. Small, fast, handsome and spacious, their natural alternative employment was as flagships. Deckhouses for staff cabin accommodation were built on the after superstructure during 1954/55, *Manxman* losing her after twin 4in in compensation, while *Apollo* lost her vestigial armament from 'B' gundeck.

Their roles became obsolete by the end of the 1950s. *Apollo* was scrapped in the 1960s, yet *Manxman*, displaying marvellous versatility, embarked on another career, this time as a Minesweeper Support Ship, her forward boiler-room sacrificed for auxiliary machinery. She was to prove the longest serving of the fast minelayers, finally disposed of, following a spell as an Engineers' Training Ship during 1968–71, after thirty years of service.

In the 1950s on fleet exercises the role of surface raider was an obvious employment for a fast minelayer. It was well known in the service that the fast minelayer 'X' had circled the fleet three times at 45kts during the war, and the stories stuck. Hence, when *Apollo* hurtled through the shipping lanes at her 33kts posing as an Orange cruiser, the ship-illuminating flares of the searching Blue aircraft would occasionally tend to move further and further ahead, until they eventually disappeared out of sight over the horizon on their 40kts-plus based search pattern.

Main Sources and Bibliography

Ships' Covers, National Maritime Museum.

Ship Movement Registers, Royal Navy Museum Library, HM Dockyard, Portsmouth.

Information courtesy of the Curator, Cowes Maritime Museum.

Captain J S Cowie, *Mines, Minelayers and Minelaying* (1949).

Captain S W Roskill, *The War at Sea* (HMSO 1954).

M P Cocker, *Mine Warfare Vessels* (Airlife 1993).

E J March, *British Destroyers* (Seeley Service, 1966).

Jane's Fighting Ships, various editions.

Conway's All the World's Fighting Ships, 1922–46 (Conway Maritime Press, 1980).

THE SINKING OF THE BISMARCK

An analysis of the damage

Long term readers of *Warship* will recall 'The Final Action' by John Roberts,[1] which described the sinking of the *Bismarck*, based almost entirely on British sources. Since this article was published in 1983, some valuable new material has appeared from survivors and the wreck has been surveyed by Dr Ballard. This new material has been published in a technical article in the USA[2] which is not readily available elsewhere. This present article, by William H Garzke Jr, Robert O Dulin Jr and David K Brown, RCNC, gives a largely factual account of the known damage inflicted on the *Bismarck* during her final voyage together with a brief commentary on that damage.

During her action with *Hood* and *Prince of Wales* on 24 May 1941, the *Bismarck* was hit by three 14in shells. The first hit the captain's motor launch and caused some trivial damage abaft the funnel. The second hit the sea just short of the port side and penetrated the hull below the belt in the region of the bridge, finally exploding against the 45mm torpedo bulkhead. Splinters penetrated into the cable passage and damaged the bulkhead between the port boiler room and the forward, port turbo-generator room. The generator room flooded quickly; the boiler room more slowly, as tears in the welded bulkhead were partially stopped with hammocks, but eventually it had to be abandoned with the loss of the two boilers and a reduction of top speed to 28kts.

The Bismarck *in 1941.*

The third hit passed through the 60mm splinter protection on the port bow and went out the other side without exploding. It flooded two compartments, one of which contained the manifolds for the forward fuel tanks, and meant that 1000 tons of fuel was unusable. The hole was above the waterline but flooded from the bow wave causing a 9 degree list to port and a 2m trim by the bow. Some void spaces near the steering gear were flooded to reduce trim[3] and the holes, 850mm in diameter, were partially covered with sail cloth.

Victorious

Nine Swordfish (the first squadron with airborne radar, ASV MkIIN) from *Victorious* attacked at dusk on the 24th scoring one hit with an 18in torpedo (warhead 388lb),

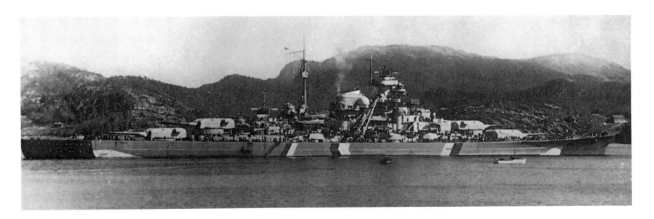

The carrier Ark Royal *arriving at Malta. Her Swordfish aircraft were to inflict the damage that was to prevent the* Bismarck's *escape from Tovey's battleships.*

using duplex pistols. The torpedo exploded on or close to the 320mm main belt amidships on the starboard side, just forward of the funnel; this damage is confirmed by one of Dr Ballard's images. There was a considerable shock effect, which killed one man and injured six more, and the hammock patches in the port boiler room were dislodged leading to the final flooding of that space. The violent manoeuvring also tore the cloth patches over the shell holes forward.

Ark Royal

Fifteen Swordfish from *Ark Royal* attacked at sunset on 26 May in a high wind (Force 9), heavy cloud and waves 25–40ft high. They scored two hits, one abaft the after superstructure which caused slow flooding, mainly through split welded seams, and one other, which was to seal the fate of the *Bismarck*, abaft the steering gear. One of the ship's survivors was sent to investigate the stern compartments aft of the steering gear complex and reported that he found extreme damage to the structure and that the smoke generator was completely wrecked. There was severe whipping, felt throughout the ship, exacerbated by the inertia of the heavy 150mm armour box round the steering gear and by its rigidity in comparison with the fairly light stern structure on which it was carried, which was a deck lower than the main hull. This severe flexing started splits in the side plating and in bulkheads, while the two decks in the stern were wrecked by the blast from the explosion, further weakening the structure.

The rudders were jammed at 12 degrees to port and access to the steering gear compartment was impossible due to the damage and because of the blast from the after

15in turrets, which were firing on British destroyers during the night. Attempts were made to steer a straight course by varying the speed of the three shafts but these proved unsuccessful.

The torpedo attack by destroyers during the night scored no hits but a star-shell did land on *Bismarck*'s forecastle and burnt for some time. The flames from this shell were probably the origin of *Maori*'s claim to have scored a torpedo hit. Evidence of this star-shell damage is shown in some of Dr Ballard's images.

The Final Action

On the morning of 27 May 1941, the weather conditions were poor with sea state at least 5, possibly as high as 7.[4] *Bismarck*, unable to steer, was yawing considerably, making accurate gunnery difficult. It seems that the extreme cut-up needed to accommodate the centre propeller made *Bismarck* directionally unstable and constant use of the rudder was necessary to hold a steady course. She had been designed with a very high metacentric height, probably 4m at the time of her last action, which would have led to high roll accelerations.

It must be remembered that with the line of fire near the fore and aft axis (the British ships were on *Bismarck*'s port bow) rolling would affect training as well as elevation, particularly with the guns at high elevation (the so-called cross-level correction). At the start of the action she also had a slight port list and, in the light of these problems, *Bismarck*'s initial shooting was quite good; she straddled *Rodney* with her third salvo at 0853 at about 24,000yds.

By this time, *Rodney* had already scored her first hits, with her second salvo at 0848, but two minutes later a false range was obtained and she did not regain the target until salvo eighteen at 0859 (21,000yds) which scored two hits. One shell of this salvo hit on the forecastle, causing a fire, and it may have been this shot which put turret Anton out of action. *King George V* was a little slower, scoring her first hit at 0853.

The unmanned examination of the wreck was incomplete for a number of reasons; the hull was buried in silt roughly up to the level of her normal waterline and the camera sled was hard to control because of the motions of the mother ship. In addition the motions of the sled shook up the silt and further reduced visibility. Examination of the complete set of videos suggest that there were some 300–400 hits out of the 2871 shells fired at her. The distribution of hits was in a beehive shaped curve centred on the forward superstructure (the statistician's 'Normal' or 'Gaussian' distribution). A very large number hit the forward superstructure which was completely wrecked, later hits merely re-distributing the debris.

Survivors suggest that most of the damage was caused by *Rodney* but there is little direct evidence to support this. In the later stage, *Dorsetshire* scored a large number of hits on the superstructure with 8in shells. Some specific areas of damage which can be identified are outlined below and are shown on Figures 1 and 2, drawn by Thomas Webb, showing *Bismarck* as she might have appeared just before sinking.

A. The bow anchor and casting are missing, together with the spare anchor and jackstaff, leaving a jagged hole.

B. All three anchors and cables are missing with a hole in the deck just forward of the starboard anchor capstan. The hole is 2–3m long and 500mm wide and shows evidence of a fire. It seems likely that this was *Rodney*'s hit of 0859, seen from *Norfolk* (though a later time has also been suggested).

C. A shell, probably a 14in, hit near the top of 'B' barbette and tore away a piece of 340mm armour some 700mm along the circumference. At the aft, port quadrant of the barbette the upper deck plating has been torn away from the barbette and survivors say that the rear plate of the turret was blown away by the explosion and the turret itself slightly displaced. (Note that the turrets fell away from the wreck during the sinking and have not been surveyed because they are completely buried on the seamount upon which the *Bismarck* rests. Evidence was found of only one turret and here only the turret operating machinery was visible, indicating that the turrets are buried upside down.)

D. An oblique video shows that the after port side of the main conning tower was hit repeatedly but it is not clear how many of these hits penetrated the 350mm plate. There are twenty-five hits visible and a survivor described the tower as looking like Gruyère cheese just before she sank. The armoured door on the port side has been blown away and there is a large hole where several shells, probably from *King George V*, hit together at about 1014.

E. The forward superstructure was hit by a very large number of shells of 5.25in calibre and upwards.

The newly completed King George V *in 1940.* (IWM)

With the help of the authors, artist Thomas G Webb depicts the port profile (at normal waterline) and plan of the Bismarck *as she might have appeared as the* Dorsetshire *approached to fire her final torpedoes. Damage to the superstructure is the result of some 300-400 shells striking the ship. Evidence uncovered by the Ballard Expedition indicates that the break in the stern was caused by failure in the weld all the way around the ship. This was a major contributing factor to the ship's sinking.*

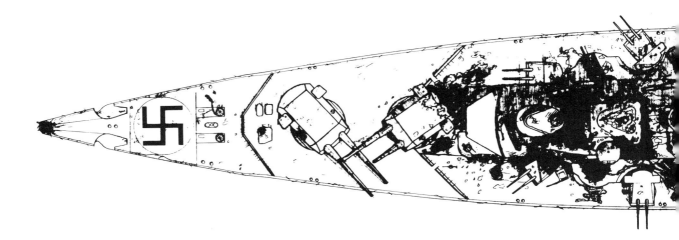

Plating and stiffeners are torn away, the forward boiler intakes were destroyed and the funnel wrecked. The deckhouse below the bridge tower was destroyed and it broke away at 02 deck level.[5] It is very probable that many of the AP shells passed through this light structure without exploding. The Admiral's bridge was, surprisingly, very little damaged (survivor's testimony). The funnel was riddled and fell away during sinking. The deck plating on the lower bridge deck has two large holes on the port side and there is a large hole below the port bridge wing. Survivors believe that these were due to two hits by 14in shells in the last minutes.

F. The 105mm mounts on the port side forward are badly damaged and unrecognisable.

G. The forward 150mm turret on the port side is wrecked with part of the roof blown off, apparently by a fire in the turret. A survivor reports that the magazine was flooded and there is also evidence of a fire outside this turret, which was mentioned in British reports. The barrels of the after starboard 150mm appear damaged but the other 150mm guns seem intact.

H. The forward AA control positions are totally destroyed by an explosion of the ready-use 105mm ammunition (survivor's testimony).

I. Little of the main belt is visible but several shells seem to have penetrated in the region of P1 150mm turret. It is possible that splinters from these hits led to the ammunition explosion in P1 mounting.

J   The forward hangars are completely destroyed and there are several holes in the after hangar. The main mast was severed at the hangar roof.

K. There is a large hole in the vicinity of the catapult on the port side. Almost certainly, this was caused by the

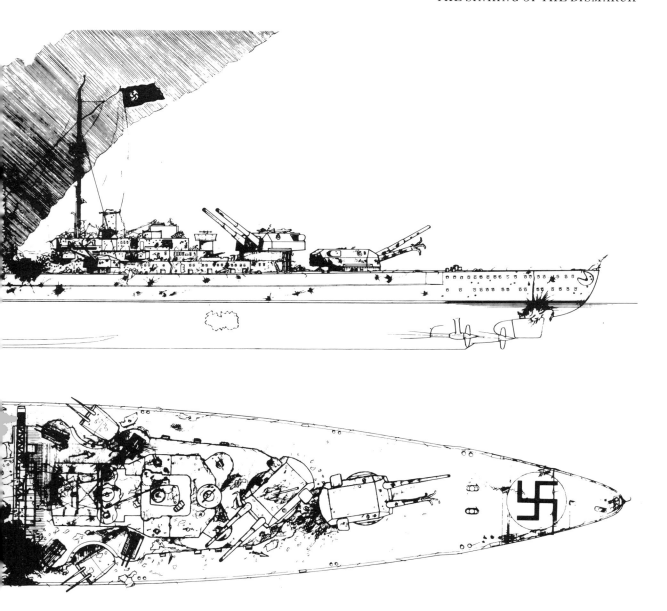

last torpedo hit from *Dorsetshire* as *Bismarck* was actually sinking and listing heavily. *Dorsetshire* reports that her final torpedo was fired on the port side of *Bismarck* at 1034, set for 16ft and was certain it hit.[6] It is probable that *Dorsetshire* had earlier scored two torpedo hits on the starboard side but, as *Bismarck* was listing some 15 degrees to port, these would have hit below the turn of bilge and the holes are not visible. Many survivors noted quantities of oil fuel in the water on the starboard side which, in all probability, came from tanks breached by these hits.

L. Many of the 105mm and 37mm mounts have lost at least one barrel and two of the 105mm mounts are virtually obliterated.

M. There is evidence of a 14in shell hit on the face of Caesar turret while it was trained towards the port bow. There is a concentration of splinter holes in 01

deck in this vicinity and survivors from this turret say that the shock of this hit disabled both elevating and training machinery.

N. The barbette of turret Dora has three hits, probably from *Rodney*, two of which penetrated. These hits started a fire in the magazine and also ripped a large hole in the upper deck.

O. There are only a few shell or splinter holes visible in the upper deck but there may be more in portions covered in sediment. The teak deck is generally in good condition except for extensive fire damage around turret Anton, the aft port quadrant of Bruno and the forward port quadrant of Dora.

P. There was a hit by *King George V* which penetrated the upper belt (145mm KC) and burst 20–30ft later in the canteen, killing 100 men including the executive officer, Commander Has Oels.

The forward 14in guns of the King George V *in October 1940.* (IWM)

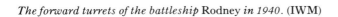

The forward turrets of the battleship Rodney *in 1940.* (IWM)

Commentary

The authors are often asked, 'Did the British sink the *Bismarck* or did the Germans scuttle her?' Our answer has always been 'Yes' to both. The order to scuttle her was given at 0930 and took some time to implement but she was already disabled between 0920 and 0930 and damage inflicted would have caused her to sink slowly and this would have been accelerated by scuttling measures. As already mentioned, *Dorsetshire*'s three torpedo hits did not contribute directly to her sinking. One must wonder if *Ark Royal*'s torpedo bombers could have sunk her with less trouble since *Bismarck*'s torpedo protection was not fully effective, even against 18in torpedoes.

Tests on armour plates removed from *Tirpitz* after the war showed that German armour was almost as good as British and both were equivalent to US plate some 25 per cent thicker. The 16in and 14in shells, at the close ranges of the later part of the action, could penetrate any thickness of armour in *Bismarck* and the state of the conning tower and 15in barbettes show that this was so. Her belt was vulnerable to 14in shells at under 15,000yds and to 16in at longer range. There seem to have been two penetrations of the deck protection by 16in shells. These probably hit the 50mm upper deck when the ship was rolling and the impact turned the shell so that it could have hit the main armour deck more nearly at right angles. One of these exploded in the port engine room and one in the starboard boiler room, both at about 0920–0930 when *Rodney* was at about 9000yds range. At close range the traditional scheme of a sloping deck edge (110mm) behind the belt (320mm) worked surprisingly well and there is no evidence that any shell penetrated both. British fuses seem to have performed very well (eg *Prince of Wales*'s second hit), detonating about 30ft from first impact with heavy scantlings. It is remarkable that all the hits on *Prince of Wales* failed to detonate; *Hood* was very unfortunate.

Bismarck as she lies on the bottom, is without her stern which seems to have fallen off during the sinking. This was due to damage from *Ark Royal*'s torpedo hit already discussed, but there are a number of other contributory factors. Similar damage was caused to *Prinz Eugen* by a torpedo hit on 23 February 1942 and, earlier, to *Lützow*. A break in deck level will always increase stresses locally and, if such a feature is essential, local structure must be considerably reinforced, usually by deep longitudinal bulkheads. In the German ships, extensive use was made of arc welding which was still in the early stages of development. The steel used was not really suitable, welding techniques imperfect and the ships were built in haste. There is clear evidence of the contribution of welding problems in an image of a plate from near the break which shows a straight fracture following the heat affected zone of a weld. Surviving major German ships had reinforcement fitted at breaks in deck level. After the

war the destroyer *Nonsuch* (ex German *Z–38*) was used for explosion trials and broke at the break of forecastle due to poor design and workmanship.

The first two authors have explored the reliability of the new eye-witness accounts and found that they match well with the pictures of the wreck, which the witnesses had not seen before giving their stories. In particular, the account of Mr Josef Statz, who was a seaman in the damage control headquarters has been most valuable. One may still wonder about the distinction which they draw between 14in and 16in hits.

In earlier battleship actions, such as Tsushima and Jutland, a rough guide was that it took about twenty hits to disable a battleship if the magazine did not explode. At first sight, *Bismarck*, with some 3–400 hits, seems at variance with this rule. However, her main armament was out of action after about 20min firing and it may well be that she was effectively disabled by about twenty hits. As mentioned earlier, later hits on the superstructure merely re-arranged the debris. The fact that the British ships fired on her from both sides tended to prevent a list developing and delayed her sinking.

Acknowledgements

This article is almost entirely based on an earlier paper by Garzke and Dulin;[2] Brown's task has been editorial and relating the new studies to British sources. The value of the article is greatly enhanced by Thomas Webb's artwork and we are grateful to be allowed to reproduce it. In turn, this depended on permission to use Dr Ballard's pictures of the wreck. Finally, we must thank the survivors, Baron von Mullenheim-Rechberg and Messrs Statz and Rudek for their accurate accounts.

Notes

1   Roberts, John, 'The Final Action', *Warship 28*, Conway Maritime Press (London 1983).
2   Garzke, William H, and Dulin, Robert O, 'The Bismarck Encounter', Marine Technology, SNAME, (Jersey City 1993).
3   British practice, then and now, is not to counterflood to reduce trim as large quantities of water are needed which sink the ship deeper in the water.
4   There is only a loose relationship between wind speed and wave height but, for the open sea with a wind that has been blowing steadily for some time, the following figures are reasonable approximations:

Sea state	Wave height (metres)	Wind speed (kts)
5	2.5–4	22–27
6	4–6	28–47
7	6–9	48–55

5   This damage is clearly shown on the dust jacket of R D Ballard's *The Discovery of Bismarck*, Hodder and Stoughton (London 1990).
6   See also the contemporary account by the *Dorsetshire* replacement campaign, *Action Stations*. They were trying to raise £2,750,000 to replace the ship, after her loss in 1942.

WAR OPERATIONS
of the Types 35 and 37 Torpedo-Boats

In operations from the French Atlantic coast to the Baltic and Norway, the German 1935 and 1937 Torpedo-Boats saw considerable service during the Second World War. Pierre Hervieux provides a brief history of that service, covering events from minor escort duties to such major events as the 'Channel Dash' of 1942.

Between November 1937 and April 1939, twelve units of the German Type 35 torpedo-boat were launched for the Kriegsmarine. The first eight, *T1–T8*, displaced 844 tons standard (1088 tons full load) and the remainder, *T9–T12*, 839 tons standard (1082 tons full load). These vessels were followed by nine Type 37 torpedo-boats, *T13–T21*, an improved version of the earlier design, launched between June 1939 and November 1941. They had a similar armament to the Type 35 but displaced 853 tons (1098 tons full load) and had an increased endurance. During the Second World War their armament was progressively improved, which resulted in a considerable variety of gun outfits between one ship of the class and another; in addition some units had their after bank of torpedo tubes landed. By way of example: at the end of the war the *T11* had one 40mm AA as a bow chaser, two single 37mm AA (one of which had replaced the after torpedo tubes) and twelve 20mm AA (four singles and four twins). Further details of the armaments are given in Table 2.

Three Type 35 boats being fitted out during the winter of 1939–40. (ECPA)

Table 1: *BUILDING DATA*

Name	Builder	Laid down	Launched	Completed
T1	Schichau (Elbing)	14 Nov 1936	1938	1 Dec 1939
T2	Schichau (Elbing)	14 Nov 1936	1938	2 Dec 1939
T3	Schichau (Elbing)	14 Nov 1936	1938	3 Feb 1940
T4	Schichau (Elbing)	29 Dec 1936	1939	27 May 1940
T5	Deschimag (Bremen)	30 Dec 1936	22 Nov 1937	23 Jan 1940
T6	Deschimag (Bremen)	3 Jan 1937	16 Dec 1937	30 Apr 1940
T7	Deschimag (Bremen)	20 Aug 1937	18 Jun 1938	20 Dec 1939
T8	Deschimag (Bremen)	28 Aug 1937	10 Aug 1938	8 Oct 1939
T9	Schichau (Elbing)	24 Nov 1936	1939	4 Jul 1940
T10	Schichau (Elbing)	24 Nov 1936	1939	5 Aug 1940
T11	Deschimag (Bremen)	1 Jul 1938	1 Mar 1939	7 May 1940
T12	Deschimag (Bremen)	20 Aug 1938	12 Apr 1939	3 Jul 1940
T13	Schichau (Elbing)	–	15 Jun 1939	31 May 1941
T14	Schichau (Elbing)	–	1939	14 Jun 1941
T15	Schichau (Elbing)	–	1939	26 Jun 1941
T16	Schichau (Elbing)	–	1940	24 Jul 1941
T17	Schichau (Elbing)	–	1940	28 Aug 1941
T18	Schichau (Elbing)	–	1940	22 Nov 1941
T19	Schichau (Elbing)	–	20 Jul 1940	18 Dec 1941
T20	Schichau (Elbing)	–	Oct 1941	5 Jun 1942
T21	Schichau (Elbing)	–	Nov 1941	11 Jul 1942

Minelaying Operations

In their first wartime operations of any importance, the Type 35 boats provided escorts for several minelaying operations in the south-western North Sea. Three defensive mine barrages, designated 'SW1', 'SW2', and 'SW3', were laid on the nights of 7/8 August, 14/15 August and 31 August/1 September 1940 respectively. The first was laid by the minelayers *Roland*, *Cobra* and *Brummer*, while, for the other two, the *Brummer* was replaced by the *Tannenberg*. The escorts for 'SW1' were *T2*, *T7* and *T8*, together with three other torpedo-boats; for 'SW2', *T5* and *T7* with four other torpedo boats; for 'SW3', *T5*, *T6*, *T7* and *T8* with four torpedo boats and three destroyers.

On 31 August 1940 the Type 35 boats gained their first success of the war, albeit somewhat indirectly. On this day, 40 miles north-west of Texel the British 20th Destroyer Flotilla ran into minefield 'SW2'. The destroyers *Esk* and *Ivanhoe* were sunk while the *Express* had her fore section destroyed as far aft as the bridge and lost both her forward 4.7in guns. *Express* was out of action for 13 months while a completely new fore end was fitted. The 20th Flotilla's commanding officer was mortally wounded.

After the 'SW3' operation the 2nd Torpedo Boat Flotilla, (*T5*, *T6*, *T7* and *T8*) under the command of Korvettenkapitän Riede, did not return to Germany but sailed for France, arriving in Cherbourg on 2 September.

Table 2: *ARMAMENT VARIATIONS*

Designed Armament of Type 35 and Type 37 Torpedo Boats:	1 × 105mm on quarterdeck; 1 × 37mm AA on after deckhouse (not fitted in ships as completed); 2 × single 20mm AA guns in bridge wings (increased to 3 by 1939); 2 × triple 533mm torpedo tubes; 30 mines could be carried when required.
Armament of T8, *1940:*	1 × 105mm on after deckhouse; 5 × single 20mm AA (1 on after deckhouse, 1 on midships deckhouse, 2 in bridge wings, 1 forward); 2 × triple 533mm torpedo tubes; 30 mines could be carried when required.
Armament of T7 *in 1942:*	1 × 105mm on quarterdeck; 5 × single 20mm AA (1 on after deckhouse, 1 on midships deckhouse, 2 in bridge wings, 1 forward); 1 × quad 20mm AA in place of after bank of torpedo tubes; 1 × triple 533mm torpedo tubes; 30 mines could be carried when required.
Armament of T19 *in 1944:*	1 × 105mm on quarterdeck; 1 × 40mm AA in place of after bank of torpedo tubes; 2 × single 37mm AA (1 on platform abaft funnel, 1 forward); 2 × single 20mm AA in bridge wings; 2 × quad 20mm AA (1 on after deckhouse, one on midships deckhouse); 1 × triple 533mm torpedo tubes; 30 mines could be carried when required.

The T3, *seen here in the summer of 1940, had an eventful career; sunk in 1940 she was salvaged and repaired but was sunk again in 1945.* (Drüppel)

On the same day the *T1* joined *T2* and *T3* in Wilhelmshaven to form the 1st Torpedo Boat Flotilla (Korvettenkapitän Rennenkampff), and these vessels continued the minelaying escort duties of the 2nd Flotilla. With the torpedo-boat *Kondor* and a destroyer, they provided escort for the minelayers *Togo* and *Kaiser*, when they laid the defensive barrage 'SW0' on the night of 6/7 September. On 10/12 September they escorted *Brummer*, *Skagerrak* and *Stralsund*, on a second minelaying operation and then sailed for France to join their sisters.

In the late afternoon of 13 September, off the western Scheldt they were attacked by RAF Blenheim aircraft. Splinters from bombs which fell 10m off the starboard side of *T2* riddled her hull, both above and below water, and six men were badly wounded, including her commanding officer, Kapitänleutnant Batge, and the engineer officer. All her fuel bunkers and double bottom compartments on the starboard side were breached and she took on a list which was corrected by counter flooding and the

A Type 35 boat early in the war, probably 1940. (Author's collection)

transfer of fuel. She was detached from the flotilla and made for Vlissingen where her damage was repaired at the Wilton Yard.

The *T1* and *T3* reached Le Havre on 15 September where they were again subjected to air raids. One bomb fell only 10m from the bow of *T1*, berthed alongside the torpedo-boat *Iltis*, but no damage was caused. The principal reason for these British air attacks was the belief that the invasion of Britain, Operation 'Seelöwe', was about to start and nightly raids were being made against the concentrations of German transports and barges in the channel ports.

In the meantime the 2nd Flotilla had provided escort for the offensive minelaying operations 'Walter' (5/6 September), 'Hannelore' (8/9 September) and 'Bernhard' (15/16 September) in the Straits of Dover. In the last-named operation the group was attacked by British MTBs but these were driven off by the gunfire of the torpedo-boats and German coastal batteries. After these operations the flotilla moved its base to Cherbourg where it was strengthened by the arrival of *T11*. However, on the night of 18/19 September, *T11* was badly damaged during an air raid by Blenheims. A bomb fell close to the port side abreast No 2 turbine room and splinters caused shock damage and started a fire; there were several casualties among the crew.

On the same night the 1st Flotilla suffered a worse loss during an air raid on Le Havre. The *T3* was hit aft on the

port side causing immediate and uncontrolled flooding. Her commander, Kapitänleutnant Bruns, seeing that there was little chance of saving his ship, ordered her to be abandoned just before she capsized and sank. Nine men were killed and twelve wounded.

At the end of September 1940, the 1st and 2nd Torpedo-Boat Flotillas returned to Germany, where they were joined by *T4*, *T9* and *T10*. This was after the latter three had escorted the cruiser *Admiral Hipper* on the first leg of her abortive Atlantic sortie. On the night of 6/7 November both flotillas, with *T1*, *T4*, *T6*, *T7*, *T8*, *T9* and *T10*, carried out a raid against the Scottish east coast, in search of convoys. However, they ran into a British minefield and *T6* (Kapitänleutnant Wolfram) was mined and sunk; the commander survived but forty-five men were lost. The operation was abandoned and the torpedo-boats returned to Stavanger.

On 3 December 1940, shortly after noon, the auxiliary cruiser *Kormoran* sailed from Gotenhafen to begin her ocean raiding cruise. She was escorted out by *T1*, *T5* and *T12*, which accompanied her until the morning of 7 December when, off Frederikshaven, they left her to sail alone to the north.

A similar duty, on a somewhat larger scale, was carried out by the *T5*, *T9*, *T10* and *Falke*, when they provided defence against aircraft and submarines for the battle-cruisers *Gneisenau* and *Scharnhorst* at the start of Operation 'Berlin' – a break out into the Atlantic to make war on commerce. The big ships sailed from Kiel on 22 January 1941 and were joined by the torpedo-boats at 1500 on 25 January. The six ships, proceeding at 22kts, passed through the Skagerrak and, at 1908, the torpedo-boats parted company and sailed for Bergen.

In January and February 1941 they were again providing escorts for minelaying operations; this time in Norwegian waters. Between 26 and 30 January the *T5*, *T9* and *T12* were covering the minelayers *Tannenberg*, *Brummer*, *Königin Luise* and *Hansestadt Danzig* while they laid defensive minefields in Operation 'Pommern' from Stavanger. On the night of 3/4 February the same minelayers, less the *Hansestadt Danzig*, were escorted by *T5*, *T9*, *T10*, *T12* and *Falke* during Operation 'Rugen' off Skudesnes.

Operations in the Baltic

With the invasion of the Soviet Union, the Baltic became a new area of operations. The *T2*, *T5* and *T11* were already in this area and they were soon joined by *T7* and *T8*. On 13/14 September 1941 a feint operation, code-named 'Westwind,' was carried out by *T2*, *T5*, *T8* and *T11*, together with several S-boats and smaller craft, against the western side of Ösel Island. On 16/17 September, with the cruisers *Emden* and *Leipzig*, the *T7*, *T8* and *T11* shelled the Soviet defenders on the Sworbe Peninsula. During the latter operation attacks by four Russian MTBs on the bombarding ships and by the submarine *Shch317* on the *Leipzig* were unsuccessful.

Three Type 35 boats moored alongside the Maritime Station in Cherbourg, following their arrival on 2 September 1940. Four boats arrived on this day: T5, T6, T7 and T8. (ECPA)

The T10 *in 1942.* (Drüppel)

At the end of September, in order to prevent a possible break-out into the Baltic by the Soviet Fleet the German Baltic Fleet was transferred to the Aaland Sea and Libau. The northern group, in the Aaland Sea, comprised the battleship *Tirpitz*, the heavy cruiser *Prinz Eugen*, the light cruisers *Köln* and *Nürnberg*, the destroyers *Z25*, *Z26*, and *Z27*, the torpedo-boats *T2*, *T5*, *T7*, *T8* and *T11* and a number of S-boats. The southern group, at Libau, consisted of the *Emden* and *Leipzig* and a few S-boats. The fleet left Swinemünde on 23 September but on the following day, after successful air attacks on the Soviet warships in Kronstadt and Leningrad, the *Tirpitz*, *Admiral Scheer* and two torpedo-boats were recalled; three other torpedo-boats were diverted to join the southern group and finally, on 29 September, the remaining ships returned to Gotenhafen.

On 12/13 October the *T2*, *T5*, *T7* and *T8*, together with the cruiser *Köln* and seven fleet minesweepers carried out another feint operation, codenamed 'Westfalen'. This was part of the operations to capture the island of Dagö, which also involved a second feint on the island's east coast while landings were made on the south coast. On the 14th the *Köln* and her group shelled Cape Ristna with their 150mm and 105mm guns, in support of the German troops ashore. By the 21 October Soviet resistance was over and, no longer required in this area, the torpedo-boats returned to operate in the Skagerrak.

The Channel Dash

On 16 November 1941 the *T4*, *T7* and *T12* sailed from Copenhagen for Kiel. Passing through the Kiel canal on the following day they stopped at Wilhelmshaven, prior to oiling at Vlissingen, and then proceeded to Cherbourg where they arrived on the morning of 25 November. Here they were detailed to escort the auxiliary cruiser *Komet*, which arrived at Cherbourg on the following afternoon, back to Germany. They sailed shortly after midnight with the fleet minesweepers *M10* and *M153* and, after a short stop at Le Havre, sailed north at 1924 on the 27 November. The escort had, by this time, been enhanced by the addition of three more fleet minesweepers and six motor minesweepers. At 0400 on the 28th, between Boulogne and Calais, the group was attacked by British MTBs. During the subsequent engagement the *T4* was damaged by both British and German gunfire and the *T7* had three men killed by British machine-gun fire. At 0710 the ships arrived in Dunkirk and on 30 November, after 516 days in enemy waters, the *Komet* was escorted safely into Hamburg.

On the same day another auxiliary cruiser, the *Thor*, sailed from Kiel and anchored in the Schilling Roads where she was joined by the *T2* and *T12* on 2 December and by *T4* and *T7* from Wilhelmshaven on the following day. Fog delayed the *Thor*'s departure and Vlissingen was not reached until midday on 4 December, where she was again delayed. On the 7th she sailed to Zeebrugge where she remained with her escort until 13 December. Sailing in the afternoon they arrived off Le Havre on the following day and, in the evening of 15 December off Brest, the torpedo-boats were relieved by the 8th Minesweeping Flotilla. The *T2* and *T4* remained at Brest while the *T7* and *T12* returned to Germany, sailing on the 17 December – the same day as *Thor* arrived off the Gironde Estuary.

In preparation for Operation 'Cerberus' (the famous 'Channel Dash' of the *Scharnhorst*, *Gneisenau* and *Prinz Eugen* on their return to Germany) the *T5* and *T11* sailed from Wilhelmshaven for St Nazaire on 10 January 1942. Joined *en route* by *T12* from Wesermünde, they arrived safely at St Nazaire on 12 January. With the *T2* and *T4*, which were already in residence, they formed the 2nd Torpedo-Boat Flotilla (Korvettenkapitän Erdmann).

Operation 'Cerberus' began exactly one month later on 12 February 1942 when the German capital ships, with an escort of six destroyers, sailed from Brest. They were joined off Le Havre by the 2nd Flotilla and off Dunkirk by the 3rd Flotilla (Korvettenkapitän Wilcke); the latter consisted of the new Type 37 boats *T13*, *T15*, *T16* and *T17*. When *Scharnhorst* was mined and stranded off the mouth of the Scheldt a number of escorts were detailed to stand by her. One of these, the *T13*, was slightly damaged by a bomb during an air attack. This was the only damage suffered by any of the Type 35 or 37 boats during Operation 'Cerberus', an operation that involved considerable risk but, by careful planning and a substantial

Two Type 35 boats off the west coast of France. (ECPA)

degree of luck, had been carried through with great success. During the operation the torpedo-boats claimed to have shot down several aircraft.

Norway

On 6 March 1942 the *T5* and *T12* together with four destroyers sailed from Trondheim escorting the battleship *Tirpitz* for an intended attack on the Russian Convoy PQ12. However, at 2010 on the same day the two torpedo-boats and one of the destroyers were ordered to return. During 19/20 March the cruiser *Admiral Hipper* moved from Kiel to Trondheim under the escort of *T15*, *T16*, *T17* and three destroyers. On 9/10 May the armoured ship *Admiral Scheer* and the fleet tanker *Dithmarschen*, escorted by *T5* and *T7*, moved from Trondheim to Narvik.

On 16 May the *Prinz Eugen*, which had just completed emergency repairs after being torpedoed by the British submarine *Trident* on 23 February, sailed from Trondheim for Kiel (Operation 'Zauberflöte') escorted by *T11*, *T12* and two destroyers. The force was attacked on the 17th by twenty-two British aircraft (twelve Beauforts, six

The T2 *passes astern of another vessel leading a Type 37 boat.* (Bundesarchiv)

Blenheims and four Beaufighters). Three of the aircraft were shot down by AA fire and Me109 fighters and no damage was done. Attacks by a further thirty aircraft were intercepted by Me109s, which shot down four British aircraft for the loss of three German. The *Prinz Eugen* arrived safely at Kiel on 18 May. On the same day the armoured ship *Lützow* started the opposite journey, leaving Kiel for Trondheim, via Kristiansand, escorted by the *T15*. She arrived on 20 May but a few days later, on 24/25 May, together with the *Dithmarschen* she moved from Trondheim to Narvik.

In the afternoon of 2 July, the *T7* and *T15* sailed from Trondheim for Altafjord, which was to serve as a base for Operation 'Rösselsprung', the attack on Convoy PQ17. On 5 July, with the *Tirpitz, Hipper, Scheer* and seven destroyers they sailed but later on the same day, following a directive from Hitler that the German ships were not to take risks, the surface ships were ordered to return and leave the convoy to submarines and aircraft.

France

On 13 July the *T4, T10, T13* and *T14* sailed from Cuxhaven for Le Havre, arriving on the 16th. There the four boats formed the 3rd Flotilla and were soon at work on defensive mining operations in the English Channel. Two operations, 'Rhein' and 'Stein', were carried out between 20 and 22 July, while a third, Operation 'Masuren', from which *T4* was absent, was completed on the night of 1/2 August.

In mid 1942 the Kriegsmarine decided to send two of its naval supply ships to the Far East. *En route* they were to supply raiders and U-boats operating in the South Atlantic and Indian Ocean and, when their duties in the Orient were complete, they were to return with cargoes of edible oils. The first of these ships, the *Uckermark* (ex *Altmark*), commanded by Kapitän von Zatorski, was given an escort of three torpedo-boats for the first part of its journey across the Bay of Biscay. She sailed on 9 August but was sighted by a British aircraft so the operation was cancelled and she returned to France. A similar out-and-back, cancelled trip was made by the supply ship *Ermland*, escorted by *T10, T13* and *T14* on 11 August. Four days later the two ships attempted to break out together, again with an initial escort of two torpedo-boats. Two days later, on the 17th, they were again sighted by aircraft. This time they were bombed and enough damage was done to necessitate their return to Bordeaux and La Pallice.

On 5 October 1942, the *T3*, which had been sunk in 1940 (see earlier) but subsequently raised, left Le Havre under the tow of the tugs *Volkmar* and *Elbe*. Despite the slow speed of the tow, in this minor version of the 'Channel Dash', she reached Germany safely where she was repaired at the Schichau Yard in Danzig.

The T2 *followed by a radar equipped Type 37 boat. Note the quad 20mm AA mounting in the foreground.* (Bundesarchiv)

Action in the Channel

Late on 13 October 1942 the auxiliary cruiser *Komet* sailed from Le Havre in an attempt to pass down the Channel and out into the Atlantic for another raiding cruise. She was escorted for her passage down the Channel by the 3rd Flotilla (*T4*, *T10*, *T14* and *T19*) and six minesweepers. Her departure had, however, become known to British Intelligence and the Admiralty despatched the escort destroyers *Cottesmore*, *Quorn*, *Glaisdale*, *Eskdale* and *Albrighton*, together with the MTBs *49*, *55*, *56*, *84*, *95*, *203*, *229* and *236* from Dartmouth to intercept the German ships. A second force, comprising the escort destroyers *Brocklesby*, *Fernie*, *Tynedale* and the Polish *Krakowiak*, was sent out from Plymouth. The German force was therefore considerably outnumbered and out-gunned.

At about 0100 on the 14th the first British group intercepted the *Komet* and her escorts off Cap de la Hague. The *T10*, outermost of the torpedo-boats, was hit by six 4in shells. The first two shells reduced her speed temporarily to 8kts and she had just worked up again to 24kts when the fifth shell brought it down once more to 9kts. Badly damaged, with eleven men killed and a number wounded, she withdrew from the action and moved close inshore. The other three torpedo-boats were slightly damaged by erratic machine gun fire from the *Komet* which resulted in several casualties, including Korvettenkapitän Wilcke. At 0215 the *Komet* was hit by two torpedoes, probably from *MTB 236*, and she blew up

shortly afterwards; none of her crew could be rescued. After damaging the *Brocklesby* the torpedo-boats escaped, suffering no further harm. Following upon this disastrous action, the 2nd Flotilla's commander, Korvettenkapitän Erdmann, suggested that a second 105mm gun should be fitted on the forecastle of the Types 35 and 37 boats. This suggested improvement, to what were comparatively weakly armed boats was, however, rejected by Konteradmiral Bey, Flag Officer Destroyers.

On 17 October 1942 the *T9* and *T12* sailed from Bogen Bay near Narvik for Wilhelmshaven where they arrived on 23 October. Three days later, they left for France in company with *T17* and reached La Pallice at the end of the month. These movements were part of the preparation for escorting the steamer *Wismar*, carrying an important strategic cargo, into La Pallice. No less than three escort groups were provided for this one ship:

1st Group: *T4*, *T13*, *T19* and *T22*.
2nd Group: *Falke* and three minesweepers from the 6th Flotilla.
3rd Group: *T9*, *T12*, *T17* and *T18*.

All three groups sailed at 1900 on 31 October. Five and a

A Type 37 boat equipped with radar but still carrying both triple torpedo-tube mountings. (Author's collection)

half hours later the *T13* had to turn back as she was experiencing trouble with her machinery; she was escorted by *T19*. Despite losing half their number, it was the first group that, following a lengthy search, located the *Wismar* and brought her safely into La Pallice at 1650 on 4 November.

A similar operation, on a smaller scale, was carried out shortly after the *Wismar* was brought home. In this case the *T13*, *T19* and *Falke* sailed at 1800 on 5 November to locate the steamer *Templin*. She was sighted at 2045 and on the following morning her escort was reinforced by three minesweepers of the 8th Flotilla. Despite several air attacks the ships arrived at La Pallice, unharmed, shortly after nightfall.

The T18 *alongside the Maritime Station at Le Havre shortly before she carried out the minelaying sortie into the Channel in early May 1943.* (Author's collection)

At the beginning of December the *T4* and *T10* returned to Germany, arriving at Kiel on the 10th. Their places were taken by *T2* and *T5*, which sailed from Germany for France on 3 March 1943, but, at the end of April, *T9* and *T12* were also withdrawn from France when they returned to Germany for refits.

On 8 March the *Scharnhorst* sailed from Gotenhafen in the Baltic for Norway, proceeding first to Bergen, then Trondheim and arriving at Bogen Bay, near Narvik, on the 12th. Initially she was escorted by one destroyer but, off Aarhus and Kristiansand, she was joined by the *T16*, *T20*, *T21*, two other torpedo-boats and three destroyers. However, the weather soon deteriorated and it became necessary for the three Type 37 boats and one destroyer to seek shelter in Bergen.

Escorted by the *T2*, *T12*, *T18*, *T23* and *Falke*, the Italian blockade runner *Himalaya* sailed from the Gironde for Japan on 28 March 1943. After her escort had departed she was located by British aircraft off Finisterre and had to return. Met by the *T5*, *T9*, *T19* and *Kondor*, she reached Bordeaux on 30 March. The *Himalaya* made a second attempt on the night of 9/10 April but, despite an escort consisting of *T2*, *T5*, three other torpedo-boats and three destroyers, she was forced to return by heavy air attacks.

A 1937 Type boat on escort duty. (Bundesarchiv)

During the spring and summer of 1943 the *T5* and *T19* were employed escorting U-boat tankers and damaged U-boats in the bay of Biscay. Between 5 and 8 May three mining operations were carried out by *T2*, *T5*, *T8* and two *Elbing* class torpedo-boats operating from Le Havre and Cherbourg. *T19*, together with four other torpedo-boats, was involved in further mining operations in the channel on 3–5 September (Operations 'Taube' and 'Rebhuhn') and on the night of 29/30 September (Operation 'Talsohle').

On 25 June the *T2*, *T5* and *T18* sailed for Germany where they arrived safely on 1 July. They were followed in August by *T19* and in November by *T14*. The latter vessel, which arrived in Cuxhaven on 5 November, was the last of the Type 35/37 boats to be stationed in France.

Return to the Baltic

In the Baltic, on 27 August 1943, the *T7* collided with the Swedish steamer *Rosa Smith* and was badly damaged.

On 29 August the Danish fleet was scuttled. The torpedo-boat *Hvalrossen* (1913, 169 tons), attempting to escape, was intercepted and turned back by *T5* but subsequently ran herself ashore, north of Bago, and was scuttled by her crew. At the beginning of September the *T20* and *T21* were transferred from Norway to the Baltic.

Between November 1943 and June 1944, the Type 35 and 37 boats were not employed operationally, being used as training ships in the Baltic for the large number of officers required by the rapidly expanding U-boat force. By the end of November *T4*, *T5*, *T7*, *T9*, *T10*, *T11*, *T14*,

T20 and *T21* were attached to the Torpedo School in Travemünde and the *T15*, *T16*, *T17* and *T18* to the U-boat training flotillas. The *T13* was part of the torpedo experimental establishment and *T1*, *T2*, *T3*, *T8*, T12 and *T19* were in dockyard hands. On 12 December the *T3*, having completed her repairs at the Schichau Yard, was recommissioned at Danzig. However, the increase in operational boats was short lived. On the very next day, during a daylight air raid on Kiel by about 600 bombers of the 8th USAAF, the *T15* was sunk – the first loss among the class since the *T6* was mined in November 1940.

In June 1944, the Types 35 and 37 boats were again transferred to front line duties to provide support for German and Finnish land forces against the increasing threat of the advancing Russians. In mid June the *T3*, *T8* and *T12* were ordered to transport ammunition to Turku in Finland and later they escorted convoys between Gotenhafen and the Baltic States, proceeding to Libau, Reval and, occasionally, Riga. During the night of 27/28 June the *T8*, *T10* and the *Elbing* class boat *T30* were involved in Operation 'Steinhäger', the assault on the island of Narvi which had been occupied by the Russians on 22 June. Five minesweepers and four motor minesweepers, together with some Finnish patrol boats and MTBs were also involved. An attempted landing by Finnish troops failed, due to a strong Russian defence and inadequate co-ordination between German and Finnish forces, and the operation was cancelled. Shortly afterwards, on the night of 15/16 July, Narvi was bombarded by *T8*, *T10* and *T30* and, during an engagement with Soviet *Tral* class minesweepers, the torpedo-boats sank the *T218* (1939, 476 tons).

On 29 July the *T2* and *T4* were sunk during a USAAF air raid on Bremen; they were both salvaged, on 27 September and 25 October respectively, but, as they required extensive repair, it was decided to pay them off – they were both scrapped in 1946.

As a show of force the *T13*, *T18* and *T20* of the 3rd Flotilla (Korvettenkapitän Verlohr) made a reconnaissance sortie into the Aaland Sea between 15 and 17 September. As they were returning, on the morning of the 17th, they stopped and searched a group of boats which were carrying refugees to Reval a few miles to the south. While in this vulnerable position, two Russian fighters appeared and attacked the torpedo-boats with rockets. Before she was able to work up speed, the *T18* was hit amidships by two of the missiles which detonated in her boiler rooms. She broke in two and sank with the loss of thirty of her crew.

On the morning of 23 September the last German convoy sailed from Reval. This consisted of four steamers and one hospital ship carrying 9000 men, escorted by *T13*, *T17*, *T19* and *T20*. Between 6 and 10 October, following the Russian break-through between Libau and Memel on the Baltic coast, the *Prinz Eugen*, *Lützow* and three destroyers shelled positions near Memel. AA and AS defence for this force was provided by the 3rd Flotilla, consisting of *T13*, *T16*, *T20* and *T21*. Although subjected to Russian air attacks, none of the ships of the force were damaged. The *Lützow* was again employed in bombardment duties on 23/24 October, this time in company with two destroyers and the *T13*, *T19* and *T21*. They shelled Russian positions on the Swarbe Peninsula, near Memel, during which time several air attacks were driven off, although the destroyer *Z28* was damaged by a bomb.

A few days later, on 28 October, the *T8* was damaged by a near miss bomb during a Russian air raid on Libau. On 20/21 November The *Prinz Eugen*, *T13*, *T16*, *T19* and *T21* were called up to provide artillery support to German troops on the Swarbe Peninsula. On the next three days this duty was taken over by *Admiral Scheer*, together with two destroyers and the 2nd Torpedo-boat Flotilla (Korvettenkapitän Paul) consisting of the *T3*, *T5*, *T9*, *T12*, *T13* and *T16*. Despite constant air attacks on the ships, they succeeded in holding back the Russian troops long enough to allow the evacuation, by barge, of the German rearguard. This task was completed on the last night, leaving the Russians to find a deserted peninsula on the following morning. The *T14* was absent from these operations because she was carrying out a post-refit work-up from Pillau.

On 15 December the *T10* was damaged for a second time by a near miss during a Russian air raid on Libau. She was sent to Gotenhafen for repairs but, on 18 December, during a raid by Bomber Command of the RAF, both she and the floating dock in which she was situated were sunk. By the end of 1944 there were only nine of the Type 35/37 boats still operational: in the Baltic there were *T1*, *T3*, *T4* and *T8* of the 2nd Flotilla and *T13*, *T16* and *T17* of the 3rd Flotilla, while, based in the Skagerrak were the *T19* and *T20* of the 3rd Flotilla.

On 4 January 1945, the *T13* was proceeding at 15kts in Danzig Bay when a submarine, displaying a red star on its conning tower, suddenly surfaced less than 100m from her bows. The *T13* rammed the submarine just abaft the conning tower and then opened fire on the submarine's crew with her machine-guns. She then went astern to free herself prior to making a depth-charge attack but the enemy vessel sank bows first and disappeared in a swirl of bubbles. Damaged by the collision, *T13* sailed slowly back to Gotenhafen. According to Russian sources, the submarine concerned was *S13* (Captain Marinesko) which, despite her damage, survived the attack and returned to base.

The T14, *mounting two 37mm AA guns, one forward and one abaft the funnel, a quad 20mm on the after deckhouse and her 105mm gun aft. She still has both sets of torpedo tubes. As she is without camouflage, the photograph was probably taken while she was on trials in June 1941.* (Drüppel)

The T21 *in company with two of her sister ships. Note she has not yet been fitted with radar.* (Drüppel)

The torpedo-boats in the Skagerrak continued to carry out their regular escort duties until the end of the war. By way of example, on 13 January the *T19* and *T20*, together with two destroyers, covered the cruiser *Nürnberg* and the minelayer *Lintz* during a minelaying operation. The group was attacked by Halifax bombers in the Skagerrak but all six of the bombs dropped missed and no damage was sustained by either side. In the Baltic, convoy operations to and from Courland continued into February and employed all available torpedo-boats without loss. On 8 February, the *T8*, with *Lützow* and two other torpedo-boats, provided gunfire support for the retreating German Army near Frauenburg.

Tragic Finale

On 8 March 1945, the *T9* was damaged by bombs in Gotenhafen. On the same day, the Russian submarine *L21* (Captain Mogilevski) laid a mine barrage off Hela which claimed the *T3* and *T5* on 14 March while the two vessels were escorting a convoy.

On 2 April, near Bornholm, the motor minesweeper *R256* was bombed and seriously damaged by Russian aircraft. Judged as beyond repair the vessel was sunk by *T11*. During the night of 9/10 April the RAF dropped 2634 tons(!) of bombs on the harbour installations at Kiel. During this raid the *T1*, which was under refit, was sunk together with several other ships, both naval and merchant.

In the Kattegat, on 10 April, Halifax bombers sank the *T13* and severely damaged the *T16*. The latter vessel became a constructive total loss, being paid off at Frederikshaven on 13 April and eventually scrapped at the end of 1945. Another tragic loss occurred in the Kattegat on 14 April when the *T17* mistook the submarine *U-235* for an enemy vessel and sank her with depth-charges northwest of Skagens Horn. There were no survivors from the submarine's crew of forty-six.

During the night of 23/24 April, the *T19*, with the destroyer *Richard Beitzen*, was escorting a northbound convoy from Frederikshaven to Oslo when, at 0335, it was attacked by a radar-equipped Halifax; the destroyer was seriously damaged. At Kiel on 3 May, the *T8* and *T9*

were scuttled: the wrecks were to be cleared with depth-charges on 10 December 1945.

At about 0800 on 5 May 1945, the *T17* (Kapitänleutnant Liermann) and *T19* (Freiherr von Luttitz), together with several other torpedo-boats, destroyers, transports and smaller vessels, sailed from Denmark to Hela to embark 45,000 refugees. On the return journey the convoy was attacked by Russian MTBs but these were all beaten off and all the ships arrived safely off Copenhagen on 6 May. Here the warships were unloaded in a hurry so they could utilise their greater speed to make a second trip to Hela. The *T17* and *T19* arrived off Hela on the following day, just before the start of the armistice. With other torpedo-boats and destroyers, they departed with about 25,000 soldiers and refugees who were disembarked at Glücksburg on 9 May.

Fates of the Survivors

T4   Allocated to USN 1945; sold to Denmark 18 June 1948 for use as MTB leader but not commissioned; broken up 1951.

T11   Allocated to RN 1945; transferred to French Navy 4 February 1946 and renamed *Bir Hakeim* – not commissioned; stricken 8 October 1951 and broken up.

T12   Allocated to Soviet Navy in 1945 and transferred at Libau in January 1946; renamed *Podvischnyi*; stricken 1957 and broken up.

T14   Allocated to USN 1945; transferred to French Navy September 1947; arrived Cherbourg 24 October 1947 and renamed *Dompaire* – not commissioned; stricken 8 October 1951 and broken up.

T17   Allocated to Soviet Navy 1945 and transferred at Libau in February 1946; renamed *Porivistyi*; transferred to East German 'Seepolizei' 1952 and employed as depot ship for motor minesweepers under the name *Rosa Luxemburg*; stricken 1957 and broken up.

T19   Allocated to USN 1945; sold to Denmark January 1947 for $5000; intended for use as an MTB tender but never commissioned; broken up 1951.

T20   Allocated to RN 1945; transferred to French Navy 4 February 1946 and renamed *Baccarat*; never commissioned; stricken 8 October 1951 and broken up.

T21   Allocated to USN 1945; cannibalised at Bremen; scuttled in Skagerrak 16 December 1946.

THE ORIGINS OF CANADIAN CARRIER AVIATION

Canadian-manned escort carriers of the Royal Navy 1943–45

The outbreak of the Second World War found Canadian naval aviation totally unprepared, although the exploits of the Fleet Air Arm and the US Navy's carriers were followed keenly by Canadian naval officers throughout the 1930s and during the early part of the war. Here, Thomas G Lynch describes how by 1942 the Canadian government could no longer afford to ignore the long-term implications of the fact that naval air forces were essential for the successful conduct of the war at sea.

Although Canada had had an abiding interest in naval aviation dating back to the First World War, it had focused chiefly on land-based maritime patrol aircraft throughout 1915–18 and even that had been allowed to lapse into near-extinction by 1920. In 1939 Canadian naval aviation possessed only biplane flying boats like the Vickers-Supermarine Stranraer, all of which were under the control of the Royal Canadian Air Force. Indeed, until 1946, naval aviation remained the sole property of the RCAF, although there were unsuccessful attempts throughout the war to establish a Canadian equivalent to the Royal Navy's Fleet Air Arm. However, during 1943–44 two officers in particular, Captains H N Lay and H G DeWolf, were to be pivotal in bringing matters to a head.

In 1942 the British Admiralty devised a scheme whereby Canadian officers could receive instruction as pilots or observers with the RN but remain members of the RCN/RCNVR. Ratings would be commissioned into the RCNVR upon successful completion of the course. Similar offers had been made in the past without result but when this proposal was placed before the Canadian Chief of the Naval Staff, Vice-Admiral Nelles, on 23 December 1942 he gave it serious consideration. The result was a memorandum in early January 1943 by the Director of Operations Division, Captain H N Lay, which stressed the importance of naval aviation to a balanced fleet. This was reinforced by another communication, this time from the Director of Plans Division, Acting Captain

H G DeWolf, stressing the role of aircraft in convoy defence and the necessity of having carrier-based as well as land-based aircraft.

After careful consideration, Ottawa signalled the Admiralty on 2 March 1943 accepting their offer and in April Lay and DeWolf wrote a joint memorandum on how the Navy could develop its own air policy. In the final paragraphs of the report, the two Directors recommended that:

1. The training of personnel with the Royal Navy for the possible formation of a Canadian Naval Air Service be expedited;
2. That a naval air division be formed at Headquarters in Ottawa; and
3. That a senior officer should be sent to the UK and the US to study all aspects of naval air operations, including the gaining of experience at sea in a carrier.

The Naval Board concurred and Captain Lay was chosen to carry out these investigations. Making a hurried trip to Washington DC in March to arrange his itinerary, he returned, only to depart again on 30 April 1943. After tours of bases in the United States, through the first half of May, he sailed to the UK from Halifax on the 17th arriving on the 24th. Tours and practical demonstrations took place throughout June and July and Lay returned to London in early August. Here planning had progressed on the implementation of the training programme and, by 13 August, all had been settled, with the FAA willing to accept fifty-five air officers and an unspecified number of

others to train as observers. However, actual implementation was deferred until the whole question of a Canadian naval air service could be studied.

At the end of August 1943 Captain Lay released a comprehensive report on his findings in which he recommended that a naval air service, modelled on the FAA but with suitable changes, should be formed as soon as possible. In addition he considered that it should concern itself exclusively with carrier operations, leaving the RCAF to conduct coastal operations with shore-based aircraft. He also suggested that the new service should start by manning two escort carriers backed by the necessary maintenance facilities.

The Manpower Crisis

Meanwhile, at the Quebec Conference in August 1943, expansion of the RCN had been under discussion, as the RN was beginning to experience a manpower shortage. At the same time NSHQ were making it quite clear to the RN that the RCN was not going to finish the war with a small ship navy. At a subsequent meeting on 8 September, the Canadian Cabinet Committee agreed to assist the Royal Navy by manning certain vessels, particularly three flotilla of major landing craft, and of gradually manning one or two cruisers and two fleet destroyers. The Chief of Naval Staff, dismayed, eloquently pleaded the case for aircraft carriers but any decision was postponed until a more thorough study could be made. A joint RCN/RCAF Committee was formed at the end of September and issued a report at the end of October, supporting the naval view that the operation of carriers should be undertaken.

Meanwhile, the manpower crisis in the UK deepened and on 30 October the escort building programme was severely curtailed. This was followed in November by an

25 January 1944 – HMS Nabob *hard aground on an uncharted silt bank near the mouth of the Fraser River on the British Columbian coast.* (DND, Dillon Collection)

Captain H N Lay aboard Nabob, *February 1944. Credited as the father of Canadian naval aviation, Lay commanded* Nabob *through her brief operational career in 1944.* (DND, Lyncan Collection)

HMS Nabob *off Norfolk, Virginia on 8 March 1944. By this time problems surrounding her mixed, RCN/RN/FAA crew had reached a head and immediate answers were necessary to address those problems.* (US National Archives, Lyncan Collection)

urgent personal appeal from Admiral of the Fleet, Sir A B Cunningham, the First Sea Lord of the Admiralty, to the CNS in Ottawa for manpower help. Accordingly, the Assistant CNS was immediately sent to London to discuss the matter. He returned with a new proposal from the Admiralty suggesting that the RCN take over two of the new American-built escort carriers then coming into service with the RN. However, the Canadian Prime Minister, Mackenzie King, scotched the suggestion at once, stating that to accept the offer would lay the government open to accepting Lend-Lease by 'back-door' methods. King, throughout the war, would maintain a 'cash and carry' policy in any acquisitions.

Faced with this situation, the Naval Service decided to explore other routes. Firstly, with the war at sea stabilising, it decided to curtail escort ship construction, since those vessels in advanced stages of building would be sufficient for foreseeable needs. The subsequent easing of manpower requirements afforded the RCN a comfortable surplus, making it possible to offer as many officers and men as needed to man firstly the CVE, HMS *Nabob*, which had commissioned at Seattle, Washington State, in September, and later HMS *Puncher*, commissioned 5 February 1944 at Seattle-Tacoma.

The command of *Nabob* was given to Captain Lay who, although Cabinet had yet to concur with this manning decision, was appointed on 15 October 1943. He immediately travelled to Vancouver to stand by his ship and by the end of December, a considerable number of RCN personnel were detailed to the carrier. However, Lay was still worried because the Cabinet had still not made a final decision on manning or acquiring escort carriers.

Finally, on 5 January 1944, the Cabinet reviewed the situation and dramatically turned down the whole idea. However, a week later, the Minister of National Defence for Naval Services, Angus L MacDonald, raised the

matter again and managed to force the manning plan through Cabinet. MacDonald had won through by arguing that operating two CVEs would cost only about C$4 million per year, since the RN was paying for the aircraft and FAA personnel. In addition, he showed that there now existed a manning surplus within the RCN, more than enough to man two CVEs. Finally, he argued that the RCN would be unable to obtain a British-built carrier of any sort for at least another full year, and that the RN would benefit from this situation by having the use of the FAA-trained Canadian personnel during that time, financed by Canada. Consequently, the Cabinet agreed to provide the ship's complements for HMS *Nabob* and *Puncher*, while the RN supplied the aircraft and flying personnel as well as retaining ownership of the ships, the latter to placate King's rabid fixation toward Lend-Lease acquisitions.

Meanwhile, personnel for the ships continued to arrive. Accommodation was at a premium, with RN and RCN personnel accommodated in buildings at Hastings Park, some of which had been cattle barns pre-war. However, this situation was alleviated on 7 December, when HMS *Thane* arrived as accommodation ship.

Nabob

Nabob (D77) commissioned into the RN on 7 September 1943 and, having completed the necessary storing, was sailed to Vancouver by a small RN crew for modifications to British requirements by Burrard Drydock & Shipbuilding Co Ltd. In January 1944 she began an extensive working-up programme, being shifted to Esquimalt on the 24th. On the following day at 1526, while exercising 'flying on' stations in the Straits of Georgia, she ran aground on an uncharted silt bank while travelling at a fair turn of speed and just two hours before high tide. At high tide, she tried to free herself by going full speed astern but the soft silt formed a perfect cradle for the hull and the suction could not be overcome.

After a number of unsuccessful attempts to free the ship, she finally floated free on the 28th, aided by two tugs and ground tackle, after 3202 tons of her dry and fluid stores had been removed by lighter and barge and the immediate area around the hull dredged. *Nabob*, under her own power, proceeded to north Vancouver where she was dry-docked. Amazingly enough, there was little damage, other than to underwater coatings and paint work.

Nabob returned to service on 8 February 1944, leaving Vancouver, bound for the Panama canal, Norfolk, Virginia and then New York. In San Francisco, the Avengers of the 852 Squadron were embarked and her first flying trials were conducted off San Diego. The ship was joined by the new Canadian frigate *New Waterford* and both ships transited the Panama Canal and arrived in Norfolk a week later, where a fair number of RCN conscripts deserted.

Faced with a clearly impossible situation, Lay first visited the British Admiralty Maintenance Representative in Washington DC to discuss problems with the crew. The victualling scale of the Royal Navy was far below that of

the RCN and the morale of the Canadian personnel suffered accordingly. This came to a head after leaving Californian ports, where the RN supply officer refused to purchase fresh fruit in any quantity although it was readily available and cheap. In addition, the average RN chief petty officer was paid about the same money as a RCN able seaman and this bred resentment among the RN personnel. The NAAFI canteen aboard was unsatisfactory, especially in light of the manager's refusal to stock certain items that were standard fare in its Canadian counterparts.

Lay travelled on to Ottawa, where he was able to impress the seriousness of the situation upon senior officers at NSHQ. After consultation with the minister

The Nabob *alongside Gladstone Dock, Liverpool on 5 April 1944 with her deck cargo of forty-five P51 Mustang fighters.* (PAC)

and the Cabinet, the decision was made that the Canadian government would pay RN personnel the difference between RN and RCN pay scales and would assume the duties of victualling standards. However, Lay's keen desire to see the ship a full Canadian unit was not acted upon, much to his disappointment.

Meanwhile, *Nabob* had been dry-docked in Norfolk and the standard propeller replaced, the original being a source of severe vibration at high speeds. On 8 March, the ship departed from Norfolk a much happier ship, bound for New York. She arrived on the 19th and was berthed at Staten Island, where the Avengers were stowed in the hangar and a deck cargo of forty-five P-51 Mustangs secured to the flight deck. Additional ratings were signed aboard, as well as twenty-seven civilians, of which fifteen were English school boys (ages eight to fourteen years), for passage to England.

On 23 March *Nabob* sailed with convoy 'UT-10' and, after a relatively uneventful passage, she arrived off Tory Island on 3 April but was forced to wait two days before entering Liverpool because of dense fog. On the 5th, she secured alongside Gladstone Dock, Liverpool, where the civilians were landed, followed by the P-51 aircraft on the 6th. On the next day she moved to the Clyde and anchored at the Tail-of-the-Bank, Greenock, where the

Avengers were catapulted off, bound for the Royal Naval Air Station, HMS *Landrail*, at Machrihanish, Scotland. *Nabob* returned to Liverpool on the 18th for alterations and additions (which included the replacement of some 20mm Oerlikon guns and the addition of HF/DF) that lasted until June. On 16 June she sailed for Greenock, and 852 Squadron re-joined on the 18th. Work-ups completed, *Nabob*, accompanied by her sister ship *Trumpeter*, left Greenock on 31 July bound for Scapa Flow, where both became units of the Home Fleet, under the administrative orders of the Rear-Admiral Commanding the 1st Cruiser Squadron. A week later the experience gained in so many exercises was put to work under operational conditions.

Norwegian Operations In Norway, enemy shipping was getting considerable natural protection by using the 'leads' or channels running between the coast and outlying islands. The Admiralty decided to mine these waters in order to force this coastal traffic out into the open sea where it could be dealt with by land-based fighters and fighter-bombers from the UK. Preparations and exercises occupied *Nabob*, with Force 4, until 9 August, when the ships under the orders of CS-1, flying his flag in the carrier HMS *Indefatigable*, sailed for the Norwegian coast on 'Operation Offspring'. At this time 852 Squadron had twelve Avengers and four Wildcats, augmented for this operation by an additional Avenger and two Wildcats.

On the morning of 10 August, *Nabob* launched two Wildcats as air cover for the fleet, which consisted of the carriers *Indefatigable*, *Nabob* and *Trumpeter*, the 1st Cruiser Squadron and eight destroyers, the latter including HMCS *Algonquin* and *Sioux*. After lunch the twelve

A Wildcat of 'G' Flight, 1832 Sqd, FAA landing on Nabob *in August 1944. Note that, while in the UK, most of* Nabob's *20mm singles were replaced by twin mountings, some of which are visible in the left foreground. Note also the landing officer to the far right with his paddles.* (PAC)

Avengers of 852 Squadron, carrying a mine apiece, were catapulted off and joined an equal force from *Trumpeter*'s 846 Squadron. Fighter protection was provided by Seafires, Fireflies and Hellcats from *Indefatigable*. The Avengers shaped course towards the Lepsorev Channel and Haarhamsfjord, with landfall made on Stornholm Light, where the squadrons dispersed and began their run-ups in flights of three.

The attack took the Germans completely by surprise and it was successfully carried out without loss, all mines being laid. The strike arrived back at the ships, were landed on, re-armed with mines and launched for a second strike. This time the Germans were ready but the mines were successfully laid, while the fighters staged diversionary raids on shore facilities. Casualties were five aircraft of the attacking force: one Avenger from *Trumpeter*, one Firefly and three Seafires. The surviving aircraft were recovered and Force 4 withdrew to the west, homeward bound, having successfully laid forty-seven mines.

Operation 'Goodwood', *Nabob*'s next sortie with the

A mighty small deck! Nabob *seen from the cockpit of one of her Wildcats while exercising landing-on stations in August 1944.* (Dillon, Lyncan Collection)

Home Fleet, was the largest with Fleet Air Arm participation ever planned. The object was to immobilize the German battleship *Tirpitz* which lay in Kaa Fjord, Norway. During the forthcoming operation there were to be diversionary fighter attacks on Hammerfest and Banak airfield, the whole to be synchronized with the passage of the thirty-three ship Russian convoy, JW-59. Force 2, consisting of *Nabob*, *Trumpeter* and five frigates, the *Bickerton* (senior officer), *Aylmer*, *Bligh*, *Kemthorne* and *Keats* of the 5th Escort Group, cleared the defences of Scapa Flow on 18 August. Force 1, consisting of the battleship *Duke of York*, the carriers *Indefatigable*, *Formidable* and *Furious*, the cruisers *Devonshire*, *Berwick* and *Kent* and six destroyers, was within visual signalling distance for the next few days and the ships

A view across Nabob's *flight deck on 22 August 1944 as she settles and develops a 7 degree list to starboard after being torpedoed by U-354. In the background,* HMS Bickerton, *also torpedoed and wreathed in smoke from a burst smoke generator, settles by the stern, while* HMS Kempthorne *carries out an Asdic sweep for the suspected U-boat.* (Dillon, Lyncan Collection)

Nabob, *badly damaged by a torpedo hit and with less than 5ft of freeboard aft. All aircraft on deck and the crew have been mustered to port to try and minimise the starboard list.* (PAC)

reached their flying-off position, inside the Arctic Circle north of Tromso, on the 20th.

Fourteen Avengers in *Nabob* were armed with influence mines in the afternoon but rough weather made it impossible to operate aircraft. Steaming westward on the 21st, the escorts were refuelled by the larger warships before returning to the launch positions on the 22nd. Once again weather interfered and a low cloud ceiling over Norway prevented mining operations. *Nabob* was relegated to flying protective patrols over the fleet while two air strikes from the larger carriers were made on *Tirpitz* with little effect, due in part to weather but also because of expert use by the Germans of smoke screens and camouflage.

With the aircraft recovered by the larger carriers, Force 2 began to withdraw to the west during the first dog-watch, as *Nabob* was preparing to fuel some of the escorting frigates. At 1716 there was a heavy explosion on the starboard side aft and *Nabob* took on a 7 degree list, her draught increasing first to 38ft aft and then 42ft. The large between-deck hatches were not watertight and flooding spread to the galley deck level where, fortunately, several vents allowed trapped air to escape and prevented the hangar deck from giving way under the mounting pressure. Water also extended to the engine room bulkhead forward and to the tanks at the extreme stern. This extensive flooding resulted from the limited number of athwartship watertight bulkheads but she settled on a relatively even keel because of a similar lack of longitudinal bulkheads.

None of the escorts had been in sonar contact with a submarine and it was assumed the ship had been struck by an electric torpedo at extreme range. The First Division of the escort group altered 140 degrees to starboard together to search for the submarine on the starboard side of the carrier when at 1714 *Bickerton*, the senior officer's ship, was also hit by a torpedo, her stern being completely blown off and more than forty men killed in the explosion. Given the torpedo's impact point, a Gnat was strongly suspected. *Kempthorne* closed *Bickerton* to take off survivors, while *Aylmer*, *Bligh* and *Vigilant* carried out a thorough anti-submarine search around the stricken ships. Both ships had been torpedoed by *U-354* which was to be sunk three days later by aircraft from the escort carrier *Vindex*.

Aboard *Nabob*, all electrical power had failed, causing the ventilation fans for the engine room and boiler room to

Her boilers relit and once more underway, Nabob *starts her slow journey back to Scapa Flow after being torpedoed on the previous day. Although the 5in guns at the stern are still in place, the twin 40mm Bofors have been ditched over the side in an effort to lighten the stern.*
(IWM, Lyncan Collection)

stop. Temperatures in both soared to 150 degrees within minutes, making it necessary to shut down the main engine and boilers. The ship's boats and carley floats were launched and secured alongside and 214 men (ten of whom were injured) were transferred to *Kempthorne*. Damage control parties shored up the vital engine room bulkhead while the engines, boilers and shaft were inspected and found to be in good order. Electrical power was restored by use of the stand-by generators and, after some cross-wiring to the main switchboard, power was restored. This in turn restored the ventilation fans and allowed the boilers to be re-lit. Flooding was stabilised by 1900 and at 2140 the ship began to gather way, beginning a long, 1100-mile trip back to home waters. *Bickerton*, damaged beyond towing, was sunk by a torpedo from *Vigilant* at about 2100.

Throughout the 23rd, the crew struggled on the canted, heaving decks to jettison or move forward all portable heavy gear in an attempt to equalise the ship's trim and maintain stability. With only 3ft of freeboard aft, the 5in guns, ammunition, cabling, etc, was unbolted and thrown over the side, while damage control parties worked feverishly to further shore up straining bulkheads and rig portable pumps to control seepage. Victualling was via makeshift facilities in the hangar deck, since the galley had been destroyed along with most food stocks, but the ship's supply branch had had the foresight to cache emergency supplies throughout the ship with just such an emergency in mind.

In the afternoon of the 23rd, an Avenger from *Trumpeter* passed overhead and aerial ASW patrols were maintained non-stop thereafter. *Nabob*'s escorts rejoined her at about 1930, and at 2000 a further 203 of *Nabob*'s crew were removed to *Algonquin*. Worsening weather on the 24th was cause for great concern but the ship, making only 10kts, rode out an 11-hour gale and finally arrived in Scapa Flow in the early hours of 27 August under her own power.

HMCS Algonquin *takes aboard 203 non-essential ratings using her own cutter and that from HMS* Keats, *those of* Nabob *having carried away the previous day while getting under way.* (PAC)

Cannibalisation After some additional bracing, *Nabob* was relieved of further top weight by the removal of her AA guns, aircraft and stores, reducing the draught aft from 42ft to 37ft. On 8 September the carrier was assisted out of the harbour by two tugs and, escorted by the destroyer HMS *Vigilant* and the ocean-going tug *Buccaneer*, set out for Rosyth where she arrived on the following day, securing at No 14 buoy by 1341.

Through 9–10 September, all ammunition in the forward magazine and walkway was removed and discharged to lighters. The decision was made by the Admiral Superintendent and dockyard officials at Rosyth that all possible stores should be removed while the ship was at the buoy, since the draught aft was still too great to place her in the graving dock. About 400 tons of pig iron ballast was added forward and, on the 28th, the catapult compartment and all undamaged oil tanks, forward magazines and the two lower bosun's stores were flooded with sea water. This produced a trim of about 29ft forward and 31ft aft, which made it possible to dry-dock her. Accordingly, two dockyard tugs shifted her into No 1 dock and the dock was slowly pumped out so that the water ballast and water within the hull could drain out evenly. At the same time, recovery of the bodies trapped in flooded compartments commenced, with fourteen of the missing twenty recovered. Total casualties amounted to eleven RCN personnel killed or missing, and ten RN dead or missing.

The torpedo had struck between stations 143 and 145, making a hole 50ft x 40ft in the ship's starboard side. It had hit immediately abreast the depth-charge magazine and depth charges were found actually welded into the ship's structure by the explosion. The force of the explosion had folded the decks immediately above the hole upwards and the bakery and stores immediately aft of the galley were inaccessible, since the deck was bent up so far it formed a bulkhead. Indeed, the damage was so extensive and British yards so overtaxed that the Admiralty decided to write her off and cannibalise the ship for spares for others of the class. Accordingly, she was paid off on 30 September and most of her crew posted to HMCS *Niobe*, the Canadian manning post in Greenock, prior to being returned to Canada. By mid-October all RCN association with *Nabob* had finished.

Nabob remained in Rosyth until the end of the war, providing emergency spares as needed. In March 1947 she was sold to a Netherlands firm, Arie Rijsdijk-Boss at Henrik-Ido-Ambaght, for scrap. On 21 September 1947 she arrived in Rotterdam, where the flight deck was stripped off and the damaged hull repaired. She was then resold to the Roland Linie Schiffart, Bremen, West Germany, a subsidiary company to the North German Lloyd Line, where she was completed as the dry cargo ship ss *Nabob*. The owners went so far as to mount a brass plaque on the superstructure commemorating the ship's former service with the RN and her torpedoing. In 1967, she was sold to Nationalist Chinese interests and renamed ss *Glory*. She was registered under the Panamanian flag until 1976, being broken up in 1978 in Taiwan.

HMS Puncher

With the paying-off of *Nabob* only one escort carrier, *Puncher*, was Canadian-manned. This ship had been built by Todd Pacific, Seattle and, following commissioning on 5 February 1944, she was steamed to Vancouver, with a reduced RN complement. Here, on 10 April, during a refit in Burrard's yard, Captain R E S Bidwell, RCN, assumed command. She then moved to Esquimalt in May and on 8 June, with HMCS *Beacon Hill* for company, she cleared Duntze Head bound for the eastern seaboard of the US. It had been hoped to obtain an operational FAA squadron and aircraft for the passage but this proved to be impossible. After transiting the Panama Canal on the 23rd, she sailed to New Orleans, where four harbour defence craft were lifted onto the flight deck for transport to New York. After delivery of her deck cargo, *Puncher* visited Portsmouth Navy Yard at Norfolk to be taken in hand for the installation of her Bofors mountings. This work took ten days and the ship returned to New York on 22 July.

With preparations underway in Italy for the invasion of southern France, cargo-carrying capability was at a premium, especially for large, bulky cargoes like aircraft. Accordingly, forty P-61 Black Widows were embarked for transport to North Africa and the ship sailed with the convoy 'UGF-13', which had assembled at Norfolk on 28 July.

The trip to the African coast was uneventful, and *Puncher*, and a USN counterpart, USS *Shamrock Bay*, were detached and escorted into Casablanca by four French chasseurs to off-load their cargo. Four days were spent in harbour and then the ship sailed as commodore's ship for four merchant ships joining the North Africa to US slow convoy 'GUS-48'. Upon joining, *Puncher* turned the four ships over to the convoy commodore and made the slow trip back to Norfolk for final fitting-out. Three days after securing alongside both watches were fully involved in hoisting aboard the aircraft and stores of the RN's FAA 1845 Squadron. Its eighteen Corsairs were struck down into the hangar while the flight deck was packed with a cargo of Hellcats, Avengers, Corsairs and one Helldiver, all of which had to be securely lashed down. Twenty-one officers and 125 ratings were embarked before the ship left for New York, where more passengers were taken aboard, including twenty-eight women and children. She was to depart New York as part of convoy 'CU-38', escorted by Task Group 21, on 4 September 1944 but was delayed a day while a special cargo of ammunition was loaded. Sailing on the 5th, escorted by USS *Enright*, *Puncher* made her best speed to overtake the convoy and joined up in the forenoon of the 9th.

Off Bishop Rock, the convoy split, *Puncher*, assuming command of one section, consisting of thirty ships in five columns. In poor visibility, course was altered to round Land's End, where she was joined by HMCS *Assiniboine*, *Chaudière*, and *Qu'appelle* who served as the advance support force for the convoy. Three separate sonar contacts were made and attacked by the support group on the way to Glasgow, evasive action being taken by the convoy, but no losses were sustained and *Puncher* secured at King George V dock in Glasgow and commenced off-loading.

After a short lay-over in Glasgow, *Puncher* returned to New York in convoy. The same pattern was repeated, the

One of Nabob's *Avengers, damaged in the barrier crash of 23 August 1944, is jettisoned over the side.*
(Dillon, Lyncan Collection)

Ditching 40mm ammunition from Nabob *in an effort to lighten the ship – 22 August 1944.*
(Dillon, Lyncan Collection)

Nabob *on 28 September 1944, after being lightened and ballasted forward to equalise her draught, is carefully moved into No 1 Dock at Rosyth to ascertain the damage and recover bodies.* (IWM, Lyncan Collection)

cargo this time being seventy-eight aircraft, and the carrier departed from New York on 6 October as a unit of convoy 'CU-42', a Jeep carrier again. Her destination this time was Liverpool, where the aircraft were landed, and by 22 October, she was secured to a buoy at the Tail-of-the-Bank in the Clyde.

On completion of boiler cleaning, *Puncher*, much to the relief of the crew, began to prepare for the role for which she was originally built. A busy trial period began with the catapult being tested by an Avenger and a Barracuda flying off and landing on twelve times. The carrier was then modified to handle a torpedo-carrying squadron and

The torpedo damage to Nabob's *hull, seen here on 28 September 1944. She was the first escort carrier in RN service to survive such heavy damage – the hole measures roughly 50ft x 40ft.* (PAC)

stores were struck down. She finally sailed on 26 November turned into the wind and received the twelve Barracuda aircraft of 821 Squadron.

Deck-landing practice was carried out in the Irish Sea during the next day but freshening winds forced cancellation in the afternoon. *Puncher* was entering Cumbrae Strait at 2020 when the alarming news was received from the engine room that the main engine had to be stopped owing to damage to the low pressure primary piston and first reduction wheel. By this time a Force 8, 40kt gale was blowing, and the carrier began to 'sail' gracefully toward the west shore of Great Cumbrae Island, while the engineers struggled to repair the damage. As the anchors were being prepared for mooring, the main engine was restarted, although at low power, and the ship proceeded on to Rothesay, where she was forced to anchor off Toward Point because of congestion in the harbour.

On the 27th the aircraft were flown off and the ship entered harbour where two tugs were waiting to assist her to a buoy, an evolution which became a shambles when the picking-up rope to the buoy and the tow line to the foremost tug parted at the same moment. For 40min *Puncher* clawed her way round the harbour, out of control half the time because the remaining tug was still secured to her and appeared unable to understand any orders given it. Finally the bridles were shackled onto the buoy and the ship swung from this buoy for the next month while repairs were made. Spares for *Puncher* came from an unexpected source, *Nabob*. Finally the ship was pronounced ready to begin sea trials on 28 December 1944; 821 Squadron were re-embarked and flying exercises commenced early in the New Year.

For most of January 1945, when weather permitted, exercises were carried out. This programme was interrupted briefly on the 15th when a signal was received that a sister carrier, HMS *Thane* had been either mined or torpedoed off the Clyde Light Vessel (she was in fact torpedoed by U-482). Two of *Puncher*'s aircraft, armed with depth charges, were the first to arrive on the scene and flew a defensive patrol over the stricken carrier for the next two hours, until the carrier was taken in tow by the frigate HMS *Loring* and towed to Greenock. *Thane*'s losses were ten men killed.

Home Fleet *Puncher* put to sea on 29 January for her final exercises but heavy snow and fog prevented them. After a visit by Angus L MacDonald, (the Canadian Minister of National Defence for Naval Services), and the Chief of the Naval Staff, Vice-Admiral G C Jones on the 30th, the ship was ordered to join the Home Fleet. She left for Scapa Flow on 1 February, with HMS *Towey* and HMCS *Iroquois* as escorts, and arrived on the 2nd. Between the 5th and 9th she was engaged in training exercises for her first operation and, on the latter day, returned to Scapa Flow to receive the fourteen Wildcats of 881 Squadron and four Barracudas of 821 Squadron. Force 1 (the cruisers *Norfolk* and *Dido* with three destroyers) left

Scapa on the night of the 10th for 'Operation Selenium I', a patrol within gun range of the enemy shipping route between Bud and Kvitholm, off the Norwegian coast.

They approached from the northwest after dark on the 10th while a second group, Force 2, made up of the cruiser *Devonshire*, two escort carriers, *Premier* and *Puncher*, and four destroyers headed across the North Sea on the 11th. Wildcats from *Premier* and *Puncher* afforded fighter cover for Force 1 during the 12th but no enemy shipping was sighted. Force 2 then went on to Operation 'Selenium II', which consisted of a minelaying sortie in Skatestrommen, abreast Skaten Lighthouse, by aircraft from *Premier*, while *Puncher* provided fighter cover. *Premier* sent seven mine-laying Avengers and four close escort Wildcats of 856 Squadron. Five mines were properly laid but one was dropped while still set on 'safe' and the seventh was jettisoned by an Avenger returning with mechanical problems. All aircraft returned safely but one of *Puncher*'s Wildcats collided with the round-down of the flight deck when the pilot was blinded by the sun. The impact broke off its tail wheel and arrester hook and the aircraft careened down the flight deck until brought to a stop by the crash barrier. The aircraft's machine guns accidentally discharged, wounding five of the deck crew in the process. Both forces withdrew to the west and steamed for Scapa Flow, arriving on the 13th after flying off their aircraft.

Puncher next ventured to sea on 17 February, where she landed on her Wildcats and Barracudas for another strike. This next operation in Norwegian waters was divided into two parts: Operations 'Shred' and 'Groundsheet'. The first was 'Shred', a minesweeping run through a suspected German minefield off Stavanger by six minesweepers of the 10th Minesweeping Flotilla. The ships sailed in the early hours of 21 February and were followed by a supporting force consisting of *Dido*, *Puncher*, *Premier* and three destroyers. Heavy seas were running off the coast of Norway but the minesweepers did

Table 1: *PARTICULARS OF THE* SMITER *CLASS* ESCORT CARRIERS NABOB, D77, (*EX AVG41*), *AND* PUNCHER, D79, (*EX AVG53*)

Displacement:	*Nabob* 8390 tons standard, 15,390 tons full load; *Puncher* 8170 tons standard, 14,170 tons full load
Dimensions:	*Nabob* 495ft 8in (oa) × 69ft 6in (wl), 107ft 2in (flight deck) × 25ft 5in; *Puncher* 492ft (oa) × 69ft 6in (wl), 102ft (flight deck) × 24ft 8in
Machinery:	2 boilers, 1 shaft Westinghouse geared steam turbines; 8500shp = 18kts at 85rpm
Oil Fuel:	3549 tons (max)
Water stowage:	874 tons
Endurance:	23,664nm at 17kts, 26,300nm at 15kts
Aircraft:	20 (max) – normally 12 Avenger torpedo bombers and 4 Wildcat fighters
Aviation Fuel:	196,091gal (max) in four tanks
Armament:	*Nabob* 2 × 5in/38 (2 × 1); 20 × 40mm Bofors (10 × 2); 34 × 20mm (14 × 2, 6 × 1 in June 1944)
Fire Control:	Mk 51 directors for both 40mm and 5in guns
Sonar:	Type 132
Radar:	SK air search, SG-1 surface search, YE aircraft homing beacon
Complement:	1000

their job, although no mines were cut. On the 22nd *Puncher* launched nine Barracudas and eight Wildcats for 'Groundsheet', another aerial mining strike. *Premier* launched eight Wildcats as top cover but landfall was

HMS Puncher *in April 1945*. (IWM, Lyncan Collection)

The Puncher *enters Halifax Harbour in June 1945, acting as a troop transporter. Notice the false bow and black pennant number over the wartime paint scheme.* (Kealy, Lyncan Collection)

made over Stavenger instead of Utsire and the fighters lost contact with the Barracudas. Intense and accurate flak claimed two of the Barracudas, while the other seven successfully laid their mines in Karmoy Channel. In addition the fighters destroyed a Dornier 24 flying boat at its moorings and shot up two silo-type buildings on the waterfront at Stavanger. The force then returned to Scapa Flow.

On 24 February, while riding at anchor in Scapa, *Puncher* started to drag on to a baffle, part of the anti-submarine defences of the anchorage. It was determined later that the mooring cable had parted at the starboard anchor swivel. The port anchor was let go, but because of the nearness of the baffle, the ship's engines could not be worked for fear of fouling the propeller and shaft. By midnight the winds were gale force and the ship was forced across the barrier but when the weather moderated on the 26th, the shaft and propeller were found to be undamaged. Continuous gales swept the Orkneys without relief until 10 March, making it necessary to keep continuous anchor watches and it was nearly impossible to communicate with the land by boat. Operationally, this was a quiet period for the Home Fleet, due to an acute shortage of destroyers to act as escorts for the larger ships.

The next deployment was Operation 'Prefix', which employed the four escort carriers *Puncher*, *Searcher*, *Nairana* and *Queen*, the cruisers *Bellona* and *Dido* and an escort of seven destroyers. They sailed for Norwegian waters on 24 March 1945. The weather was still poor but, on the morning of the 26th, a strike was flown off by *Searcher* and *Queen* to attack shipping in Trondheim Leads and towards Kristiansand north. Conditions improved off the Norwegian coast and, at 300ft, two German ships proceeding up Tustna/Stablen Fjord were attacked.

Meanwhile, eight to ten Messerschmitt fighters were sighted and engaged by two flights of Wildcats, which shot down three and damaged two more. The Avengers, however, were not so lucky – finding no suitable targets, they jettisoned their bombs and returned to the carriers. Operation 'Muscular', a night strike by *Nairana*'s planes was cancelled by the weather and no flights were possible on the 27th for the same reason. The last part of these operations, 'Strike C' of Operation 'Prefix', was a raid on enemy shipping at Aalesund by fighters. Two vessels

alongside a jetty were attacked and the wireless station at Vikeroy Island was shot up. Less one Barracuda, which did not return from its A/S patrol, the carriers then returned to Scapa Flow.

A powerful force consisting of *Puncher*, *Searcher*, *Queen*, *Trumpeter*, the cruisers *Bellona* and *Birmingham* and eight destroyers was sent to sea in early April for Operation 'Newmarket', an attack on the U-boat depot at Kilbotyn, Norway. The ships crossed the Arctic Circle in squalls and mountainous seas on 7 April and the ships spent the next five days being battered by gale-force winds before the operation was finally cancelled. Returning to Scapa, *Puncher* flew off her aircraft before entering harbour; her career with the Home Fleet was drawing to a close.

After a final review by Admiral McGrigor, she was escorted to the Clyde by the destroyers *Savage* and *Scourge* for boiler cleaning. She entered dry-dock near Glasgow and was still there on 8 May, VE-Day. The ship was finally undocked on the 11th and proceeded down river for trials. On 15 May, she was transferred to the administration of the Flag Officer Carrier Training (FOCT). The Admiralty had decided that *Puncher* would not be tropicalized for the war in the Pacific and from the middle of May until the second week in June she was employed in affording landing practice opportunities to 1790 and 1791 Squadrons of the FAA. The only incident of any note in this period occurred during the first day of landing-on exercises, when a Firefly of 1790 Squadron had its arrester hook broken off on contact with the arrester cable. The aircraft then plunged through the crash barrier and hurtled over the bows and into the sea. Two men of the crew were rescued but the observer drowned.

Troop Transport In mid-June 1945, the Admiralty decided to use the ship as a troop transport, ferrying Canadian personnel back to Canada and RN personnel back to the UK. The FAA personnel were landed and the ship went back to Tail-of-the-Bank where workmen welded in a large number of double-tiered bunks in the hangar spaces and converted workshops into bathrooms.

In the last week of June, the ship embarked 491 personnel, including some fifty WRCNS, in the Clyde and then left for Halifax, NS, arriving on 2 July in dense fog. During the eleven days alongside, the ship's crew was reduced to a ferrying complement. An engine defect was discovered on the 10th and the Admiralty decided to have it repaired at the Portsmouth Navy Yard, Virginia. The ship arrived on the 14th and, after completing repairs and embarking a load of aircraft, she sailed to New York and discharged her cargo.

Another trooping voyage started on 3 August and a week later, off the west coast of Ireland, *Puncher* picked up a message directing a frigate to proceed to the rescue of the crew of a Hudson bomber, which had ditched some 130 miles to the north of the ship. Informing the C in C, Western Approaches of her intentions, *Puncher* immediately altered course and increased to full speed to close the last reported position of the downed aircraft. Reaching the area at 1800, it was found that the six-man crew had been saved by the 5300 ton ss *Jamaica Producer* at 1700, after the plane had sunk. The survivors were transferred to *Puncher* and course resumed for the Clyde.

On 19 August 1945 *Puncher* was officially loaned to the Canadian Government to act as a troopship and from then until Christmas she made trips back and forth between Halifax and the Clyde, ferrying Canadian personnel. Stores and a draft for the new Canadian light fleet carrier *Warrior*, building at Belfast, were brought over in October. On her last two westerly voyages *Puncher* encountered a good deal of bad weather, having to heave-to on 14 November in a 55kt wind, which increased to a full gale from the west on the 16th. The forward edge of the flight deck and the supporting structure underneath were moderately damaged. On the final return trip she passed through the centre of an atmospheric depression that caused the barometer to plunge to 839 millibars and resulted in a 48hr delay in her ETA at Halifax.

In the new year *Puncher* steamed south to Norfolk and arrived on 16 January 1946 where the White Ensign was lowered for the last time, the ship reverting to the USN under the terms of the Lend-Lease agreement. Thus ended the career of this, the last escort carrier to be manned by the RCN. Sold in 1948, she was converted to mercantile trade, becoming the British *Muncaster Castle* in 1949, renamed *Bardic* (1954) and then *Bennevis* (1959); she was finally broken up in Taiwan in 1973. The *Nabob* and *Puncher* had afforded the opportunity to train hundreds of RCN personnel in the mysteries of operating an aircraft carrier at sea. This experience was to prove priceless when the RCN embarked upon a far more ambitious programme of fully manning light fleet carriers post-war.

THE SOVIET CRUISERS

of the *Chapayev* and *Sverdlov* classes

With their construction delayed by the Second World War, the *Chapayev* class cruisers
were eventually completed to a modified design in 1950. They were followed by the
derivative *Sverdlov* class, the last of the large gun-armed ships of the Soviet fleet,
and the foremost big ships of the Russian Navy in the 1950s and early 1960s.
V V Jarovoj and René Greger describe the design background,
construction and subsequent history of the two classes.

Stalin's 1938 Naval Programme provided for the construction of twenty cruisers. Seventeen of these ships were to be of a new type which, compared with the recently completed *Kirov (Project 26)*, were to have improved protection and carry an armament of nine 152mm guns in place of nine 180mm. The latter requirement resulted from the Soviet Union becoming a signatory to the London Naval Treaty (which limited gun calibre to 6in) in July 1937.

The initial technical requirements were given to Chief Designer A I Maslov (who had also produced the *Kirov* design) early in 1938. These requested an 8300-tonne, 35kt ship (utilising the same machinery as *Kirov*), protected by a 100mm belt and 50mm deck and armed with nine 152mm guns in three triple turrets, eight 100mm guns on combined HA/LA mountings and twelve 37mm AA guns. The ships were intended to operate with the battle fleet, for which purpose the new 152mm gun, with its high rate of fire, was expected to be quite sufficient. Contrary to some sources of information, the 180mm gun was never considered for this design; it had not proved a success, having exhibited a high rate of bore erosion,

The Chkalov *fitting-out at the Baltic Yard in 1949*. (Author)

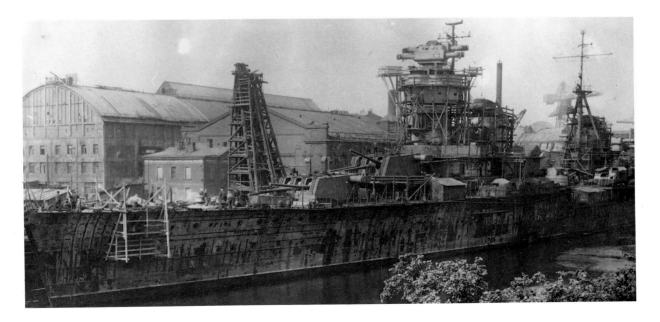

while its triple mounting, which employed a common gun-cradle, had also given trouble. The new 152mm gun had been developed for the *Sovetski Soyuz* class battleships, for which it was to be mounted in twin turrets. For a while an alternative source for the armament was anticipated and the development of a triple turret for the cruisers did not begin until after the outbreak of war with Germany (see below). A number of these 6in guns were employed during the war on railway mountings.

Project-68

Maslov's preliminary design resembled an enlarged *Maxim Gorki* but it was concluded that it was undergunned for its displacement, now 9500 tonnes, and he was asked if he could fit in a fourth triple 152mm mounting. The modified design, with twelve 152mm, was submitted by the Construction Bureau (CKBS-1) early in 1939 but Stalin, who took a strong personal interest in and

Table 1: *PARTICULARS OF* PROJECT-68 *AND ITS PRINCIPAL VARIANTS*

	Project-68 Chapayev 1939	Project-68K Chapayev 1947	Project-68bis Sverdlov 1947
Standard displacement (tonnes):	10620	11450	13600
Normal displacement (tonnes):	11330	12183	15126
Full load displacement (tonnes):	13420	14105	16553
Length oa/wl (m):	199/195	199/195	210/205
Beam max/wl (m):	−/18.7	−/18.7	22/21.2
Draught at std displ (m):	5.88	6.22	6.88
No of boilers:	6 × Type KV-68	6 × Type KV-68	6 × Type KV-68
shp (normal):	110,000	110,000	110,000
shp (forced):	126,500 (designed)	126,500 (designed)	118,100 (actual)
Max speed (kts):	33.5	32.6	32.5
Endurance (nm/kts):	5400/20	5400/20	9000/18
Gun armament (mm/cal):	12 × 152/57	12 × 152/57	12 × 152/57
	8 × 100/56	8 × 100/56	12 × 100/70
	24 × 37/58*	24 × 37/67*	32 × 37/67
Torpedo tubes (mm):	2 × 5 − 533	none	2 × 5 − 533
Aircraft:	2 KOR-2 flying boats	none	none
Side armour (mm):	100	100	100
Deck armour (mm):	50	50	50
CT armour-sides (mm):	150	150	150
Complement:	742	1183	1250

* *The* Chapayev *class were originally to be fitted with a new model 37mm twin AA mount with a shorter barrel than the model 37/70 fitted in the* Kirov *class and other ships of the period. These guns were under development during the Second World War but were later superseded by a new watercooled 37mm, twin mounting known as model V-11.*

The Chapayev *Class cruiser* Zheleznyakov *on the river Neva.* (Author)

The Komsomolec (*ex* Chkalov). (Author)

influenced the design of all the Soviet Navy's warships, decided that the endurance was insufficient for ocean warfare. Maslov replied that this could be improved at the cost of the economic speed or by an increase in displacement – Stalin agreed to both and *Project-68* was born, the design being formally accepted by the principal authorities on 13 June 1939.

The 1938 Programme called for the construction of fourteen *Project-68* cruisers, which were to become the *Chapayev* class, five of which were laid down in 1939 and were expected to be completed by the end of 1942. Although *Chapayev* was the name ship of the class, her sister ships *Chkalov* and *Frunze* were laid down five weeks earlier – a reflection of the Soviet system where all was subordinated to 'the plan'.

The radical change in the political situation in Eastern Europe in the autumn of 1939 and the signing of the Soviet-German pact provided some new opportunities for

Soviet warship designers and builders. Both technical and material help was promised by Germany in the construction of battleships and cruisers. In December 1939, CKBS-1 was informed by the Commissariat for the Navy that Germany had promised to deliver not only the new cruiser *Lützow* but a number of guns, including a 150mm model mounted in a triple turret. Consequently, Maslov was requested to revise the *Project-68* design to accommodate both the German 150mm mounting and their twin stabilised 105mm AA mountings; the revised design was known as *Project-68I* (I = Importnyi = Imported).

The Frunze *in Sevastapol's Northern Bay in 1960.* (Author)

This photograph, looking forward from the Sverdlov's *quarterdeck, was taken shortly before the ship's departure for Britain to take part in the 1953 Coronation Review.* (CMP)

However, doubt was cast on this decision when Soviet Navy ordnance experts, having tested production models of the Russian 152mm gun, discovered that the German weapon was ballistically inferior to the Soviet design. Consequently, it was decided to order only four, plus one reserve, triple 150mm mountings, all of which were to be mounted in the *Chapayev*. By the autumn of 1940, however, it was becoming obvious that deliveries from Germany were going to be extremely slow and it was decided to cancel these also. It was, however, still hoped that the *Chapayev*, and possibly her later sisters, would receive the twin 105mm DP mounting, complete with its fire control system, from Germany.

The last variant was known as *Project-68S*; it is uncertain if the 'S' signified 'Skoda' or '*stabilizirovannyi*' (= stabilised) as 105mm stabilised twin mountings were ordered by a delegation, led by (the later Marshal) Ustinov, from the Skoda works in Czechoslovakia in 1938. The development of these mountings continued, without interference, after the German occupation of Bohemia and Moravia on 15 March 1939. However, late in 1940, with the prototype just tested and deliveries due to commence early in 1941, the German authorities ordered all work on the mountings to cease.

The Sverdlov *at Spithead on 10 June 1953, shortly before the Coronation Review.* (CMP)

War Construction

Initial progress with the construction of some of the first five cruisers was rapid, particularly at Nikolaev which, although not one of the preferred (Leningrad) yards, launched the *Frunze* on 30 December 1940. On the following day, a sixth member of the class, the *Ordzhoni-kidze*, was laid down on the vacated slipway. The *Kuybyshev* was launched a month later from the second yard in Nikolaev (Zavod No 200) she too being replaced by another sister, the *Sverdlov*; in this case on the same day. The two vessels newly laid down were due for launching in the first half of 1942 when they in turn were expected to be replaced on the slipway by projected sisters *Parhomenko* and *Kotovski*.

Progress in Leningrad, by contrast, was slow, each of

The Admiral Ushakov *approaches Stockholm in July 1954.* (CMP)

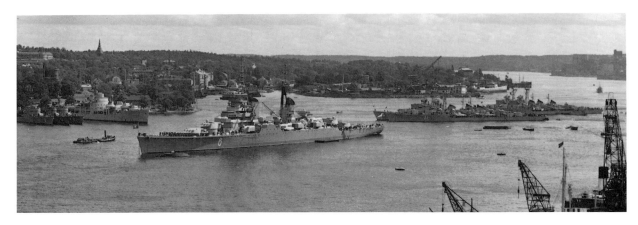

The Admiral Ushakov *and her escort at anchor in Stockholm harbour on 16 July 1954. This was an exchange visit, at the same time the Swedish cruiser* Tre Kronor *was visiting Leningrad.* (CMP)

the two shipyards having launched only one cruiser by the end of June 1941, while the third (*Chkalov*) had to wait until October 1947. Considering this situation, it is difficult to understand why, in October 1940, the Communist party decided that four further ships of the class were to be ordered from the Leningrad yards. Three of these new vessels were to be named *Lenin*, *Dzerzhinski*

A close-up of the after section of Ordzhonikidze *at the start of an official visit to Helsinki in July 1954.* (CMP)

and *Avrora* (it is possible that the fourth ship was to be named *Zhdanov* but this is uncertain); in the event none was laid down.

The reader may be surprised that only two units of the class were envisaged for such an important area as the Pacific and Far East. These two cruisers, *Lazo* and *Shchors*, were planned for construction at the new shipyard (Zavod No 199) in Komsomolsk on the Amur but, due to the technical and economic problems associated with constructing large ships in this yard (their capacity was fully utilised constructing the smaller *Project-26bis* cruisers *Kalinin* and *Kaganovich*), neither was built. For the same reasons no *Sverdlov* class ship was built in the Komsomolsk yard.

On 10 July 1941, following the German invasion of Russia, all work on the *Chapayev* class was halted. At this point the stage of completion for each ship was as follows:

Table 2: *BUILDING DATA*

Name	Builder	Yard No	Laid down	Launched	Commissioned	Fate
CHAPAYEV CLASS – PROJECT-68K						
Chapayev	Shipyard No 189	305	8 Oct 1939	28 Apr 1941	16 May 1950	{Hulked 1960, scrapped 1964
Chkalov	Shipyard No 189	306	31 Aug 1939	25 Oct 1947	5 Nov 1950	Scrapped 1981
Lenin	Shipyard No 189	309	Projected 1941	–	–	
Dzerzhinski	Shipyard No 189	310	Projected 1941	–	–	
Zheleznyakov	Shipyard No 194	545	31 Oct 1939	25 Jun 1941	19 Apr 1950	Scrapped 1976
Avrora	Shipyard No 194	555	Projected 1941	–	–	
Frunze	Shipyard No 444	356	29 Aug 1939	30 Dec 1940	15 Dec 1950	Scrapped 1961
Ordzhonikidze	Shipyard No 444	364	31 Dec 1940	–	–	
Kuybyshev	Shipyard No 200	1088	31 Aug 1939	31 Jan 1941	22 Dec 1950	Scrapped 1966
Sverdlov	Shipyard No 200	1090	31 Jan 1941	–	–	
Parhomenko	Shipyard No 444	–	Projected 1942	–	–	
Kotovski	Shipyard No 200	–	Projected 1942	–	–	
Shchors	Shipyard No 199	–	Projected 1942	–	–	
Lazo	Shipyard No 199	–	Projected 1942	–	–	
Sverdlov CLASS, PROJECT 68BIS						
Sverdlov	Shipyard No 189	408	15 Oct 1949	5 Jul 1950	15 May 1952	Stricken 1989
Zhdanov	Shipyard No 189	419	11 Feb 1950	27 Dec 1950	31 Dec 1952	Stricken 1991
Admiral Ushakov	Shipyard No 189	420	31 Aug 1950	29 Sep 1951	8 Sep 1953	Stricken 1987
Aleksandr Suvorov	Shipyard No 189	436	26 Feb 1951	15 May 1952	31 Dec 1953	Stricken 1990
Admiral Senyavin	Shipyard No 189	437	31 Oct 1951	22 Dec 1952	30 Nov 1954	Stricken 1991
Dmitri Pozharski	Shipyard No 189	445	31 Mar 1952	24 Jun 1953	31 Dec 1954	Stricken 1987
Kronshtadt	Shipyard No 189	453	1953	11 Sep 1954	–	Scrapped 1961
Tallin	Shipyard No 189	454	1953	1954	–	Scrapped 1961
Varyag	Shipyard No 189	460	1954	Jun 1955	–	Scrapped 1961
Ordzhonikidze	Shipyard No 194	600	19 Oct 1949	17 Sep 1950	30 Jun 1952	Sold to Indonesia 1962
Aleksandr Nevski	Shipyard No 194	625	30 May 1950	7 Jun 1951	31 Dec 1952	Stricken 1989
Admiral Lazarev	Shipyard No 194	626	6 Feb 1951	29 Jun 1952	30 Dec 1952	Stricken 1986
Shcherbarkov	Shipyard No 194	627	1952	24 Apr 1953	–	Scrapped 1961
Dzerzhinski	Shipyard No 444	374	31 Dec 1948	31 Aug 1950	18 Aug 1952	Stricken 1986
Admiral Nakhimov	Shipyard No 444	375	27 Jun 1950	29 Jun 1951	27 Mar 1953	Stricken 1961
Mikhail Kutuzov	Shipyard No 444	385	23 Feb 1951	29 Nov 1952	30 Dec 1954	
Admiral Kornilov	Shipyard No 444	395	6 Nov 1951	17 Mar 1954	–	Hulk PKZ 130, 1957
Molotovsk	Shipyard No 402	301	15 Jul 1952	25 May 1955	30 Nov 1954	Stricken 1987
Murmansk	Shipyard No 402	302	28 Jan 1953	24 Apr 1955	22 Sep 1955	Stricken 1992
Arhangelsk	Shipyard No 402	303	1954	–	–	Scrapped 1961
Vladivostok	Shipyard No 402	304	1955	–	–	Scrapped 1961

Notes to builders:

Shipyard No 189 is the Baltic Yard (Baltijskij zavod) in Leningrad.
Shipyard No 194 is the Admiralty Yard (Admiraltejskij zavod) in Leningrad.
Shipyard No 444 (ex No 198, renumbered after the War) is the Marti Yard (ex Naval) in Nikolaev.
Shipyard No 200 is the Chernomorski Yard (ex 61-Kommunara Yard) in Nikolaev.
Shipyard No 199 is in Komsomolsk on the Amur.
Shipyard No 402 is in Severodvinsk (formerly Molotovsk).

Kuybyshev 70 per cent; *Frunze* 75 per cent; *Chkalov* 52 per cent; *Chapayev* 50 per cent; *Ordzhonikidze* 20 per cent; *Sverdlov* 5 per cent. To avoid capture, the two ships fitting out at Nikolaev, *Kuybyshev* and *Frunze*, were towed to Caucasus ports. German troops occupied the town and its shipyards on 15 August 1941, and seized the hull of *Ordzhonikidze*, together with that of the battleship *Sovetskaya Ukraina* and several other vessels.

Post War Redesign

In 1946 the Soviet government decided that the surviving five hulls of the *Chapayev* class should be completed to a modified design with improved underwater protection, for the war had demonstrated that the *Kirov* class were weak in this respect. Despite the abandonment of the aircraft arrangements and torpedo tubes of the original

The Zhdanov *arrives at the Yugoslav naval base of Split on 12 September 1957 at the start of a six-day visit. She was accompanied by the destroyer* Svobodni. *(CMP).*

design, this resulted in a substantial increase in displacement and a reduction in the metacentric height from 0.89m to 0.77m. The modified design, known as *Project-68K* (K = *Korrektirovanyi* = corrected), was approved on 28 August 1947.

All five *Chapayev* class ships were commissioned in the Soviet Navy during 1950. They carried the armament originally specified except that the air-cooled 37mm AA guns were replaced by new modern, water-cooled, 37mm AA guns on twin mountings. None of these ships remained long on active service, being soon replaced by the *Sverdlov* class. *Chapayev* (renamed *Komsomolec* in 1957), *Frunze* and *Kuybyshev* were relegated to training ships in April 1958, followed by *Zheleznyakov* in 1961. *Chapayev* was completely disarmed in October 1960 and

became the hulk PZK 25. By December 1965 three of the class had been scrapped but *Zheleznyakov* and *Komsomolec* remained in service until 1976 and 1981 respectively; in later years as stationary units only.

The Sverdlov Class

To provide a standard cruiser for his new 'Ocean Navy', Stalin wanted ships larger than the *Chapayev*. However, he also wanted them quickly and, to save time, the *Chapayev* was taken as the basis for the new design, an enlarged version of *Project-68*, designated *Project-68bis*. The design was approved by Stalin and the government

Oktyabrskaya Revolutsiya, *formerly the* Molotovsk, *one of many Soviet ships renamed as a result of political change.* (Author)

on 27 May 1947, three months before the approval of the 'corrected' version of the *Chapayev* class design.

Project-68bis, which was to become the *Sverdlov* class, employed the same machinery, main armament and protection as the *Chapayev* but had a much increased fuel capacity and, consequently, endurance. The principal innovations were the adoption of an all-welded hull and a new system of underwater protection. The latter included a hull divided by watertight bulkheads into twenty-three totally isolated main compartments and a double bottom extending over 75 per cent of the ship's length. Also new was the radar equipment, which included the fire control and rangefinding types *Rif* and *Zalp*, and fire-control type *Jakor* for the new 100mm, 70cal, AA guns.

Originally, it was intended to lay down thirty *Sverdlov* class ships in Leningrad and Nikolaev but five were dropped from the programme in favour of three battle-cruisers (*Project-82*, the *Stalingrad* class) which had Stalin's personal support. As a result of the change in Soviet military doctrine after Stalin's death, the class was further reduced to twenty-one units before construction

began and, of these, only fourteen were completed.

Three of the class were to be laid down as quickly as possible after the finalisation of the detailed design. The Chief of the Soviet Navy ordered that these three vessels should be named after those cruisers of the *Chapayev* class whose construction had been prematurely ended by the German invasion of 1941: *Sverdlov*, *Ordzhonikidze* and *Dzerzhinski*. The first two were to be built at Leningrad and the third at Nikolaev. As with the *Chapayev*'s, the name ship of the class, *Sverdlov*, was that to be built by the traditionally preferred yard at Leningrad, shipyard No 189 or the Baltic Yard (at this time known as the Ordzhonikidze Yard, it has since reverted to its original name); the order to this effect was given on 3 December 1947.

The reconstruction of the Soviet shipbuilding industry after the war proceeded very slowly and, although it was intended that the construction of all three of the new cruisers should begin in 1948, only one, *Dzerzhinski*, was laid down in this year and that on the very last day, 31 December. The builder was the Marti Yard in Nikolaev,

The Zhdanov *in the Arctic in the 1960s.* (Author)

The Sverdlov *during a naval review on the Neva.* (Author)

which had been almost completely destroyed by the retreating German Army in 1944. The *Sverdlov* was not laid down until ten months later but her builder, the Baltic Yard in Leningrad, was provided with 'official support' to restore its reputation and the ship did, in fact, complete as the first of the class, being commissioned on 15 May 1952.

The steam trials of *Sverdlov* proved very satisfactory, she made 32.69kts with 114,000shp and 33.04kts when forced to 121,700shp. The fuel consumption was exceptionally good and provided for a range of 9000nm at economic speed, 1600nm more than expected. The standard displacement also provided a pleasant surprise in coming out at 13,230 tonnes – 370 tonnes below the design figure.

Construction

During 1949–52 a total of fifteen *Sverdlov* class ships were laid down, including two vessels building in Leningrad for

The Oktyabrskaya Revolutsiya *at Leningrad in 1967.* (Author)

completion in Molotovsk. These ships were well under way when the Navy decided that all the later units should be built with protection against radioactivity. The first ship to the modified design, known as *Project-68zif*, was the *Shcherbarkov*, laid down in 1952 but neither she nor her six sister ships were ever completed. In the mid 1950s the new leadership of the Communist Party, under N S Khrushchev, decided to end the construction of all large, gun-armed warships and, early in 1956, work on the *Sverdlov* class was stopped. This was despite the fact that construction of some ships was well advanced, *Admiral Kornilov*, in particular, being nearly complete. In 1959 the Soviet Government ordered that all the unfinished cruisers (except *Admiral Kornilov* which became a hulk) were to be scrapped by the end of 1961.

A Sverdlov *class cruiser in the Mediterranean in 1969.* (CMP)

In 1960 the *Sverdlov*s were the largest ships in the Soviet Navy and the majority were serving as flagships. They were fairly evenly distributed between the four main Soviet Fleets, with four in the Pacific, three in the Arctic, three in the Baltic and four in the Black Sea/

The Admiral Ushakov *in the late 1970s with new light AA weapons and an increase in radar and other electronic equipment but otherwise little altered in external appearance.* (Author)

Mediterranean. The Pacific Fleet ships made their way east by the 'Northern Way', along the Siberian Coast, during 1955–56. As construction of two of the cruisers building at Molotovsk, the *Arhangelsk* and *Vladivostok* (ex *Kosma Minin* and *Dmitri Donskoi* respectively, renamed 25 September 1953) was stopped, the *Aleksandr Nevski*, built in Leningrad, was transferred to Murmansk to take their place in the Arctic Fleet.

In 1957 all ships carrying names connected with the Stalin regime were renamed, which affected one cruiser from each of the *Chapayev* and *Sverdlov* classes. The *Chkalov* was renamed *Komsomolets* and the *Molotovsk* (the first unit to complete in the new shipyard of the city of the same name, now known as Severodvinsk) was renamed *Oktyabrskaya Revolutsia* after the recently scrapped battleship of that name.

Modernisation

In the late 1950s it became evident to the Soviet naval authorities that the guided missile was going to be the naval weapon of the future. After testing a guided weapon system on the destroyer *Bedovyi* in 1955, it was decided that a number of new cruisers and large destroyers should be rearmed as guided-missile ships. The first of these ships was the *Admiral Nakhimov* which was rebuilt during 1955–57 to carry a very large, antiship (winged) missile installation in place of her forward 152mm turrets. After an extended period of testing it was concluded that neither the missile nor its launcher were a success and the ship was stricken in February 1961. She was subsequently used as a target, to test a new generation of anti-ship missiles, off the Crimea, near Tendra.

The Project 70-E conversion, Dzerzhinski, *with her twin 'Guideline' (Volkhov) missile launcher in place of X turret.* (Author)

During 1960–62 another ship of the class, *Dzerzhinski*, was modified to carry a guided missile launcher. This time, however, the alterations, known as *Project-70E*, called for the replacement of the third turret with an AA missile system – Type *Volkhov* (NATO code name *Guideline*). Proposals to convert a second cruiser were refused and, instead, two of the class, *Zhdanov* and *Admiral Senyavin*, were rebuilt during 1970–72 as HQ ships. In 1971 *Zhdanov* (refitting under *Project-68U1* [U = *Upravlenie* = Command]) was fitted with four of the newly introduced twin 30mm Gatling mountings, for close-range defence against aircraft and missiles. She was also fitted with a large after deckhouse in place of 'X' turret, with a SAM launcher on its roof. *Admiral Senyavin*, whose reconstruction began a year later under *Project-68U2*, was fitted with eight twin 30mm mountings, a large helicopter hangar (with SAM launcher on its roof) in place of both after turrets and much improved interior spaces for the staff. The last modernisation for the class was *Project-68A* which included the fitting of eight twin 30mm and an improved radar outfit. This was applied to *Oktyabrskaya Revolutsia* in 1976 and to *Admiral Ushakov* in 1979 but no further major modernisations were provided for the class.

Perestroyka brought an end to the service of the older, traditional, ships of the fleet, and to the employment of many 'hulks'. It was decided to scrap all obsolete ships as soon as possible and in 1986 the *Admiral Lazarev* and *Dmitri Pozharski* in the Pacific and the *Oktyabrskaya Revolutsia* in the Baltic were stricken. In 1989 the *Sverdlov* in the Baltic and the *Aleksandr Nevski*, which had been laid up in Polyarnyi for many years, followed. The last two ships of the class in Vladivostok, *Alexsandr Suvorov* and *Admiral Senyavin*, were stricken in 1990 and 1991 respectively. The *Zhdanov*, in Sevastopol, was also stricken in 1991 and was immediately sold for scrap, while the *Murmansk*, which had lain for many years in reserve in the Arctic, followed in 1992. The last ship of the *Sverdlov* class, *Mikhail Kutuzov*, is now (1993) at Sevastopol awaiting her fate.

THE COLD WAR
Korea and US minesweepers

Within five years of the end of the Second World War, the US Navy was designing a new generation of minesweepers, survivors of which are still in service in many navies. In this article Norman Friedman describes how, far from springing from the unhappy experience of North Korean mining at Wonsan, as is often claimed, the programme was in fact well under way before the outbreak of the war and was developed in response to new technology developed during the Second World War.

Like the Royal Navy, the US Navy ended the Second World War with a large fleet of minesweepers, yet the 1950s were to see a large US design programme for a new generation. Similarly the Royal Navy found itself building numerous new sweepers well before the wartime craft might have been expected to wear out. The new US design incorporated not only technology developed during the Second World War but some radical new technology of its own. In both senses the new-generation minesweepers correspond to such postwar developments as the new-generation large-deck carriers and the new fast submarines. However, they have not received the same attention because the technology involved is generally more obscure.

The two outstanding new mine developments were much more sensitive magnetic mines and pressure mines. According to early postwar accounts, the new magnetic mines were fifteen to eighteen times more sensitive than their predecessors. Magnetic mines in themselves were nothing very new and steel-hulled sweepers could be degaussed to avoid setting off wartime mines. The wartime US response to this threat was to provide all sweepers with powerful diesel generators and with space for towing a large reel-carrying magnetic sweep cable. For example, the prewar-designed *Raven* (AM 55) class was redesigned (as the *Auk* class) with diesel-electric rather than geared-diesel power specifically to provide sweep power (they could divide their installed power between propulsion and magnetic sweeping). Wartime and postwar sweepers also needed power to run acoustic sweep devices, though not on anything like the scale magnetic sweeps demanded.

Numerous small wooden sweepers, most prominently the 136ft YMS, were built in wartime but their hull material was adopted to allow construction in small boatyards; the choice had nothing to do with reducing magnetic signature. The wooden sweeper programme was analogous to the wooden subchaser (SC) programme or, for that matter, to attempts in Britain to increase aircraft production by designing wooden bombers (such as the Mosquito).

Pressure Mines

Pressure mines were a more difficult proposition. They responded to the reduction in water pressure (suction) as a ship passed overhead. A small ship, such as a sweeper, might well provide too little suction to trigger the mine. To sweep it, she would have to tow something the mine would confuse with a real ship. Pressure mines could be triggered by the turning of the tide (they could be designed to look for sudden rather than gradual changes in pressure, however). It seemed likely that future ones would use magnetic sensors to confirm that the change in pressure had indeed been caused by a real ship passing overhead. Several wartime attempts to build ship simulators ('egg crates', etc) failed. The postwar US concept was a large 'unsinkable' cylinder, XMAP. In theory, XMAP could duplicate not only the pressure signature but also the magnetic signature of a real ship. However, to be towable it had to be of limited dimensions. That in turn limited the extent to which it could deceive pressure mines.[1]

As an interim measure, the US Navy became interested in mine hunting. It developed a variety of underwater object locators, most of them magnetic, culminating in the early postwar UQS–1 high-frequency sonar. Mines detected by sonar might be investigated by divers or, it was hoped, destroyed by mortar rounds fired from the ship carrying the sonar. However, sweeping was infinitely preferable, since a sweeper did not have to examine each mine-like object in detail. This expectation was not to be defeated until the mid-1950s.

By 1945, then, it seemed obvious that to be viable future sweepers had to produce much smaller magnetic signatures, and needed enough power to tow ship-sized pressure mine countermeasures, such as XMAP, and to provide increased sweep current for a wider swept path. These demands conflicted. The smaller the sweeper, the smaller its basic signature (which would be further reduced by degaussing). However, a small sweeper could not accommodate enough powerplant to tow XMAP, nor enough to power new magnetic sweep gear.

Post War Programmes

Early postwar US shipbuilding plans (through FY49) included no new sweepers. However, the list of shipbuilding projects included installation of a new underwater object locator on an amphibious craft, initially an LCT, later an LSM (SCB 18 project). Earlier equipment had been widely installed in preparation for the invasion of Japan. Mine clearance remained a postwar priority due to the need to deal with US pressure mines in Japanese waters. As of mid-1946, underwater object locators were on board ten LCI(L) and LCTs, but they were not satisfactory. BuShips protested that the sonar was the important part of the system, that no specialized mine-hunting ship was yet needed. The Ship Characteristics Board felt that it was pointless to install the new sonar in a newly-converted ship; better simply to replace the existing equipment in a craft already assigned to mine location. SCB 18 was dropped from the programme. Instead, installation was conducted using modernization (MIP) money.

As the Cold War began, US interest focussed on the problems of maintaining sea communications with Europe in the face of a likely Soviet naval offensive. Work

The USS Sheldrake *(AM 62) was one of the* Auk/Raven *class, the principle US large minesweepers of the Second World War. She is seen here on 30 September 1954 after conversion to a survey vessel (AGS 19). (L & L van Ginderen)*

on a new minesweeper, initially designated AMS (ie, successor to the wartime YMS, rather than to wartime ocean sweepers AM) began in late autumn of 1948, in the expectation that twenty would be included in the FY50 programme. These craft were expected to be larger than the existing 136ft YMS, with non-magnetic hulls, silenced engines, mine-detecting sonars (UQS–1) and more powerful sweep generators (10,000 amps), capable of towing heavier sweeps (30,000lbs drag at 10kts), particularly XMAP. Their mission was 'to sweep mines in shallow water unapproachable by large minesweepers', ie, enjoying much-reduced magnetic signature (soon specified as 0.5 milligauss, mg, at 30ft depth). It soon turned out that any craft capable of towing XMAP would be about the size of an ocean minesweeper.

The planned programme comprised the XMAP-towing AMS (later AM, SCB45), the XMAP pressure mine countermeasure and a small minesweeping boat (MSB, SCB62). In theory, the large sweeper would be safe in water as shallow as 30ft; in shallower water its signature at the bottom would be enough to set off the new sensitive mines.

The United States produced no non-magnetic diesels, yet machinery would be a major contributor to magnetic signature. Worse, to tow the new XMAP the only available diesels with sufficient power, as of December 1948, were submarine engines; the GMC16–278A, the Fairbanks-Morse and the 'pancake' designed for the new *Tang* class. Although the pancake was not yet notorious, it was already expected to require over-frequent overhauls and it would be difficult to attach sweep generators to its

vertical crankshaft. General Motors was developing an aluminum–cylinder block diesel (Model 110) for trucks but twenty-four would be needed for a minesweeper (for a combined sweep/propulsion diesel-electric powerplant). All those generators (and four propulsion motors) would add so much magnetic material that the nearly non-magnetic properties of Model 110 would count for very little. One alternative was to split the plant between sweep (four diesels per generator) and propulsion (four geared to each shaft).

However, the sheer size of the planned programme offered a much more attractive possibility. It would justify some R & D expenditure, even in tight postwar times. That might pay for non-magnetic versions of the two attractive submarine diesels. In the end, General Motors produced two such engines (GM8–268A and 8–278A); the others were a series of more radical lightweight Packards (V–8, V–12, and V–16).[2]

Alternative powerplants (sweep and propulsion) were two GM 8-268A and three 8–278A; three Packard V–8 and four V–16; and six Packard V–12 (the choices in ships actually built were somewhat different). The GM plant gave 1600bhp for propulsion; it could tow two XMAP at 7.2kts. The 7–Packard installation gave 3200bhp for propulsion but that was reduced to 1600 when sweeping; it could tow two XMAP at 8.6kts. The 6–Packard plant gave 2400bhp (free route), reduced to 1200 when sweeping). It could tow two XMAP at 8.1kts. Specified sweep current, originally 10,000 amps, was reduced to 7200 amps at 360 volts (pulsating DC); it was expected to increase the width of the swept path from 124 to 175 yds.

This figure could not be met with the existing 0.04 ohm sweep cable; currents would be only 4300 (GM) or 5000 amps (Packard, both alternatives). However, a new 0.02 amp sweep cable would increase current to 5100 and 7200 amps, respectively. The wider sweep width improvement was essential, since it would be impossible to build anything like as many sweepers as the conventional steel wartime types. In fact the new cable never appeared, so, to achieve anything like the required current, the MSO needed a much more powerful sweep generator.

Several hull materials were considered. Initially the design used inherently non-magnetic aluminium. This was not altogether satisfactory so some alternatives were considered in the fall of 1949. The most promising was Jessop (austenitic) steel. It would add about 150 tons to an aluminium ship. Aluminium (riveted and welded) was second best, followed by composite (wood with aluminium framing) and then by wood with a Jessop steel frame. Titanium, magnesium and plastic may also have been considered but no details of ships designed to use them seem to have survived.

The USS Firm *(MSO 444), of the ubiquitous* Agile/Aggresive *group, on 7 November 1957.* (L & L van Ginderen)

Early Designs

The first sketch design showed an aluminium ship about the size of a wartime fleet sweeper: 220 x 37 x 8–6ft, 910 tons light (925 tons standard, 1180 fully loaded). It used five 1500bhp low-magnetic diesels, two for propulsion (driving CRP propellers via reduction gears, to make it easier to choose between high free-route speed and low towing speed), and three for sweep current. As of mid-1949 BuShips was considering GM, Fairbanks-Morse and Cooper-Bessemer engines. Armament would be a single 3in/50 (with Mk 63 FCS) and four twin 20mm; all ammunition was to be carried as high as possible to avoid underwater explosions. The 3in/50 might be abandoned to reduce magnetic signature.

Unfortunately, aluminium might be in short supply in wartime. In the Second World War US consumption suddenly went from 120,000 to about 1 million tons per years; in 1949 the United States was using 360,000 tons per year. Aluminium was one of three materials under the Controlled Materials Plan because sources of high-quality bauxite ore had already been heavily depleted. Production required great electrical power and in November 1949 BuShips feared that the United States (whose economy was not booming) was already running at nearly full generating capacity.

The Aggressive *class ocean minesweeper* Gallant *(MSO 489) on 7 January 1963.* (L & L van Ginderen)

The preliminary designers found themselves looking for some way to cut the size of the aluminium sweeper. In December 1949 BuShips suggested studies of a 180ft aluminium hull and of a 160ft wooden hull. In November 1949 BuShips had a preliminary design for a 180ft aluminium sweeper (180 x 33 x 8–3ft, 527 tons light [of which 132 tons was machinery], 573 tons standard, 751 tons fully loaded). It had seven engines: two 750bhp V–12s for propulsion, two for magnetic sweeping, one 375bhp six-cylinder engine with a variable-frequency hydraulically-driven generator for acoustic sweeping and two more 375bhp ship service generators. Estimated cost was $4.5 million, compared to $6 million for the 220-footer.

It appeared that the 180-footer was the smallest which could meet the requirements, including the ability to generate 10,000 amps of magnetic sweep current. It capitalized on three new features: (i) six 16–cylinder, 850bhp diesels of a new lightweight design, similar to a new six-cylinder 350bhp unit, and much superior to the engines of the 220-footer; (ii) two of the main engines could be used either for propulsion or for sweeping; (iii) the 3in gun was manually-controlled, with ready-service ammunition only (in June 1950 it was replaced by a twin 40mm, adding 2 tons, and the weight of the towing machine increased considerably). Volume liberated by eliminating the magazine would be used to provide the requisite 10,000 amps of magnetic sweep current. The SCB distributed characteristics (staff requirements) based on the 180ft design on 11 April 1950. By June, the machinery section of BuShips was cautioning that the

V–16 engine was not as good as had been hoped; it might not meet simultaneous loads when all sweeps were running.

That raised an interesting question. It might be possible to limit sweep generator load to 1000 amps for the 'dog blankets' used to increase XMAP's magnetic signature but an acoustic sweep would always need 200kW. The designers had hoped that there would never be a need for both at once from one diesel. The only solution would be to use one ship service diesel generator for the 1000 amp load, but then the generator would have to provide DC power instead of the usual ship service AC. Worse, providing 200kW of acoustic power demanded about 270kW of electric output, since conversion was only 75 per cent efficient. The planned 300bhp six–cylinder engine had to be replaced by an eight–cylinder diesel (the choice fell on a 400bhp, 250kW, Packard running at 2000rpm, feeding a variable-speed hydraulic transmission for acoustics). A second such engine could run the dog blankets.

The Wooden Sweeper

There was still interest in a smaller wooden sweeper, which would cost just over half as much as the aluminium ship. The largest possible wooden ship would be 165ft long and could not accommodate anything like the power wanted. It was limited to four 650bhp engines, hence enjoyed only 55 per cent of the power output of the

180-footer. It could not accommodate a 3in gun (it would be limited to two twin 20mm).

The 180-footer could not quite match the range of a 220-footer (4000nm) but it could come close (3750nm). A wooden sweeper would have to use temporary tanks for any long ocean transit. It was not really very attractive so the designers looked for some compromise between the 180- and 200-footers.

First characteristics were distributed on 2 November 1949. They required 15kts on 3000bhp (and thus to be able to keep up with existing amphibious forces), with long endurance (4000nm at 15kts). Towing (sweep) speed was to be 10kts pulling a 33,000lb tow while furnishing 300hp, or capable of pulling 21,000lbs while furnishing 4000hp for a magnetic sweep. The compromise aluminium design was 200 x 35 x 8ft(max), 750/900 tons (trial). Estimated cost was $6,374,000. By way of comparison, it was estimated that *Albacore* would cost $7.5 million, and that a DDE conversion would cost $8.3 million.[3]

Unfortunately, estimated lead time to obtain a non-magnetic diesel was three years so BuShips was looking at non-magnetic, aircraft gas-turbines, at least for sweep power. It might well have to use much more degaussing than in previous classes. For example, it seemed unlikely that a non-magnetic 3in gun could be obtained; its magnetic moment would have to be cancelled out. The

uss Dash, *name ship of the MSO 428 sub-group, at Malta on 20 May 1959.* (L & L van Ginderen)

designers were by no means sure that they could meet the required magnetic standard. To approach it, it had to use critical materials (nickel, chrome, copper) lavishly to provide non-magnetic fittings.

Then aluminium construction had to be abandoned. Quite aside from any expected shortage, rolling and pitching would induce eddy currents (which in turn had magnetic consequences) in the conductive aluminium hull. On this basis the US Navy later convinced the Royal Navy to abandon aluminium decks and bulkheads in its own coastal sweeper programme. That left BuShips with an unpleasant choice: a very large wooden hull with virtually no metal components (eg, sheer straps). Revised draft characteristics (reflecting the new design) were released on 25 May 1950 and a preliminary design was ready by July. Experience with the 165ft design showed that conventional wood construction was far too heavy to provide the required payload.[4]

The Ocean Minesweepers

The new sweeper would be the largest all-wood warship in the US Navy. As such it had to incorporate new construction techniques. It became much more expensive. To carry the considerable payload, a new kind of hull structure had to be developed, far lighter than conventional all-wood construction, using techniques

MSO 427, Constant, *in July 1968*. (L & L van Ginderen)

from the civilian plywood industry (which, incidentally, was enjoying great prosperity in the postwar US housing boom and hence had considerable capacity). BuShips eventually claimed that its new type of construction saved about 50 per cent in hull weight.

Large hull frames (24 x 32ft) were laminated in a single piece extending from the deck edge, through the keel and up to the deck edge on the other side. The two thicknesses of side planking were laid diagonally to transmit shear stresses to the decks and bottom. A thin outer layer of planking was red oak pressure impregnated with copper naphenate to protect the hull against attack by marine borers. Using plywood, builders did not need the large perfect timbers formerly associated with building large wooden ships.

Even so, wood construction drastically limited overall size; the AM was initially characterized as 165ft long (later it was 171ft). Fortunately, the new type of construction proved so strong that the last ships of this basic design could be lengthened from 171 to 186ft. The hull form was adapted from that of the Second World War YMS but with a fuller midships section (coefficient 0.80 rather than 0.716) to increase available displacement without increasing .dimensions unduly (this hull was 165ft on the waterline, 171ft 6in oa x 34ft x 9ft 9in full load, with a depth of 15ft amidships, or 22ft 6in to the forecastle; it would displace 800 tons fully loaded, 704 tons light, and 723 tons standard). The hull was made somewhat full at the ends (longitudinal coefficient 0.62) to protect the ends from drooping. Arrangement generally followed that of the satisfactory wartime PCS, with bronze strapping. The

upper deck was carried aft to over the after machinery space bulkhead to add strength and improve seakeeping and also to add usable space (which was limited in a YMS deckhouse).

The big magnetic sweep reel was placed above the main deck over the after machinery space to avoid cutting a hole in the strength deck, to provide space for the combined minesweeping winch and towing machine (for XMAP) and to keep the towing machine as far forward as possible.

The planned powerplant was four 16–cylinder non-magnetic 800bhp diesels (Packards). Two would drive via reduction gears, for propulsion only. The other two could be used either for propulsion (eg, to help pull XMAPs) or for sweep current. The propellers had to be controllable-pitch to cover so wide a range of power and speed (free-route or towing various loads). All four engines would be in the same room.

The really radical step was to add a variable de-gaussing system which could compensate automatically for variations in the ship's position in the earth's magnetic field due to roll and pitch as well as to change of heading. This special system was the truly secret element of the design. The design also included special equipment to minimize stray magnetic fields and specially degaussed storage for tinned foods and ammunition, which could not be made inherently non-magnetic. By 1955, BuShips was

claiming a base signature of 0.1 to 0.3mg, which rose to about 0.6mg due to stray fields. By way of comparison, a large steel ship (45ft draught) had a signature of about 34mg at a depth corresponding to its beam.

The big wooden sweeper came very close to an aluminium ship, but it could not accommodate a 3in/50; instead it would be armed with a single manual 40mm gun.

All of this was expensive: about 1954 the sweeper was considered among the Navy's most complex (and innovative) ships, only matched in cost per ton by submarines.

There was also another problem. The big AM was an essential element of an amphibious assault. Ideally, the assault sweepers had to transit to the objective area with the assault ships, protected by the same escorts. By about 1948, the US Navy had accepted that future amphibious assault ships should all transit at about 20kts (attempts to design a 20kt LST bore no fruit until the 1960s). However, small minesweepers could not possibly maintain such speeds; they are too short.[5] This problem was never really solved. For the Persian Gulf, US ocean sweepers transitted at acceptable speed on board a semi-submersible (flo-flo) merchant ship, rather than on their own bottoms.

In 1953–60, the US Navy built a total of ninety-three ocean minesweepers of the *Agile* and modified classes (twenty-eight for foreign navies), plus four slightly im-

The USS Exploit *(MSO 440) at Little Creek on 14 June 1968. Note the panelling of the wooden hull and the fore and aft lines of the planking.* (L & L van Ginderen)

proved *Acme* (MSO 508) class ships and three enlarged *Ability* (MSO 519: 190ft rather than 172ft long) class ships. They were enlarged to relieve overcrowding in the engine room and CIC (ie, in the mine plot), and to provide better unit commander facilities. The extra length automatically bought more cruising range and it permitted installation of more powerful commercial diesels (which increased sweep current to 6900 amps), as well as space for some engine silencing (to avoid falling victim to acoustic mines). The MSO 509 and 519 classes had divisional flag facilities. Engine installation varied but all types had four diesels:

MSO 421 (*Agile*) class: 3040bhp Packards

MSO 422 class (*Aggressive:* MSO 422–427, 432–449, 455–474, 488–496): 2280bhp Packards

MSO 428 class (*Dash* class: MSO 428–431): 1520bhp GM (2 GM 8-278A), sweep capacity 5100 amps. These ships could accommodate new 5700 amp sweep generators but they lacked sufficient space to install the GM 12-278A engine needed for more current.

MSO 508–511 (*Acme*) class: 2280bhp Packard

MSO 519–521 (*Ability*) class: 2700bhp GM (two 12-278A; GM offered a supercharged version of its smaller 8-278A, 8-278CS, 1300bhp in less space than the 12-278A).

Units for transfer abroad all had 1600bhp GM diesels: MSO 450–454 for France; 478–479 and 486–487 for Portugal; 480–485 for the Netherlands; 498–499 for Norway; 500–502, 505, 512–513 for France; 503–504, 515–516, and 522 for Belgium; and 506–507, 517–581 for Italy. It is not clear whether the transferred ships had the US type automatic degaussing system.

Minesweeping Boats

Work on the companion 56ft MSB apparently also began in 1948. The Navy obtained four MSBs built (by Norfolk Navy Yard and by Mare Island) for the Army in 1945; it is not clear just what their army role was to have been. The MSB would go overseas on board larger vessels. To minimize its weight, it would be made of aluminium. By 1950, however, wood had been substituted for fear of eddy currents, and the MSB (now 57ft long) was expected to use the same expensive construction technique as the AM. At first BuShips was interested in powering it with the new GM Model 110 (power would be 240 rather than 300shp, but sweep current would be 5200 rather than 5000 amps). However, the final design introduced gas turbines to the US Navy in the form of sweep generators; only a gas turbine could provide enough power in the available space. About 1951 the MSB was rated at 11kts (free route; 6.5kts sweeping). At this time she had two

The Belgian minesweeper De Brouwer *at Zeebrugge on 24 October 1983. She was originally built as part of the MDAP and became the Norwegian* Nansen *shortly after completion in 1955. She was transferred to Belgium in 1966.* (L & L van Ginderen)

sweep generators, each producing about 1075 amps at 213kW. Endurance was 24hrs free route, 16hrs sweeping, or 12hrs sweeping with full magnetic sweep.

First preliminary characteristics were distributed on 29 May 1950; forty-eight were eventually authorized. MSB 23 burned while under construction, and was completed with a plastic rather than a wooden hull.

Unfortunately the MSB turned out to be too heavy for conventional cargo booms. It could go overseas only on board a heavy-lift cargo ship or in the well-deck of an LSD. In September 1953, in connection with the FY55 programme, BuShips noted fleet interest in converting an LSD to an MSB carrier/tender (it offered to submit a proposal). In 1953/4 MinRon Ten evaluated an LSD as an MSB carrier. MSB 29 was built to a new large design (by John Trumpy & Sons of Annapolis), reportedly because the MSB was now so clearly overweight that there was no longer any point in restricting its dimensions to make it easily transportable overseas.

For an assault, the alternative was to develop a boat small enough to fit a standard Welin davit on board an amphibious ship. Late in the Second World War 36ft landing craft (LCVPs) were used as extemporized shallow-water sweepers and this practice continued postwar. For example, in December 1952 the allowance for Minesweeping Boat Division One was thirteen LCVPs. The next step was a specially-built minesweeping launch. Four 30ft wooden Mk 1 (for training) were followed by twenty-five wooden Mk 2 (MSL 5–29, register numbers C 3067–91, built by Sagsted Shipyard, Seattle, under the FY56 programme), then by a single plastic Mk 4 (MSL 31–56, register numbers C 13419–44, built in the mid-1960s by United Boat Co.[6] The Mk 5s were two Mk 1 and one Mk 2 converted to diesel power (two 300bhp engines) in 1967. MSLs were intended to operate in groups of four: one moored, one acoustic, two magnetic (the MSL hull was designed to take any of the three sweeps). The sweeps were launched aboard 50ft LCMs, which transferred them to the MSLs. At least Mks 3 and 4 used 200hp gas turbines for both sweep and propulsive power. An accompanying project (SCB 123) called for conversion of a war-built minelayer/transport (CM or LSV) to an MCM headquarters ship (MCS, SCB 123), carrying twenty MSLs in davits (and helicopters on deck). Money was too tight, in the mid-1950s, for such a conversion but all five LSVs, no longer needed for amphibious assault, were redesignated MCS in 1956. Only two were ever converted (in the 1960s). An MCS converted from an LST was also proposed. The war-built LST 1069 became MCS 6 (*Orleans Parish*) in January 1959, having served as a mine support ship for some years under her LST designation (there was no formal conversion). The LSD *Epping Forrest* could accommodate MSBs (or ten MSLs). She was redesignated in November 1962. Unfortunately, the MSLs proved too small to tow useful sweep gear; they and the MCSs were discarded in the late 1960s.

Helicopters, which have survived, were another attempt to develop a truly mobile mine countermeasures force. Like the MSBs and MSLs, they cannot do the job by themselves. Almost forty years later, there is still no entirely successful solution to moving minesweepers into place at sufficient speed.

Underwater Locators

The companion AMCU conversions were intended to survey and buoy limits of minefields; to direct sweepers to safe courses for sweeping and check completeness of sweep; to conduct harbour and channel bottom surveys; and to lead columns of ships through mined waters. In an August 1950 (ie, pre-Wonsan) proposal for the FY52 budget, the AMCU was priority 3, after a new ocean escort (DE) and a missile cruiser conversion. The three AM were priority 14, the MSBs priority 17. The AMCU was defined as a minimum conversion of existing hulls (AMCU 204, AGSC 13 and 14 and 28 LSIL) with the UQS–1 sonar, precision navigation gear, and facilities for a large-scale plot. Their big well decks provided space for a mortar mine destruction system then under development.[7] All had provision for a power (diver)boat. The main problem with the converted landing craft was its inability to maintain course, due to its lack of a keel.

About 1952 work began on a specially-designed mine-hunter (AMCU, later MHC; SCB 109 project). Specified maximum magnetic signature was 0.5mg, 35ft below the keel and it was to have had minimum acoustic signature. This was a keel-type hull. Required trial speed was 14kts; armament was one 40mm, two 20mm and one mine destruction projector (X–1, with twelve, later twenty-four charges, associated with the UQC–1 sonar). The designers found the wartime YMS hull too slow so they tried a series of wood and plastic hulls of various lengths, seeking the smallest ship which could make 14kts. They found that a plastic hull would allow a fuller midships section, which gave it a decided advantage. However, it was expensive, and an attempt to fabricate a plastic landing craft (LCVP) had just failed. That shifted them back to wood; they knew they could meet the required speed using Packard diesels in a 138ft hull (ie AMS length – see below).

Minehunting made slow-speed manoeuvrability particularly important. The designers considered cycloidal propellers but rejected them for excessive magnetic signature. Instead they used twin activated rudders for position-keeping and for propulsion at up to 6kts (existing commercial units met the magnetic standards).

The designers hoped to avoid changing the AMS design, merely exchanging mine-hunting gear for sweep diesels and gear. They found they had to extend the open bridge from side to side so that those on the bridge could see the ship's waterline. The controls for the main engines, active rudder and steering were all moved from the pilot house to the open bridge, leaving only steering control and an engine order telegraph in the pilothouse. With replacement of sweep generators by smaller motor-generator sets for the active rudders, the forward machinery space could be shortened to increase berth space. The hull form itself was not changed.

The ship emerged as USS *Bittern* (MHC 43). The designations MHC 44 and 45 were allocated to two planned (but abortive) sisters. Her X–1 was never fitted but otherwise she generally followed the 1952–53 design. Early in 1954 five war-built YMS were reclassified as minehunters (AMCU, later MHC, 46–50). When plans for the two repeat *Bittern*s were cancelled early in 1955, two more YMS were redesignated MHC 44–45; it is not clear to what extent these ships were modified.

Modernizing the YMS

NATO was formed in 1949. Initially, the United States saw it not as a military alliance but as a Mutual Defence Assistance Programme (MDAP) to build up the standing forces, including the navies, of the NATO allies.[8] Much effort went into anti-submarine measures but clearly the Soviets, like the Germans, were just as likely to attempt to stop supplies in Europe by attacking Western European ports. MDAP therefore had to include minesweepers for the NATO navies. It was assumed that the Soviets would be able to reproduce German-style sensitive magnetic and pressure mines. BuShips saw little point in developing anything as exotic as its new ocean sweeper. Instead, it decided to modernize the wartime YMS.

Work began early in 1950. In May, BuShips decided to redesign the YMS for reduced magnetic signature and improved seakeeping. The earlier hull could not be adapted directly because the YMS already lacked sufficient stability and freeboard. Instead, the AMS used a reduced version of the hull form of the 165ft ocean sweeper, with shallow draught and minimum dimensions. Hull scantlings were based on those of the successful wartime YMS. Compared to the YMS, the new hull had a longer forecastle deck (for dryness and a greater range of static stability) and was 15in deeper. It was slightly longer (144ft oa vs 136ft for the YMS) and beamier (26ft 6in vs 23ft 4in), displacing 65 tons more standard (370 vs 305).

The YMS had two 500bhp propulsion engines, a 500bhp sweep generator and a ship's service generator. The AMS design showed four 12-cylinder 600bhp Packard non-magnetic diesels: two for propulsion, two for sweep generation, plus two 4-cylinder GM diesels driving 60kW ship service generators. BuShips hoped that simple measures, such as adopting non-magnetic diesels, would reduce the ship's magnetic signature but it did not expect anything like that expected of the radical SCB 45 sweeper. It did plan to use the same sort of non-magnetic wooden construction, with laminated wood framing. In March 1951 the estimated magnetic signature (at 30ft) of an AMS powered by four of the radical new lightweight Packards was 0.7 to 1.2mg. At that time some AMS were planned for the US Navy; BuShips decided that all AMS for MDAP would have proven 440bhp GM8-268A engines (signature at 30ft was 1.0 to 1.7mg).[9]

The AMS could not tow an XMAP. It would tow the same moored and acoustic sweep gear as the YMS. Sweep current was limited to 4700amps (4340 with 440bhp GM engines vs 3300 for the YMS) because, to save time, the new ship used the same type of sweep cable. Compared to the YMS, armament would be reduced from one 40mm and two 20mm to one twin 20mm, with many fewer rounds, and there would be no searchlight ASW sonar (nor did the design include a mine detection sonar).

The new sweeper would make 8 rather than 7.5kts, towing magnetic and moored sweeps, and maximum speed would be 14 rather than 13.6kts. Given the limited size of the sweeper, there was no hope of gaining either much more speed or much more range.

Between 1953 and 1960, the US Navy built a large series of AMS of closely related designs, all but twenty-two for transfer: MSC (AMS) 60–171, 190–209, 214–221, 238–240, 255–267, 268–288. AMS (later MSC) 60 used GM engines; the later MSC 121 class was similar but Packard-powered, for the US Navy. US boats used roll-compensated degaussing. It was possible to degauss sufficiently to overcome the extra magnetic moments of the GM engines but there was some fear that they would not provide enough power to reach minimum sweep speed. The last series were lengthened (from 144 to 152ft) and powered by 1200bhp rather than 880bhp GM diesels. Other MSCs were built abroad to US orders, using either the British *Ton* design (MSC 172–189, 210–213, 222–237, 241–253) or the US design (MSC 214–217 in Italy, MSC 254 to a hybrid design powered by 4000bhp Mercedes-Benz diesels).

The FY59 programme included a redesigned MSC (SCB 69A design). As of May 1957, it was expected to be slightly larger (150ft pp x 30ft, 490 tons light, 3200bhp = 16kts), with a new Rotovac acoustic device. The prototype was expected to cost $4 million, compared to $2.7 million for a repeat SCB 69. An alternative was to lengthen the existing MSC by about 6ft (25 tons added), with the Rotovac ($3.8 million). Two ships (MSC 289 and 290) were moved up to the FY58 programme to replace two (MSC 200 and 202) transferred to Spain. *Albatross* (MSC 289) was built with gas turbine sweep generators. All but two of those built (MSC 289–418) were transferred abroad.

Inshore Minesweepers

In effect the last of this series was the inshore sweeper (MSI, SCB 136), conceived in 1955 as a purely defensive type, a more seaworthy hull carrying MSB sweep gear. It was partly inspired by Trumpy's 85ft MSB 29; the US designers also considered modelling it on the very successful 95ft Coast Guard and on the British 106ft *Ham* class. The first preliminary design was modelled on the Coast Guard boat 'which has earned a good reputation for its sea-keeping qualities'. The Ship Characteristics Board (SCB) rejected this enlarged MSB; it wanted a fisherman-type single screw hull, limited to a waterline length of about 100ft, but capable of carrying and operating MSC 60 class sweep gear and of conventional construction (for mobilization). The SCB rejected gas turbine sweep generators (which the designers considered the best solution to the problem): they would consume far too much fuel. To accommodate a sufficiently powerful standard diesel generator (440bhp, 3000 amps), the designers had to lengthen the ship 5ft and accept a lighter sweep cable. The propulsion diesel produced 580bhp. The arrangement was unusual: this diesel was placed *forward* of the sweep generator because the latter required more length; that moved the uptakes forward, leaving more space for a sweep deck. Since the minesweeping engine had to be offset to starboard to clear the single shaft, the propulsion diesel had to be to port, to balance it. Two (*Cove* and *Cape*) were included in the FY56 programme. Eventually the SCB's decision was reversed; their sweep diesels were replaced by gas turbines to give them an influence sweep capability comparable to that of the MSC 289 class. Another twelve were built for transfer, plus five improved MSI 15 class, which added minehunting capability.

Construction Programmes

In April 1948, the draft FY50 programme (for the year ending 30 June 1950) included twenty small minesweepers (AMS, successors to the wartime YMS). Another was planned for FY51. At about the same time XMAP was assigned SCB number 59 and the mine countermeasures designation PAM–1. The SCB wanted the two prototype XMAPs for the FY51 programme, but they were so important that they were moved back to FY50. Then funds tightened dramatically. The minesweeper programme was cut to a single ship, which had to be financed by transferring funds originally assigned to a FY49 repeat ASW cruiser (*Norfolk* class; some of this money also went to six DDE conversions). In May 1949 the projected FY51 programme included a second sweeper (now AM, an ocean sweeper) and two XMAPs, as priorities 3 and 4, after more DDEs and *Essex* class carrier conversions.

In January 1950 the proposed FY52 programme included not only three more minesweepers (AM) but also five new minesweeping boats (MSB), as priorities 3 and 1 (priority 2 was DER conversions for Continental Air Defense). Two more MSB were included in a special $75 million ASW programme. It seemed likely that eleven AM would be included in the FY53 budget and fourteen more in FY54; and that twenty-five MSB would be included in each of those two budgets. No more XMAPs were

planned, presumably on the theory that they had to be tested first. In April 1950 all AM were cut from the FY52 programme because not much could be spent on them that year (the MSBs survived). Then savings in the FY50 programme allowed the high-priority items from FY52, including the three MSBs, to be shifted back into FY51.

In June, just before the Korean War broke out, the planned FY52 programme showed two MSB and two AM. Then the war released money. By early July, BuShips was calculating the cost of a programme including twelve AM and fifteen MSB.

The FY51 programme was drastically enlarged. It paid for the prototype ocean minesweeper *Agile* (AM 421). To that were added ten in the first FY51 supplemental (the two originally planned had been dropped); another eighteen were included in the second supplemental and another fifteen in the third, for a total of forty-four. The programme also included eighteen MSB (two in the base programme, fifteen in the first supplemental and fifteen in the third) and two prototype AMS for MDAP (third supplemental; plus up to sixteen for transfer to foreign navies, depending on funding).

In August 1950, a revised FY52 programme showed nine AMCU (minehunters, converted from one AMC, six LSI(L) and two AGSC), three AM, and ten MSB. By the

The Spanish minesweeper Guadalquivir, *seen here at Barcelona in May 1985, was built as the* USS Persistant *(MSO 491) in 1955 and transferred to Spain under MDAP in 1971.* (L & L van Ginderen)

end of 1950, the planned FY52 programme showed thirty-one AMCU conversions, five AM, and fifteen more MSB, for a total of fifty-nine AM and forty-eight MSB.

By this time mine countermeasures craft were badly wanted. A tentative FY53 budget drawn up in May 1951 showed fifty AM, sixteen AMCU conversions and thirty MSB. These numbers were excessive. In December 1951 a revised (Secretary of Defense mark-up) programme showed ten AM and thirty AMS (as a less expensive alternative to the high-technology AM), twenty MSB and sixteen AMCU. About this time the AM was priority 3 and the AMS was priority 4; the MSB was priority 15, the AMCU priority 23. Numbers continued to fluctuate, so that a 20 December 1951 shipbuilding status report showed an FY53 programme of ten AM, sixty AMS, thirty MSB, and sixteen AMCU. It is not clear how many of the AMS were for MDAP; BuShips would have listed them with the US ships. Plans called for installation of UQS–1 on board at least some of the AMS, perhaps as a first step towards the MHC described above. The programme actually adopted included ten AM and twenty AMS but no MSB.

Still there were not enough mine countermeasures craft. First studies for the FY54 budget showed forty AM (OpNav staff comments would have supported a total of sixty) but these figures were drastically cut in the three

The Acme *class minesweeper* Affray *(MSO 511) at Malta on 28 March 1964.* (L & L van Ginderen)

budget alternatives BuShips offered (for totals of $2, 1.5 and 1 billions: thirty, thirty and twenty respectively). The planners initially included no AMS at all but OpNav comments supported sixty; their alternatives were thirty, zero and zero. The planners began with thirty MSB (thirty-three could be justified); their alternatives were thirty, ten and ten. The new AMCU (MHC) was proposed but it could be bought only under the high-budget alternative. The SCB proposed thirty AM, thirty MSB and a single new AMCU (no AMS).

In November 1952 BuShips proposed ten AM for FY55 as priority 14, to maintain a mobilization base and approach the large number envisaged for war.

However, interest declined with the arrival of the new Eisenhower Administration, whose military strategy emphasized nuclear weapons rather than the sort of amphibious assaults the minecraft were designed to support. Thus the FY54 programme actually bought only four AM (but it did pay for the prototype new-construction AMCU). By September 1953 BuShips listed eight AM. A January 1954 list showed the three AM actually included in the FY55 programme, the last of their type for the US Navy for about a quarter of a century. They were soon redesignated MSO, ocean minesweepers.

From its inception about March 1954, the FY56 programme included two new sweepers. By June they were listed as MSI (it is not clear whether originally a new class of MSO was planned).

FY57 lacked any minecraft at all. DCNO (Logistics), who was in charge of the SCB, wanted two MSO included in the FY58 budget to ensure 'orderly development of this

essential type' but they lacked priority. Instead, the programme included two replacement MSCs.

By this time the XMAP experiments had clearly failed. The alternative was to convert a full-size merchant hull into a pressure minehunter, preferably carrying devices to increase all her signatures so that she would trigger mines at a distance. She could be filled with buoyant material, her controls moved to a shock-mounted bridge and her engines protected. Converted merchant ships had already been used as 'guinea pigs' to proof-test swept fields: three Liberty ships were converted under the FY53 programme, two at Yokosuka (YAG 36 and 38) and one (*John L Sullivan*, YAG 37) at Norfolk. YAG 37 was powered by T34 turbo-props. She was very successfully tested in 1957–58. The engines survived explosions which would have sunk a cruiser; BuShips concluded that of all mines in an area through which the ship steamed in a random path, well over half would be swept safely. By 1959, the proposed FY62–67 programme showed four MSS (SCB 159, later redesignated SCB 500.66). BuShips hoped to simulate the pressure signature of a 20,000 ton ship. New engines might increase speed to 15kts; by keeping its speed high during a sweep, the 'guinea pig' should simulate the signatures of larger ships moving more slowly. Plans initially called for turboprop power, modified degaussing and pulse coils (to increase magnetic signature, for sweeping), possibly even hydrofoils to increase pressure signature. Studies then showed that diesels on deck, driving outboard propellers through right-angled drives, could be as effective but much less expensive. They were used in the single operational MSS converted, the Liberty ship *Harry L Glickman* converted under the FY66 programme. The only other MSS was a converted LST (1166) used to proof-test the swept channel at Hanoi-Haiphong in 1973.

Programme Cuts

The new MHC was clearly an appropriate companion type. Thus an April 1957 draft of the FY59 programme showed a repeat MHC and a prototype MSS conversion alongside three MSC. All were soon dropped from the FY59 programme; by October 1957 the FY60 proposal included the MHC and MSS. This MHC was an enlarged version of the earlier one, modified to tow a mine detection/classification sonar through a hull well (CXRP, a UQS-1 fitted with the classification sonar of a British Type 193; it later became SQQ-14). The new MHC was also expected to use a new side-looking towed sonar, Shadowgraph, and probably such exotica as a very sensitive magnetic gradiometer and a bottom-following towed vehicle. It was expected to grow slightly, to 160 x 30 x 10–4ft (350 tons). Although the ship was never built, the sonar survived (as SQQ-14) to appear on board modernized ocean minehunters. The MSS was included in the FY60 programme. Then it was cancelled in favour of an oceanographic research ship (AGOR).

The Bluebird *class coastal minesweeper* Meadowlark *(MSC 196) in 1954.* (L & L van Ginderen)

Minecraft continued to be included in draft programmes but they often failed to survive into final ones. Money was very tight; numerous programmes had to be cut or killed to pay for very urgent ones, such as Polaris and the FRAM fleet modernization. Thus in November 1958 the Long Range Objectives group (LRO-58) proposed that two ships be converted to MSC in FY60 and FY62 (one for each ocean). Replacement minecraft were clearly needed: two in FY60, two in FY61, four in FY62, four in FY63, four in FY64, four in FY65, eight in FY66, a total of thirty-two in FY67–69. In fact none was built. Two ships were converted to MCS (FY63 and FY64); the MSS was finally converted in FY66.

A new MSO was projected for FY66. In 1964 the FY66–73 programme showed four in FY66, five in FY67, seven per year in FY68–70, then eight per year in FY71–3, a total of fifty-four to replace the existing MSOs. As an interim step, existing units were to be modernized under the FRAM II programme. About April 1964 the SCB working level group concluded that a modernized MSO would actually be better than the new ship in some ways (given money limits and its smaller tonnage, which generated a smaller pressure signature). On the other hand, the modified MSO would lack sweep power (4500 vs 7500 amps in ships with GM diesels); would be noisier (the FY66 sweeper had shrouded propellers and noise-mounted diesels); would not achieve the same sweep speed

The coastal minesweeper uss Thrasher *(MSC 203) in 1956.* (L & L van Ginderen)

(the FY66 ship would tow a combined magnetic/acoustic sweep at 8.5 rather than 7kts); would not meet current habitability standards and would lack any growth margin.

The BuShips design section argued that it would be nearly pointless to begin a new series of ships which essentially duplicated enlarged MSOs. Much new technology was nearly ready: plastic hulls, catamarans. It would be better to hold off a new design until FY70 or FY71. The existing wooden MSO hull was now characterized as over-heavy, not daringly light; it could probably be reduced by 50 to 60 tons (out of about 300). However, before that could be done, the new scale of reduced scantlings would have to be tested successfully. Plastic (which the British were already testing) might be far better.

The FY66 funds were used to accelerate the MSO FRAM programme. Initially fifty-six MSOs were involved, then it grew briefly to sixty-one. Four were included in the planned FY66 programme but they were deleted because necessary equipment could not be provided in time (work could begin in the latter part of FY67). Major bottlenecks were delivery of new engines (eight re-enginings had been begun using FY65 refit funds) and the new precision navigation system needed for minehunting.[10]

Ultimately only nineteen MSOs began refits, and modernization of five (MSO 460, 468, 470, 472, and 519) was cancelled and the hulks scrapped. This work was funded under the FY68 (MSO 433, 441–3, 445, 446, 449, 456) and FY69 (MSO 437, 438, 448, 488, 490) programmes,

For minehunting, the ships were to be fitted with a short-range, high-resolution classification sonar (ultimately SQQ-14 was chosen). Their fantails were rearranged to stream the new Shadowgraph side-looking imaging (detection/classification) sonar (three towfish) and to fire Sea Nettle anti-mine torpedoes (to stow at least twenty). Shadowgraph was expected to guide the short-range Sea Nettles in the hope, never realized, that its images would be so precise that mines would not have to be examined one by one before being neutralized. In the event, Shadowgraph/Sea Nettle was never deployed, although the basic idea has survived. A precision navigation system was installed. Except for the MSO 428 class, all the rebuilt ships were to have new sweep and propulsion engines, for better reliability and maintainability. Sweep power was to suffice for 7500 amps. The 40mm gun, 24in searchlight, 26ft motor whaleboat and towing winch were all landed as weight compensation (the prominent SQQ-14 winch replaced the 40mm gun).

The abortive new MSO (SCB 501 in a new 500-series for minecraft) planned for FY66 would have combined MSO and MHC capabilities, using Shadowgraph/Sea Nettle and SQQ-14. To limit size (hence pressure signature), it would have been operable in any of three configurations: normal sweep, hunt/destroy (using Sea Nettle and SQQ-14).

In effect, that ended the story of the first postwar generation of US mine countermeasures craft. Any hope of immediate replacement ended about 1971, when Admiral Elmo Zumwalt decided that future assault sweeps would be conducted by helicopters. The MSOs survived long enough for it to become obvious that the helicopters would not suffice, despite their success in clearing the Suez Canal in 1974. By the late 1970s there was intense interest in a new generation of sweepers, primarily to deal with a new threat; rising mines, which might threaten US strategic submarines going to their patrol areas. That is a very different story.

Notes

[1] XMAP (SCB 59) was a 2880-ton cylinder of STS, 4.5 to 10.5in thick (251ft x 28ft 6in, drawing 19ft 6in). It carried magnetic and acoustic generators drawing power from the towing ship. XMAP could duplicate the pressure signature of a ship of up to about 5000 tons and was intended to withstand fifty mine explosions, each equivalent to 2000lbs of TNT in 40ft of water. A sweeper was expected to tow two XMAP either in tandem or side by side. Two dummy hulls proved that the shape towed badly; a test explosion-resistant hull sank.

[2] By about 1954, BuShips was proud of this dual development programme, which it said had succeeded despite many gloomy forecasts. However, in 1967 Richards T Miller ('Minesweepers', in US Naval Institute *Naval Review* for that year), mentions only the Packard programme. He states that it was hurried disastrously from orderly development to war-scale production 'before its detailed design problems had been completely defined and corrected . . . [it] required

The US minesweeping boat MSB 51 at Zeebrugge on 30 May 1981. (L & L van Ginderen)

aircraft-type maintenance. It took some eight years to correct the many mechanical ills with which it was plagued, and that led to its acquiring an unsavoury service reputation.' As of 1967, plans called for replacement of the Packard by a commercial type of diesel. According to Miller, the Packards weighed 5 to 6lbs per bhp, whereas the commercial-type diesels (GMs) replacing them in newer sweepers and in modernization weighed 10 to 12lbs bhp. He claimed that the loss of power in changing type had little effect on speed but did not comment on its effect on magnetic sweep or on towing capability (which presumably was not as important, given the demise of XMAP).

3   Formal Characteristics for a 180-footer (as an alternative to the *220-footer*) were issued as late as June 1950; they included twin rudders for manoeuvrability.

4   Design work on improved wooden designs apparently began early in 1950; some designs were reported on 11 April. At the verbal request of the General Board (surely one of its last few), the designers developed a series of 160/165ft designs which they reported on 10 May. They were: (i) a 165-footer with additional power at the expense of crew space; (ii) a wooden sweeper with substantially the performance of the 180-ft aluminium ship; (iii) a 175-ft wooden sweeper; and (iv) a 195ft wooden sweeper. In the 165-footer, sixteen-cylinder engines could be substituted for twelve-cylinder units, increasing sweep current from 6000 to 7200 amps and tow speed from 8 to 9.8kts with one XMAP (from 6.8 to 8.6kts

with two). The designers argued that it was better to add structure than to lengthen the hull, because efficient joints could not be made between the ends and edges of wood planks. The wooden equivalent to the 180ft aluminium sweeper would be 230ft long and of dubious strength; lengthening to 175 or 195ft would buy very little. These studies drove the designers to use double-diagonal planking outboard and fore-and-aft planking inboard, with laminated oak frames. Presumably the AM actually selected later in 1950 was derived from these studies.

5   Speed performance depends largely on speed-length ratio, the ratio of speed in knots to the square root of length, in feet. A speed-length ratio much above 1 defines a fast ship, much of whose weight and volume should go into machinery. For a 180ft sweeper, this point is reached just below 13.5kts. The needs for towing power and for generator power (for the magnetic sweep) further complicated any attempt to build a fast sweeper.

6   Register numbers for Mk 2 and Mk 4 are from lists maintained by the small craft office of NAVSEA. Unfortunately it has not been possible to find register numbers for Mk 1 and Mk 3. The register lists only three 30ft MSLs, No *5377–79*, without further details. The four prototypes were probably built under the FY54 programme. The FY56 programme included twenty-six MSLs, which is probably twenty-five Mk 2s plus one Mk 3. The Mk 4s probably date from FY66 or FY67.

MSB 16 *at Zeebrugge, 30 May 1981.* (L & L van Ginderen)

This X–1 device was abandoned because UQS-1 detected too many false targets; ammunition use would have been prohibitive. It appears that initially small cargo ships (AKL) were considered as alternatives to LSI(L)s. The LSI(L) was chosen because it was available and was deemed 'not unacceptable' but operations by units at Charleston and Norfolk showed that it was not particularly attractive, largely because it could not easily hold position without a keel. The alternative SCB 135 was deleted from the FY53 programme because it was so much more expensive than an LSI(L) conversion, then reinstated.

MDAP was eventually a huge programme of US-built ships. There was also a programme of Off-Shore Purchases (OSP), in which the US Government financed construction of approved types (evaluated by BuShips) in foreign yards. OSP funds were provided via MSA, the Military Supply Agency (they were also called AMP, additional military procurement). In March 1952, for example, AMP was financing five AMS 60 for Norway, eight for Belgium and twelve AMS 61 for Italy. That was in addition to ninety-seven building in the United States under MDAP. At this time coastal (AMC) and inshore (AMI) sweepers of indige-nous design were planned for OSP under the FY53 programme. In September 1952, there were two existing AMC designs not yet approved, the French version of the *Ton* class and the German R-boat. The Italians were working on their own version of AMS 60 as an AMC (modified to US standards) and the French and Italians were working on versions of British *Ham* class AMI. As planned in October 1952 the programme called for four Italian AMC (AMS 60 variant) and twenty AMI (British *Ham* class or Italian design); fourteen French AMC (*Ton* class; six for the Vietnam War); two Portuguese (*Ton* class); and fifteen British AMI (*Ham* class; the Admiralty paid directly for others). In the final programme, the fifteen British-built AMI went to France.

9   Estimated magnetic signatures are taken from a 24 March 1951 BuShips report on 'current minesweeper designs'

written specifically for the CNO. It compared the AM(MSO) 421, AMS (MSC) 60 and a British coastal design (*Ton*) powered by Deltic engines. At this time Canada was generally following the British design and the Dutch were interested in the AMS (by March 1952 they were getting *Ton*s). The *Ton* was slightly larger than the AMS (hence was superior) but produced much less sweep current (3000 vs 4550 [GM] or 5000 [Packard] amps) and had a larger signature (1.7 to 3.2mg). The reduced sweep current would limit the British ship to a swept path 64yds wide, compared to 124 for the Packard-powered AMS or 120 for the GM-powered version. BuShips considered the British sweep current insufficient to trigger relatively insensitive mines intended to destroy large ships, nor could it be relied upon to sweep sensitive mines in shallow water. The *Ton* described in the paper was the original version using aluminium frames, decks and bulkheads, and African mahogany planking. At the time of the paper it was being redesigned with US-style laminated-wood framing. Initially the British argued that eddy currents were not a realistic problem, since they would become important only if the sweeper were rolling so severely that she could not sweep. Canadian tests bore out US fears. US evaluators pointed out, too, that the British sweepers used magnetic materials in their Mirrlees and Deltic engines. The declassified 1951 paper is in the 1951 'double zero' files held by the US Navy Operational Archives. Actual, as opposed to estimated, magnetic and other signatures have not been declassified.

10   Fifty new engines (six per ship, with two spares) were ordered but in May 1965 the GAO cancelled the contract because of a disputed bid award. There was now no reliable 600bhp engine so the modified ships would have to use paired 1200bhp propulsion engines, as in some Canadian sweepers (similar to the GM 800bhp units in the MSO 428 class). These engines were too heavy; they were acceptable only if the sweep engines could be replaced by lightweight gas turbines. The moral of the story was that even a small slow ship could have her design jeopardized by excessive engine weight.

SWEDISH POSTWAR SUBMARINES

In this article, David Miller gives a detailed account of the post-war design evolution of the Swedish submarine, together with some background detail on their origins and intended role. It demonstrates that even a country with a relatively small population and industrial base can maintain a position in the fore-front of naval technology without foreign assistance.

Swedish inventors were among the first underwater pioneers, the earliest known design being that of Dr Thunberg in 1770. Two submarines were built in 1869–70, although with what success is not known, and later the industrialist Nordenfelt produced several boats in partnership with the British pioneer, Garrett, including two that entered service with the Greek and Turkish navies. It was not until the start of the twentieth century, however, that the Royal Swedish Navy (RSwN) took an

active interest and Engineer Commander Richson's first design was commissioned as HSWMS *Hajen* in 1904. Like many other contemporary navies, the RSwN next bought an Italian boat, *Hvalen*, and created something of a stir by sailing her 4000nm from La Spezia to Stockholm on her delivery voyage in 1908. Since then, however, every submarine has been of Swedish construction, with the sole exception of a British two-man X-craft bought in 1958, although foreign design ideas have been incorporated from time to time.

Sweden is in a unique strategic situation and for many years her armed forces have been responsible for keeping her out of a war, whilst being ready, if that fails, to repel an invader. The most likely enemy was either Germany or Russia, which meant that the primary area of operations would be the Baltic. Thus, the Navy is responsible for the

The Hajen *class submarine* Bävern *leaves one of the many bunkers excavated from the cliffs along the Swedish coast; the design of this class incorporated the lessons learnt from examining the German Type XXI U-3053.*

defence of a long coastline, populated with many hundreds of islands.

The Baltic is generally shallow, so the submarines tend to be small, and the acoustic conditions are difficult, which explains why all modern Swedish torpedoes are wire-guided. A further significant factor is that Sweden's policy of neutrality dictates that the armed forces must be totally independent and rely on national industrial assets to a major extent. As a result Sweden has built a succession of submarine classes, whose designs have become more innovative and striking as the years have gone by.

That Sweden is correct in keeping up its military guard, despite its neutrality, is demonstrated by the repeated underwater incursions that have been made into its territorial waters since the 1970s; incursions which continue even in 1994. Many of these have been detected, of which none was more public than that by the Russian *Whiskey* class diesel-electric submarine, which ran onto the Swedish coast near the Karlskrona naval base on 27 October 1981.

Situation in 1945

Sweden managed to maintain its neutrality throughout the Second World War, during the course of which two submarines were sunk. One hit a German mine and the other collided with a merchant ship but both were raised and one, *Sjöborren*, was returned to service. When the war ended in 1945 the RSwN was equipped with twenty-four submarines of four classes, most of them of relatively recent construction. There were two patrol classes, the *Sjölejonet* and *U-1*, and two minelaying classes, the *Delfinen* and *Neptun*.

The first of the *Sjölejonet* class was launched in 1936, followed by one each in 1937 and 1938, four in 1940 and the final two in 1941, making it the most numerous class

built for the RSwN up to that time. Displacing 760 tons, their conventional design was derived from that of the *Delfinen* class minelayers (see below), although the disposition of their six torpedo-tubes was relatively unusual: three were in the bows, one in the stern, and two in a traversing mount on the upper deck, a feature popular with the French Navy. There were also two 40mm guns on disappearing mountings, a surprising feature, since such mounts were both complicated and heavy, making them an unnecessary complication for such light weapons. All nine were reconstructed in the 1950s, with the guns and traversing torpedo-tubes being removed, but they were stricken between 1959 and 1964.

The other wartime patrol type, the nine 450-ton boats of the *U-1* class (U = *Ubåt* = submarine) of 1941, were given numbers rather than names. They were slightly smaller than the *Sjölejonet* class and were, again, of very conventional design, except for the torpedo armament, which consisted of two bow tubes, one stern tube, and a single tube in a traversing mount on the upper deck. The gun armament consisted of a single 20mm cannon for AA defence. *U-1* and *U-2* were stricken in 1960, followed by *U-3* in 1964, while the remainder were rebuilt as the *Abborren* class, as described below.

The use of submarines as minelayers was one of the naval successes of the First World War and for many years thereafter many navies, including that of Sweden, maintained a small number of such specialised boats. The RSwN adopted the French Normand-Fenaux system and the layout was similar in the three successive classes, all of which carried twenty mines. The first minelayer was *Valen*, a single boat (730 tons, commissioned 1925, stricken 1944), which was followed by the three-strong

The Valen, *720 tons, one of the six-strong* Hajen *class, commissioned between 1954 and 1958.*

Six of the 'U' class were rebuilt as ASW hunter/killers and fitted with large bow sonars and a rotating torpedo magazine abaft the sail. This is Abborren, *lead-ship of the modified group.*

Delfinen class (720 tons, commissioned 1934/35, stricken 1953) and, finally, the three *Neptun* class boats. The latter were the major minelaying class to serve on into the post-war period. All were laid down in early 1942, launched later that year and completed in mid-1943, a remarkably quick process, which showed the impetus provided by the combat being waged all around them. They were the last minelayers to be completed for the

The Nordkaparen *in 1970, a* Draken *class submarine, the first operational class to be fitted with a single, slow-rotating propeller rather than the then customary twin propellers.*

Navy, carrying a wartime load of twenty mines in addition to their five torpedo-tubes, a single 40mm and a single 20mm cannon. All were stricken in 1966 and sold for scrap in 1970.

U-3503

At the end of the Second World War the RSwN found, like every other navy, that its submarine designs had been outdated at a stroke by new German designs, particularly the Types XXI and XXIII. Naturally the victorious Allies protected their newly-acquired German secrets very carefully and it could have taken neutral Sweden many years to gain access to this new technology. Fortunately for them a brand-new German Type XXI, *U-3503*, was scuttled in Swedish territorial waters.[1] This boat was recovered in 1946 and taken to Karlskrona where it was examined in great detail before being scrapped

Hajen *class*

The next class of patrol submarines should have appeared in the late 1940s but this was delayed while the lessons of the new German designs were absorbed. This produced the *Hajen* class, laid down in the early 1950s and commissioned between 1954 and 1958. Although somewhat smaller than the Type XXI, these six 720-ton boats were the largest built for the RSwN thus far and their long, smooth hull, careful streamlining (especially of the fin) and high battery power resulted in a very effective design, and their twin propellers gave them an underwater speed of 16kts. They were designed for fast diving and were the first Swedish submarines to be fitted with schnorkels.

The Sjöormen *class, commissioned 1967/68, introduced a revolutionary short, stubby hull design, together with X-configured after hydroplanes; this is* Sjöhunden, *third of five boats in the class.*

Draken

The six submarines of the *Draken* class were commissioned in 1960–61 and, although they continued the long, thin hull design then standard in every navy, they incorporated a major innovation in the use of a large,

This view of the Näcken *shows the interior packed with weapons, machinery and equipment. Note the very heavy torpedo battery forward, the command centre beneath the sail and the large slow-revolving, back-skewed propeller aft.*

The rebuilt Näcken, *on 23 November 1988, after being lengthened and having a Sterling engine and special fuel tanks installed, enabling her to operate completely submerged for up to two weeks at a time. Such non-nuclear-powered air-independent submarines pose a totally new threat to surface warships and merchant vessels.*

single, slow-revving propeller and cruciform after control surfaces. They displaced 770 tons submerged and were armed with four torpedo-tubes, all in the bow. They were replaced by the *Näcken* class in the early 1980s and at one stage two were offered to Malaysia, for initial training of a submarine arm prior to an order for modern submarines, but the plan fell through.

Abborren

By the 1960s the *U-1* class was twenty years old but the Navy proved that there was life left in the design by taking six in hand and giving them a thorough, and, in some ways, revolutionary modernisation. They emerged between 1962 and 1964 designated *kustubåtar* (coastal submarines), the opportunity having been taken to clean-up and streamline the hull, as had been done in other navies (eg, the US Navy's GUPPY programme), to improve underwater performance. In the RSwN, however, the purpose of the conversion was quite different, since these boats were intended for one role only: as ASW 'hunter-killer' submarines.

A large sonar array was fitted in the bows but the truly revolutionary feature was the addition of a rotating magazine for specially-developed ASW torpedoes fitted in the after ballast tank. For launch the torpedo was lined up with one of two hatches, the hatch opened and the torpedo swam out and, since the magazine was conical in section to match the contour of the hull, the torpedo departed at an angle of some 30 degrees. This installation required that the entire afterbody was redesigned and rebuilt, with the original stern-tube being removed and a single-propeller arrangement replacing the original twin-shaft installation.

Twelve wire-guided TP40 torpedoes were carried, the forerunner of the TP42. The *Abborren* class remained in service for some years, being stricken in 1970–76 as the *Sjöormen* class came into service.

Sjöormen

Up to the mid-1960s Swedish submarines were very conventional in design with long, thin hulls, and frequently incorporated foreign ideas, particularly, as has been described, from the German Type XXI. In the late 1960s, however, this changed and a definite 'Swedish submarine' appeared, the first being the *Sjöormen* (Type A–11B) class, which introduced a new short, stubby hull design with a length:beam ratio of 8:1. This class also had a large sail positioned well forward and the forward hydroplanes mounted on the sail instead of in the bows.

The key to the high manoeuvrability of this class was

The hull shape of the Västergötland *is clearly shown in this 'dry-dock' shot. The six 533mm torpedo tube caps are all open and the mouths of the three 400mm tubes can just be seen below.*

Two Västergötland *class submarines in company on the surface.*

the X-form control surfaces. This configuration was to a certain extent influenced by that of the USS *Albacore*, but the Swedish solution was different in one very major respect. In the *Albacore* the control surfaces were mechanically connected in a diagonal manner, with the upper starboard surface connected to the lower port surface, and the upper port to the lower starboard.

In the Swedish solution, however, the four control surfaces are entirely independent of each other, each having its own shaft and hydraulic control circuit. This provides much greater flexibility in control and provides a virtual guarantee against detrimental effects through jamming. Either of the upper, lower, starboard or port control surface pairs provide reasonable underwater control. Pairs are also supplied from two hydraulic circuits and their servo valves from two electric circuits with additional battery back-up. This arrangement was extensively tested before it was accepted for service and

The Swedish Type 471 design won the Australian order against very intense international competition. These six large boats (submerged displacement 3000 tons) are under construction as the Collins *class and are the most sophisticated conventionally-powered submarines in the world.*

has proved a great success. It has been used in all subsequent Swedish submarine designs, including that of the Australian *Collins* class.

Five of this class joined the fleet in 1967–68. Two are to receive a mid-life update, which will include new towed sonar arrays, improved hull-mounted sensors and a new fire-control system, and will serve on into the twenty-first century. The other three will be stricken in the late 1990s as the *Gotland* class becomes operational.

Näcken

With the *Näcken* (Type A–14) class the hull design was altered again, with the very angular sail moved further aft, indicating that the control room is once more amidships. These submarines are characterised by a high number of launch-tubes (six 533mm and two 400mm) and a substantial number of torpedoes for the boat's size: eight Type 61B/613 533mm and four Type 422/431 400mm.

The RSwN has put tremendous effort into achieving greater automation, which is needed not only to produce greater combat effectiveness but to reduce the highly-trained and expensive manpower needed to run a submarine. After a ten-year development programme the Censor 932 central digital computer was produced for the *Näcken* class, which undertakes the control and management of combat information data and weapons systems, as well as managing the platform functions. This computer-control and automation led to the reduction of the crew size to twenty-four.

Two boats of the class, *Najad* and *Neptun*, are being given a mid-life update to bring them, as far as possible, up to the standard of the *Västergötland* class. The name-ship of the class, however, HSwMS *Näcken*, was taken in hand in 1987 and retrofitted with an 8m 'plug' containing an Air-Independent Propulsion (AIP) system based on two Stirling heat engines for energy conversion and liquid oxygen (LOX) for support of the combustion. Prior to this successful retrofit the AIP conversion was developed and demonstrated at Lockum's yard ashore and then in a floating test vehicle. With its new power-plant the *Näcken* can now remain submerged for over two weeks and is currently the only conventional submarine in

the Western world to be fitted with an operational and fully militarised AIP system.

Västergötland

The design of the *Västergötland* (Type A–17) class started in the late 1970s with project definition in the early 1980s and detailed design in the mid-1980s; the four boats were laid down in 1983–86, launched at Kockums 1986–8 and commissioned 1987–90. The class is a further evolution of the *Näcken* class but with some significant differences in the general arrangement and the command-and-control system, the latter being assisted by a system of microprocessors.

The launch-tubes for the full length 533mm torpedoes are arranged in one horizontal row, with reloads immediately behind for rapid and simple reloading (ie, there is no vertical movement to add to the mechanical complexity of the loading machinery). Launch-tubes for the short, 400mm weapons are fitted horizontally below the full-length launchers. At one stage it was planned to install four vertical launch-tubes for short-range surface-

The Gotland *class is currently under construction for the Swedish Navy. It is similar to but somewhat smaller than the Australian* Collins *class and continues the Swedish idea of a mixed armament of 533mm and 400mm torpedo-tubes.*

to-air missiles but this was abandoned. Patrol endurance and stealth characteristics have been considerably enhanced in this class.

Gotland

Construction of the *Gotland* class started in 1992 and they will be operational by 1998. They are rather larger than

The Type 2000 submarine, now being designed by Kockums will be of a very sophisticated design, one possibility being this 'flounder' shape. Note the remotely-controlled underwater vehicle which has been released from the mother-ship and is operating near the surface where it is communicating with friendly surface units.

the *Västergötland* class, with a submerged displacement of 1490 tons as compared with 1070 tons, although the design is conceptually similar. Improvements have been made in operational endurance, stealth capabilities and sensor suite. However, the most important innovation is the total integration of the Sterling engine, making this the first non-nuclear submarine to be designed, built and fitted with an integral AIP system. The enhanced submerged endurance which results will greatly increase their combat efficiency and survivability.

The main weapons system is the 533mm Type 2000 wire-guided and homing, high-speed, wakeless torpedo, for which there are six tubes and six re-loads. Below this are three 400mm tubes for Type 43CO short torpedoes (with three reloads); these ASW torpedoes are electrically powered and have both wire-guidance and an active/passive homing system. In addition, like all modern Swedish submarines, the *Gotland* class can be fitted with an external mine girdle. which enables twenty-two mines to be carried without affecting the number of torpedoes carried. Alternatively, 533mm, self-propelled, long-range mines can be carried, but, in this case, at the expense of torpedoes. Following the success of the Australian *Collins* class, an export version of the *Gotland* design will be available, designated the T 96.

Internal view of a Västergötland *class submarine, showing the neat, almost clinical, layout of the control stations.*

Collins

Swedish submarine designs have been admired for many years by foreign navies but they were generally considered to be specialist vessels designed for Sweden's particular needs. In the mid-1980s, however, a Royal Australian Navy (RAN) competition for a replacement for their ageing British *Oberon* class patrol submarine was won by the Swedish submission, the Type 471, having overcome strong competition from France, Germany, Italy, the Netherlands and the UK. The designs of both the *Gotland* class and the Type 471 are based on that of the *Västergötland* class and all three have a similar external appearance. However, it is often not appreciated that while the *Gotland* is slightly larger than the *Västergötland*, the Type 471 is, in fact, very much larger than either of them (see Table 1).

It is claimed that the six *Collins* class boats will be the quietest and most shock-resistant submarines in the world. They are intended to meet a mission requirement of a 3500nm operational radius at 10kts submerged, coupled with forty-seven days on station at 4kts. Their large battery capacity gives them an exceptional underwater endurance of 120hrs at 4kts.

Unlike the Swedish submarines the Type 471 is equipped only with 533mm tubes, the RAN having no tactical requirement for the smaller 400mm torpedoes. The 533mm tubes are, however, fitted to launch Sub-Harpoon missiles as well as Mk 48 torpedoes and a total of

Table 1: *COMPARISON OF RECENT SWEDISH SUBMARINE DESIGNS*

	Västergötland	**Type 471**	**Gotland**
Displacement (submerged):	1140 tons	3000 tons	1300 tons
Length:	48.5m	75.0m	52.5m
Beam:	6.06m	7.8m	6.06m
Torpedo tubes:	6 × 533mm, 3 × 400mm	6 × 533mm	6 × 533mm, 3 × 400mm
Torpedoes:	12 × Type 613 6 × Type 422	23 Mk48 torpedoes/ Sub-Harpoon SSMs	12 × Type 613 6 × Type 422
Crew:	20	42	20

twenty-three torpedoes/missiles are carried. The *Collins* class is also reported to make greater use of electronic and microcomputer controls than any other known non-nuclear submarine.

Submarine 2000

The RSwN continues to forge ahead with its submarine designs and with the *Gotland* class now under construction work is well in hand on the design of the next class, known as 'Submarine 2000'. In this class Kockums intend to enhance yet further the AIP capability and stealth characteristics of their submarines, whilst increasing their

The air-independent propulsion installation in the rebuilt Näcken. *(Right)*

The Ubåtsraddningsfarkost *(Submarine Rescue Vehicle), seen here in 1979, is another advanced Swedish development, located at the Naval Diving Centre, Berga. It is transported by truck to the nearest port, then towed at 10kts to the scene of the accident. It carries two divers and can accommodate up to 23 survivors. The RSwN operated an ex-British X-class midget submarine (*HSWMS* Spiggen, *ex* HMS Stickleback) in the 1960s but this has been stricken and today a Jugoslavian* Mala *class swimmer delivery vehicle and another midget, the* Spiggen II, *intended to simulate intruders, are in service. (Below)*

Table 2: *Particulars of 20th Century Swedish Submarine Classes*

Class	Commissioned	Displacement: surfaced/ submerged (tons)	Dimensions: length × beam × draught (m)	Speed: surface/ submerged (kts)	Torpedo tubes (b = bow; s = stern)	Guns	Crew	Stricken
Hajen (1 boat)	1904	107/127	21.6 × 3.6 × 3.0	9.5/7	1 × 457mm (3)	—	11	1922
Hvalen (1 boat)	1909	186/230	42.5 × 4.3 × 2.1	14.8/6.3	2 × 457mm (4)	—	17	1924
UB-2 (3 boats)	1909	138/230	26.8 × 3.6 × 3.0	8.8/6.6	1 × 457mm (3)	—	12	
Svärdvisken (2 boats)	1914	252/370	45.1 × 4.2 × ?	14.2/8.5	2 × 457mm (4)	1 × 37mm	21	1936
Delfinen (1 boat)	1914	260/370	42.5 × 4.3 × ?	13.6/9.4	2 × 457mm	1 × 37mm	21	1930
Laxen (2 boats)	1914	140/170	26.7 × 3.6 × ?	8.8/6.6	1× 457mm		10	1931–35
Abborren (2 boats)	1916	174/310	31.0 × 3.6 × 3.1	9.5/7.4	2 × 457mm (4)	—	14	1937
Hajen (3 boats)	1917–18	422/600	54.0 × 5.2 × 3.5	15.5/9	4 × 457mm (8)	1 × 75mm	30	1942–43
Bävern (3 boats)	1921	472/650	57.0 × 5.8 × ?	15.2/8.2	4 × 457mm	1 × 75mm	31	1944
Valen (1 boat)	1925	548/730	57.1 × 7.1 × 3.1	14.8/7.4	4 × 457mm	1 × 75mm, 1 × 25mm	31	1944
Draken (3 boats)	1926–30	667/850	66.2 × 6.6 × 3.3	13.8/8.3	3 × 533mm (b), 1 × 533mm (s)	1 × 105mm, 1 × 25mm	35	1943–48
Delfinen (3 boats)	1934–35	540/720	63.1 × 6.4 × 6.4	15/10	2 × 533mm (b), 2 × 533mm (s)	1 × 57mm, 1 × 25mm, 20 mines	34	1953
Sjölejonet (9 boats)	1936–1941	580/760	64.2 × 6.4 × 3.4	16/9	3 × 533mm (b), 1 × 533mm (s)	2 × 40mm	35	1959–64
U-1 (9 boats)	1941–44	367/450	49.6 × 4.7 × 3.8	14/9	3 × 533mm (b), 1 × 533mm (s)	1 × 20mm	26	U-1 to U-3 1960–64
Neptun (3 boats)	1942	550/730	62.6 × 6.4 × 3.4	17/9	3 × 533mm (b), 2 × 533mm (s)	1 × 40mm, 1 × 20mm, 20 mines	34	1966
Hajen (6 boats)	1954–58	720	65.8 × 5.1 × ?	16/16	4 × 533mm	—	44	1980
Draken (6 boats)	1960–61	770	69.3 × 5.1 × ?	16/?	4 × 533mm	—	36	1982
Abborren (mod *U-1* class)	1962–64	388	49.8 × 4.3 × ?	14/9	3 × 533mm	—	23	1970–76
Sjöormen (5 boats)	1967–68	1130/1400	50.5 × 6.1 × 5.1	10/20	6 × 533mm	—	23	
Näcken (3 boats)	1978–79	1030/1125	49.5 × 5.7 × 4.1	10/20	6 × 533mm, 2 × 400mm	—	19	
Västergöiland (4 boats)	1986	1070/1140	48.5 × 6.1 × 6.1	11/20	6 × 533mm, 3 × 400mm	—	20	
Gotland	1997–2001	–/1500	60 × 6.1 × 5.60	12/20	6 × 533mm, 3 × 400mm	—	20	
Collins	1995–1999	2450/2700	75.0 × 7.8 × 6.8	10.5/21	6 × 533mm	—	42	

The Swedish-built Australian submarine Collins.

resistance to attack by modern weapons and enhancing the submarine's own weapon characteristics; the result promises to be the most advanced non-nuclear design yet. Kockums state that while the technological advances between the four most recent classes have been moderate, that between the *Gotland* class and the Submarine 2000 could be significant.

Conclusion

Since the end of the Second World War the Royal Swedish Navy has pursued a consistent course and has designed and constructed its own submarines, tailored to its own strategic and tactical requirements. The Navy has generated just enough orders to maintain the design and construction base needed, but it has worked. In 1994 Swedish submarines have a reputation second-to-none and in the *Collins* and *Gotland* classes this small country has produced probably the finest and most capable non-nuclear submarines in the world.

Notes

[1] *U-3503* (Oberleutnant zur See Deiring) was scuttled off Götenborg (57° 39′N, 11° 44′E) on 8 May 1945. She was raised by the RSwN on 24 August 1946 and, after detailed examination, broken up.

WARSHIP NOTES

This section comprises a number of short articles and notes, generally highlighting little-known aspects of warships history.

THE PADDLE SLOOP JANUS

The following extracts are from The Practical Mechanic and Engineer's Magazine, Vol 1, second series, *and were published in December 1845 and February 1846 respectively. They give a contemporary view of the experimental, and unsuccessful, paddle sloop* Janus, *the design of which was the responsibility of the Earl of Dundonald (Lord Cochrane), and which was constructed in Chatham Dockyard during 1843–46.*

THE STEAM FRIGATE [sic] 'JANUS'

'On a former occasion we noticed this *outre* specimen of Naval Engineering, and expressed our doubts of the success of the experiment. Both vessel and engines have been fully tried, and so far as we can judge, have proved signally unsuccessful. In proof of this, we might quote several published accounts of experimental trips, but confine ourselves to the following by the correspondent of the Times, because it has been formally replied to by the Earl of Dundonald, with whom it will be remembered; the whole scheme originated, and to whom its execution was entirely entrusted.'

"The *Janus* steam sloop has again returned to her former moorings by the sheer hulk, opposite to the dockyard, having been towed up on Fri-

day, the 21st inst, by the *Wildfire* steam vessel, she having broken down at sea. This unfortunate vessel, it appears, left Cockham-wood Reach at twelve o'clock at noon, on Wednesday, the 18th inst, as reported, for Portsmouth, whereas she was to take a cruise in the Channel, having on board Captain W H Shirreff, RN, Captain Superintendent of her Majesty's yard, accompanied by Vice-Admiral the Earl of Dundonald, the constructor of her engines, and manned by the seamen of the ordinary; and reached Sheerness in about two hours and a half, the paddle-wheels revolving about thirteen times to the minute, and on her arrival outside the river, touching the sea-water, her pace became slackened, and it gradually decreased, and on her arrival near the Mouse, her speed was so reduced that her wheels only made eleven revolutions in the minute, although she had a strong wind in her favour, and, in attempting to turn her, she drifted astern; consequently it was found necessary to anchor her for the night, as it was rough, and blew a strong gale. The next morning the engineers could not get the wheels to turn until noon, when they revolved about five times to the minute, and at which rate the engines continued working until eight o'clock at night. The next morning (Thursday), the weather being fine, it was attempted to run the vessel over to the Downs, but it was found that, by using every exertion, she would not make head against the sea. Further trial was therefore deemed useless, and the vessel was beat up again for Sheerness; and on her arrival in the river water she returned to her former speed. On passing her Majesty's vessel *Trafalgar*, however, her engines broke down, and she was obliged to

anchor for the night; and on Friday she was towed to this port. On raising her anchor it struck her bow, and made a hole in it. It is now clear that this vessel, according to her present construction, will never go ahead, having now failed in a hundred experiments, and having had all the resources of Chatham-yard lavishly expended on her for the last year, without the least improvement. Her engine is stated to be very defective. The rotary engine of this vessel, it appears, is fitted with four tubular boilers, equal in bulk and expenditure of fuel to 500-horse power boilers, and with engines estimated at 220-horse power, but withal, the boilers have never worked up to 60-horse power. The boilers are divided into two sets, with a stokehold between them, which forms a kind of pandemonium, where the unfortunate firemen are scorched by six furnaces on each side of them, and by the cylinders full of steam above their heads, while their feet and ankles are immersed in hot-water, and where they are deprived alike of air and light. It is stated that this machinery is not fitted with the appendages which experience has shown to be essential to the safety of a steam-vessel, because they cannot be attached to a rotary engine without extraordinary complication. Yet, notwithstanding these omissions, it occupies 38 feet fore and aft, and great part of the upper deck; while a perfect pair of engines of 200-horse power, with tubular boilers, and every appendage for safety and convenience complete, with ample airy stokehole, and free access to every part, would not occupy more than 34 feet.

"During all the expensive experiments on this unfortunate craft not

the least improvement has been made. With wheels proportioned to her nominal power, she would not make two miles an hour, and when sent to sea in this instance she did not make headway against a light sea, whereas another vessel would have run full speed.

"The *Janus* on going out, had only forty tons of coals and four tons of water on board. She is now two feet lighter than she was during her first trips, and has one and a half-streak of her copper painted black, to make her appear deep in the water. Her engines, since her arrival, are being taken to pieces."

'This account is feebly parried by his lordship in the following statement, in which he seems to labour under a belief that success yet awaits this *chef-d'-œuvre* of his engineering skill – that, in fact, he has hitherto been defrauded of success by something else than the inherent evil principle which he has embodied in his scheme; and would lead us to infer that jealousy, and perhaps a little malevolence, have more to do in the matter than the form of his vessel or the design of his engines. We cannot, however, perceive the necessity of having recourse to any other agency than that generated by the perversion of his own ingenuity, to account for his non-success; although, therefore, we insert his defence, we cannot subscribe to the opinion that it seems intended to produce. The evil seems to us radical and inherent, nothing occult, and essentially physical.'

Memoranda, being Facts relative to the Progress and Performance of the Revolving Engine on the Principle of those in her Majesty's Sloop Janus.

"The Earl of Minto, when First Lord of the Admiralty, having learned from his brother, Rear-Admiral Elliott, that rotary engines had been successfully used (in two small steam-boats), and that their compactness, levity, and celerity of motion rendered that kind of engine peculiarly suited to the naval service, ordered a trial to be made of the power of a condensing engine on that principle by pumping water from a well in Portsmouth Dockyard.

"This engine had been at work for full twelve months when the present Admiralty made their first official visit to the yard, and their Lordships had an opportunity of witnessing the energy and power it then displayed, which by constant work, has now increased to such a degree, that not

The paddle sloop Janus. (NMM, courtesy D K Brown)

one of the thirteen engines in the yard (most of which are on Watt's principle) has produced a better vacuum, or required less repair, as is testified by Mr Taplin, the chief engineer and machinist of that yard.

"The result was not, however, obtained without great anxiety and trouble. Thirty times at least within 18 months of its erection was this engine taken to pieces, and at times parts of it were sent to London to be altered, under the impression that some defect or other prevented its efficient performance. Such, indeed, was the prejudice originally existing, augmented by repeated failures to work the engine, that it was on the point of being finally rejected by the authorities, when it occurred that perhaps the cold water pipe leading to the condenser might be choked. Admiral Sir Edward Codrington, Rear-Admiral Bouverie, Capt Sir Thomas Hastings, Mr Taplin and Mr Blake, the master shipbuilder, were present to witness the result of, perhaps, the last trial; and they and others saw the injection-pipe cut, and a plug of wood withdrawn, which blocked the passage, so that not one-fourth of the water required, could enter the condenser; indeed, after the pump was re-joined on the following day, the engine could scarcely work two of the three pumps it was destined to put in motion; it was therefore again pulled to pieces, and also the air-pump (which had never before been suspected as a cause of obstruction); nevertheless it was found that the delivery valve was not only open, but was retained open by its cover being screwed down upon it, thereby effectually preventing the formation of a vacuum, even by the most free introduction of injection water and the most complete condensation.

"It may here be noticed that a ball of rope yarn and a hank of strands were subsequently extracted from the injection-pipe; and that within the last two months, on examining the lower valve water-pumps at the bottom of the well, in the middle suction-pipe a plug of solid elm wood was found, which completely blocked up that pump, and consequently during five years and a half defeated the trial of the engine by the pumping of water. In confirmation of this, Mr Taplin says, in a note dated the 18th of September, – 'The plug must have been there from the time the pumps were first put in motion. As a proof of this, we never had such a supply of water as at present.'

"It need, therefore, be no matter of surprise if the large engines of the *Janus* have been delayed in the performance of their duties, or that numerous trials failed to produce a satisfactory result. On Saturday, the 15th, however, the engines started well, and were accelerating, when the wedges of the clutches of the paddle-wheels (being slackly driven) slipped, and the engine flew round and broke the chain of the air-pump, which being repaired on Monday, the *Janus* proceeded down the Medway purposely at a moderate rate, in order to ascertain if any damage had been done to the engines themselves by the accident of Saturday. There being no visible indication of derangement, the vessel proceeded, and was anchored near the Mouse Light at dusk, on account of the difficulty of passing through the shoals at night. On the

following morning on setting the engines to work, no vacuum could be formed in one engine, which having thrown the whole labour on the other, it soon became manifest that some partial derangement had taken place therein; and a search having been made, it was discovered that one of the snift valves had been misplaced since the preceding evening; consequently the atmospheric air had thereby free access to the condenser. This impediment having been detected and removed, it was further discovered that the end plate of the air-pump (lately withdrawn for inspection) had been improperly jointed, so as to suspend its useful action. Every person conversant with the mechanism of engines will fully understand how totally independent these impediments are of the principle of the engine, yet how fatal to its operations, which I have no doubt, like the Portsmouth engine, will be rendered quite efficient. Indeed, the brief specimen exhibited on Saturday confirms this opinion, having accelerated from 18 to upwards of 20 revolutions before the accident.

"With regard to the boilers of the *Janus*, it is hereby fearlessly asserted, that having been first tested by the authority of the Admiralty, under the immediate inspection of the officers of Chatham-yard, and their greatly superior evaporative power having been doubted, an application was made to the Admiralty to direct the engineer department of Woolwich Dockyard to test the boilers. The result was that their power amounted to 314 cubic feet of water evaporated per hour, at the economical rate of 12.9 pounds, by each pound of Llangenneck coal – a result testified by the engineer's official report of the trial, now in the records of the Admiralty, dated the 19th of last November; the importance of which result, in a maritime point of view, every person acquainted with steam navigation is competent to appreciate. Lastly, in regard to the temperature of the 'stoke-hold', although the furnaces are opposite, it may be truly asserted, that the temperature is less than at the same distance from any tubular boilers in her Majesty's service."

Dundonald

THE EARL OF DUNDONALD'S ROTARY ENGINE

'(Having on a former occasion made some remarks on the non-success of the *Janus* steam ship, we think it only justice to the Earl of Dundonald to insert the following report on his Rotary Engine, erected by the late Admiralty at the Portsmouth Dockyard, the performance of which seems to be highly satisfactory)':–

"Report on the Earl of Dundonald's Rotary Engine, erected in her Majesty's Dockyard at Portsmouth.

"On the 22nd of December, 1845, two years and nine months of constant performance of the rotary engine expired, during all which time it has been working in the most effectual and satisfactory manner, no derangement of consequence ever having taken place.

"It is presumed that these two years and nine months of constant and laborious operation (requiring no more than slight attention by the workmen) have gone far to establish that quality which, until now, had not been sufficiently developed – namely, durability, and consequent continuity of operation.

"The principal repair this engine has required was taken in hand about nine months ago. This was so trifling that six men could have accomplished it in one day, but having been much pressed with work at the time, one man only could be spared, which consequently protracted its completion for one week.

"Thus after four years and nine months constant working as a prime mover, two years and nine months of which have been so successfully performed, nothing more can be wanting even by the most sceptical to establish its merits as a powerful, economical, and durable engine, equal in point of efficiency to any reciprocating engine in her Majesty's service.

"Should additional evidence be sought to establish further claims as a rival in steam mechanism, it is to be found in the simple fact, that this first essay on the Earl of Dundonald's principle, although first altered and mutilated to bring it to perfection, is nevertheless at the present time perfectly free from those indications of weakness and declining energy which any other engine, under similar circumstances, might probably evince, as is proved by its exhibiting a vacuum at all times equal to 28 inches of mercury.

"Another fact which gives great confidence in the utility and applicability of this principle is its freedom from liability to internal derangement, and consequently the service in which it is engaged is scarcely ever inconvenienced by stoppages.

The engine has not been opened for examination since July last."

R. Taplin, Engineer and Machinist. Her Majesty's Dockyard, Portsmouth, Dec 1, 1845.

SHIRAKUMO AND ASASHIO

D J Lyon describes two torpedo boat destroyers built by Thornycroft for the Japanese Navy at the turn of the century.

The following notes are taken from my unpublished 'Thornycroft List' – a catalogue of the Thornycroft collection of plans and documents held at the National Maritime Museum – which was compiled quite a few years ago. It took the form of detailed notes taken almost entirely from the collection itself, grouped under entries on each vessel or class of vessels built by that firm. The catalogue form explains the particular style of the entries. The intention was to provide summaries and extracts from documents in the collection rather than complete histories of the vessels involved, together with a listing of plans held in the Collection at Greenwich (from which copies can be provided – please contact the Museum's ship plans section for information about availability, prices etc: National Maritime Museum, Greenwich, London SE10 9NF, UK)

The following is a fairly typical set of notes for a class of destroyers built at the period when the firm was still based on the Thames at Chiswick:
Thornycroft Yard Numbers 356 and 357 – Shirakumo and Asashio

Dimensions:	216ft 9in (oa), 215ft 9in (wl) × 20ft 9in × 13ft 9in × 8ft 3in
Displacement:	400 tons light, 432 tons full load
Guns:	One 12pdr, five 6pdr
Torpedoes:	Two 18in tubes
Machinery:	Two sets triple expansion engines, (cyl 22in/29½in/31in/31in dia × 19in stroke); four Thornycroft/Schultz water-tube boilers; contract speed 31kts with 7500hp
Complement:	59
Ordered:	7 or 16 November 1900

Costs Jones Burton and Company received £721 net commission for their work as agents (A\7 – 4 December 1901 [this is a reference to a document in the Thornycroft Collection]). There are indications that Thornycrofts, having cut their original tender price to secure the order, were later at least in danger of making a loss on the transaction.

Order As early as December 1899 SW Barnaby was considering the possibility of using four boilers in the new proposed 31kt boats, but initially turned the idea down because it would have meant lengthening them. On 20 April 1900 (D\18 [another Thornycroft Collection Document reference]) Thornycrofts wrote to the Japanese Navy's Inspector General (Admiral Kamimura) offering designs HO 9964 A and B for an improved 31kt destroyer (210ft oa x 20ft 4in x 7ft 7in). Larger engines and boilers than those fitted in the Japanese 30kt vessels were proposed but the arrangement of armament would be the same as in these earlier destroyers. There would be slightly more accommodation for the 60 officers and men proposed. Three boilers of the *Daring* type would discharge their smoke from two funnels: 'This better arrangement forms an important feature of our torpedo boat destroyers as it is difficult to distinguish them from torpedo boats at a distance – a condition which was considered indispensable by the British Admiralty in the earliest boats, which condition, however, had to be relaxed on account of the different types of boiler used by other builders'. The beam was greater than the earlier Japanese destroyers, ensuring sufficient stiffness for stability whilst decreasing the period of rolling. One destroyer to this design would cost £56,000, two

General Arrangement Plan for Shirakumo and Asashio from the Thornycroft Collection, National Maritime Museum, Greenwich. (courtesy of the author)

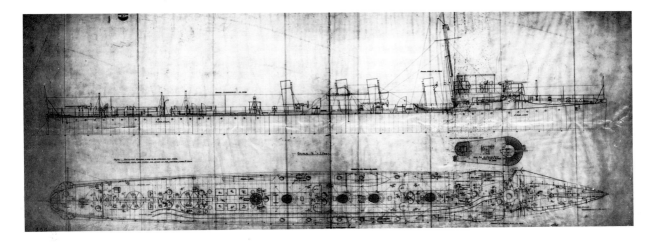

£55,500 each and four £55,000 each. On 25 May 1900 another letter to the same officer referred to the conditions handed to the firm by Captain Takagi and Lieutenant Yamamoto, which meant that a larger vessel would be necessary than those tendered for in the previous letter. As new patterns and plans would therefore be needed, it would not be possible to deliver within the requested time, which was fifteen months – a time that was supposed to be strictly adhered to – 'We therefore judge delivery time is of considerable importance and in view of this ask whether the Government is disposed to order a modified *Albatross*, in which case we have the machinery drawings and patterns all ready and undertake to deliver such a vessel in fifteen months . . .'. She would carry a 40–50 ton load, could be guaranteed for 31kts, would offer considerable advantages in price over the original *Albatross* and could be built for £64,000. This would offer the great advantages of 'larger capacity and seaworthiness, more powerful machinery and at the same time our guarantee of delivery in the time you specify'. Another letter to Admiral Kamimura, written on 1 June 1900, stated that, in order to meet the Japanese conditions, a longer vessel would be required, and the price would be £57,250 if only one was ordered. Delivery would be eighteen months but best endeavours would be used to deliver in a shorter time, if possible fifteen months. On 30 June 1900 Thornycrofts had just heard that the Japanese Government were probably going to order more than one destroyer and, as an inducement to order from them, Thornycroft produced new prices of £57,250 for one, £56,750 for each of two and £56,250 for each of three. A letter dated 24 August 1900 was sent to Constructor Commander Takagi stating that the firm 'do not see any way to guarantee more than 31kts speed, although we expect that the vessels will do considerably more . . . We would remind you that in all the boats built for you we have exceeded our speed by at least half a knot more than that guaranteed in our contract and we prefer not to depart from our practise, viz: that of always having a margin of speed in hand . . . we think fears of air pressure are groundless'. The firm was putting in four boilers instead of three and these of an improved type, and it was to be expected that air pressure would be as low as that in other types of boiler. The firm was prepared to make a further reduction in price of £1000 per vessel if two were ordered.

Trials On 22 February 1902, in a letter (B/104) to Messrs Farlow and (?), Jordan stated that: 'our vessel *Asashio* made fast to the buoy at Greenhithe and was in the act of being moored . . . The master of your client's barge *Sepoy* was warned when it was observed he was weighing anchor that he would have to be careful, but he took no notice of this and continued to smoke his cigar in a very unconcerned manner, and in passing the *Asashio* he allowed his barge to fall alongside with the resulting damage.'

On 14 March 1902 (B/104) Thornycrofts wrote to Matthew Paul and Company: 'with regard to compensation for the loss of several trials we are fully aware that we have no claim on you for consequential damages by terms of your contract.

'We think, however, that sooner than allow us to bear the full loss owing to the failure of your fan engines you should admit some liability in the sense of sharing cost of extra trials.

'It is a matter more of whether you care to leave us so dissatisfied with the results of having adopted your fan engines for these boats without in any way trying to adjust matters by compensation.'

A letter of 17 May 1902 notes that the engines of *Asashio* had been damaged in trials. New cylinders, etc. were required. Earlier, on 31 January 1902, Thornycrofts had written to the Admiralty offering a place at the trials to an Admiralty observer (the Japanese had given permission) and pointing out the rapid building time of this new design.

History These vessels were steamed out to Japan. The Swedish destroyer *Magne* (Yard No 378) was built to the same lines. Both were taken out of service in 1922 and scrapped in 1923.

Plans: Lines 9522 (damaged)/9522A (both ½in = 1ft scale); Arrangement of deck fittings (profile and weather decks) 10630 (3in = 1ft scale); Conning tower and chart house 10268; Searchlight platform and stand 10813; Lower deck and hold 10480B/10906B: (both ¼in = 1ft scale); Sections 10734A (Forward)/10734B (engine room)/10734C (aft) (all ½in = 1ft scale); Model lines 11244 (¼in = 1ft scale); Rigging 10605 (½in = 1ft scale); Platform and standard for standard compass 10665.

Photos Engines/model

Documents None separate – but see references in the text.

A NOTE ON THE TORPEDO PROTECTION OF THE KING GEORGE V AND THE JOB 74 TRIAL

Some background notes by D K Brown, RCNC, on the quality of the underwater protective system of the King George V *class battleships and why it did not, apparently, come up to prewar expectations.*

The Problem A full-scale trial of the torpedo protection of the battleships of the *King George V* class was carried out during the development of the design and this test section successfully resisted the explosion of 1000lb of TNT. In war, the torpedo protection of the *Prince of Wales* seems to have failed sufficiently to allow some flooding under attack by a torpedo with a warhead of only 330lb.

Job 74 The test structure, Job 74, was a pontoon 73ft long, 60ft wide and 50ft deep (keel to deck) and is illustrated in Warship 24[1]. One side represented the torpedo protection of the *King George V*, the other that of the *Ark Royal*. A 1000lb TNT charge was exploded in contact with each side in turn. The outer plating on the *King George V* replica was destroyed over an area 25ft long by 16ft high, the intermediate longitudinal bulkheads failed – as they were designed to do – over a length of 36ft and the holding bulkhead was deflected 18in but did not rupture. The holding bulkhead was 13ft from the skin and consisted of two thicknesses of 0.875in (35lb) D1 plate riveted together so that the butts in each plate were staggered, half the plate

The launch of the ill-fated battleship Prince of Wales *at Cammell Laird's Yard in Birkenhead on 3 May 1939*. (courtesy J Roberts)

The Prince of Wales *in August 1941, a few months before her loss.* (MoD)

width apart. The trial against the *Ark Royal* system failed, mainly at the welds in the single, 1.5in (60lb), thickness holding bulkhead.

The surprising feature of the *King George V* trial is the small size of the hole, which one would expect to be about 50 per cent bigger, but damage from underwater explosions is very variable.

Variation in Underwater Explosion Damage The battleship *Malaya* was hit in March 1941 by a torpedo with a warhead equivalent to 1000lb of TNT which caused quite limited damage and only slight leakage. Her torpedo protection was old fashioned (bulge) with a holding bulkhead of two thicknesses of 1in plate, only 13ft from the skin. In contrast, when the carrier *Indomitable* was hit by a smaller torpedo (700lb TNT equivalent warhead) in 1943, her modern sandwich protection (13ft 6in deep to a 60lb D1 holding bulkhead) failed. This damage was, however, exacerbated, the explosion having broken a plate of the 4in cemented armour, pieces of which were projected into the boiler room, though it was believed that the bulkhead would have failed anyway.

A more general impression of the variability in the extent of damage caused by a torpedo hit is provided by a postwar review of war damage to

establish the probability of failure of a transverse bulkhead at different distances from a torpedo hit. Success or failure was noted at 5ft intervals and there were, typically, some thirty cases at each distance, although these were mainly ships without torpedo protection. The extent of flooding would be one or two compartment lengths longer.

The Probability of Failure of a Transverse Bulkhead at Given Distance

Probability (%)	25	50	75
Distance (ft)			
21in torpedo	43	36	29
Distance (ft)			
18in torpedo	34	29	25

It so happens that the length of the hole in the shell plating is about the same as the distance in the table above, ie, for Job 74 one might expect a 36ft hole, 50 per cent of the time and a 24ft hole less than 25 per cent – not impossible, but not likely.

There are many aspects, both of the explosion and of the target, which may contribute to this variation in damage. On detonation, the charge is converted to gas in some 40 micro seconds, initially occupying the same volume, at a pressure of several hundred tons/in^2. This generates a shock wave, moving at the speed of sound in water and containing over 25 per cent of the energy of the explosion, a proportion very sensitive to any air-filled cavity adjacent to the charge. The gas bubble will expand

and oscillate. It will be repelled from the surface or soft boundaries and attracted to the bottom and hard surfaces. The shell of a ship is intermediate and the bubble may be attracted or repelled, a feature critically dependent on the separation between charge and target. One would like to know how the Job 74 charge was suspended – was it fixed to the side or dangling, allowing it to move away a little?

Job 74 was rectangular and the bulkheads were parallel to the side throughout their length, whilst in a real ship the curved side would move in towards the ends. A structure will tear at hard spots of which there are more in a real ship, such as drain pipes passing through the protection. Garzke[2] says that rivets were more widely spaced in Job 74. It may well be that the building of a trials vessel was more closely supervised than that of a production ship.

The *Prince of Wales* sank as a result of flooding caused by damage to two shafts by hits outside the protection. She was also hit three times on the side protection system by torpedoes with a 330lb warhead. In the first attack there was an explosion close to frame 206 on the port side, though accounts differ as to the severity of the explosion. There was flooding reported by survivors from the auxiliary machinery spaces inboard of the torpedo protection in this area. Garzke suggests[2] that the explosion had buckled the transverse bulkhead at this frame, leading to flooding. Whilst this may well be correct, it is at least possible that the flooding had come up the shaft passage from flooding aft. It seems that, at best, the protection was barely adequate and may just have failed. In the second attack the protection at frame 236, starboard, seems to have worked well with little or no flooding. The protection at frame 109 had been compromised by counterflooding of the voids and would not be expected to resist a hit. There was evidence that the height of the side protection was insufficient so that the deck was ruptured, allowing flooding to spread.

Hindsight One can be sure that the trial was honestly and competently conducted. The trials officer was Dudley Offord, who had been in charge of DNC's damage section for some years and was meticulous over detail. However he had designed the protection to withstand a 1000lb charge and it is human nature not to question evidence which shows your work to be successful. Specifically, there were too few trials to show the variability of damage effects and, in the thirties, few engineers thought in terms of probability – a test either succeeded or it failed.

It seems that Job 74 and *Prince of Wales* lay within the bounds of probability – just – and known factors suggest an above average performance for the trial and below average for war.

Notes
[1] DK Brown, *Attack and Defence, Part 3*. Warship (24 October 1982)
[2] WH Garzke, *Battleships*. USNI Press (1980).

THE LOSS OF THE DESTROYER LANCIERE, 23 MARCH 1942
Amgiraglio di Squadra G Pollastri and D K Brown, RCNC, provide some notes on the relatively rare occurrence of the loss of a Second World War destroyer as a result of the weather, rather than enemy action.

(NOTE. This account is based on material supplied by Admiral Pollastri, who, as a lieutenant, was a survivor of the sinking of the destroyer *Lanciere*, edited and amplified by David Brown. Thanks are also due to Mr E Cernuschi for making this possible. Passages in quotes are taken directly from Admiral Pollastri's account. Some additional material has been supplied by Andrew Smith.)

Losses of large modern warships due to stress of weather (see Table 1) are happily rare and the few such tragedies are deserving of careful study in the hope of preventing further losses.

The *Lanciere* sailed from Messina on 22 March 1942 with an Italian force operating against a British convoy which was to culminate in the Second Battle of Sirte. Initially, the weather was quite good but rapidly deteriorated, the seas getting increasingly rough.[2] Just after 1000 speed was increased to 30kts, the maximum which could be used in the prevailing waves. 'In the afternoon, the breakers started hitting more and more fiercely her superstructures until, in the evening, due to water seepage, the main gun sight system

[Director?] broke down.' *Lanciere* was not closely engaged during the battle but did locate the British ships on sighting AA shells bursting in the sky above the convoy.

During the late afternoon the weather forced a reduction in speed, first to 26kts and then to 22kts, but these reductions did not provide much benefit. There was, however, no apparent cause for alarm when she began her return to port, though some hatches and the engine room skylight were buckled, 'wind hoses were stripped by a depth charge' and there was floodwater in some spaces. The condition of the ship became worse when water contaminated the fuel, causing loss of speed. Despite all the engineers could do, the steam pressure was only partly restored and even then it was only available for short periods – 'It was a very long night.'

Signals from *Lanciere* reported in the Official History (Summarised)
22 March
2030 unable to maintain speed.
2245 stops to repair machinery.
2315 heaves to, slow speed on one engine.
23 March
0531 will have to remain hove to all day.
0547 condition of ship much worsened due to considerable quantity of water in after engine room; hove to with one engine.
0958 SOS in plain language.
1007 We're sinking. Long live Italy – Long live the King – Long live the Duce.

By the next morning (23 March), power was continuing to drop and a dynamo had stopped; she no longer answered her helm, was full of water and was heeled over on her beam ends to leeward. An attempt was made to bring her upright which seemed to succeed, but in a few moments she fell over to the other side. This shows that the heel was not list due to asymmetric weights but loll caused by negative metacentric height, a condition in which counterflooding is often fatal. 'Then a wave which to me looked enormous fell over the stern and went inside. The ship trimmed and began to sink by

Table 1: *LOSSES OF DESTROYERS DUE TO STRESS OF WEATHER (POST FIRST WORLD WAR)*

Ship	Country	Date	Cause
Tomozuro	Japan	16 Mar 34	Capsized
Branlebas	France	14 Dec 40	Broke in half
Lanciere	Italy	23 Mar 42	Lost power and foundered
Scirocco	Italy	23 Mar 42	Unknown (see text)
Sokrushitelnyi	USSR	22 Nov 42	Pooped on 20 Nov, lost power and later broke in half
Warrington	USA	13 Sep 44	Lost power and foundered
Hull	USA	18 Dec 44	Capsized
Monaghan	USA	18 Dec 44	Capsized
Spence	USA	18 Dec 44	Capsized

the stern, with her stem upwards.' It is thought that she sank in about 4 minutes at 1017.

Lt Pollastri found himself on a Carley float with 20–30 people either on it or clinging to the side. In the big waves, with breaking crests, the float capsized two or three times. 'What is still very clear in my mind is the absent look of those who, though wearing their life jackets, put their face into the water and went down under the waves, the loss of our food supplies and, towards the night, our efforts to hoist a red rag on an oar.' By sunset there were only four men left and one of these was dying. Later that night Lt Pollastri was rescued by the hospital ship *Arno*. Five other survivors were rescued from two other rafts.

Lanciere was a modern ship, launched in 1938, and, by the standards of the day, quite large.

Admiral Pollastri recalls her as a generally good ship; capable of high speed, easily steered and well subdivided though her freeboard was low

The quarterdeck of an Italian destroyer awash in heavy seas. (courtesy Admiral Pollastri)

Table 2: *Particulars of Lanciere*

Displacement	1620 tons standard, 2250 tons deep
Length	106.7m
Beam	10.15m
Freeboard	5.7m at forecastle, 3.3m to upper deck
Armament	4 × 120mm, 8 MG, 6 × 533mm torp tubes
Speed	38kts max (trials)

and her superstructure exposed to damage from waves. He blames her loss on weakness both in the superstructure and in exposed hatches. The lack of asdic and radar were more serious operational defects.

There were only two ratings saved from the *Scirocco*, which was lost at the same time as *Lanciere*, and they were unable to explain what happened. They were below deck, unaware of any problems, defects or power failures and, suddenly, were swimming for their lives! Apparently, the general opinion at the time was that she simply went under when pitching heavily.[3] The signals summarised below suggest that her story may have been very similar to that of *Lanciere*.

Signals from *Scirocco* reported in the Official History (Summarised)

22 March

2045 Port engine fails. 14kts on starboard.

23 March

0539 stops, drifting.

0545 sinks (probable time)

It should be noted that several other ships in company were in considerable difficulty, though surviving:–

Bande Nere suffered from dangerous rolling in quartering seas, later damaged by weather.
Trento suffered from serious leaks.
Oriano had an engine room hatch carry away and suffered later from contaminated oil filters.
Geniere had both turbo generators out of action, speed reduced to 8kts.
Fuciliere had both rudders out of

action, large quantity of flood water, damage to electrical system.
Ascari dangerous list.
Grecale serious damage (unspecified)

Comment Admiral Iachino (Le due Sirte) says that all ships which sank, or found themselves in serious difficulty, suffered more or less the same fate. They leaked through scuttles and hatches which were not watertight, or had been damaged in the heavy seas, and this water caused failure of electrical supplies. In turn, this led to loss of pumping capacity and a build-up of flood water, reducing buoyancy and stability. Bucket trains were organised but the steady ingress of water was too great and, as the crews became exhausted, slowly but surely, boilers, engines and rudders failed. Iachino suggests that standards had fallen in refit due to the loss of skilled men and to the arduous escort work undertaken by destroyers. In the case of *Lanciere* he says that a heavy deck locker broke loose, causing leaks, and that several

tubes failed in No 2 boiler, leading to the initial loss of power.

This tragic story is all too common, even today. Slow flooding is insidious and can be serious before it is recognised. It can lead to loss of power, either from water in the fuel, as in the case of *Lanciere*, or electrical failure, as in the USN destroyers lost in the Pacific. Extensive flooding leads to loss of stability and few navies understood the difference between list and loll in 1942 (Mountbatten saved *Kelly* because he did recognise this problem and jettisoned top weight rather than trying to correct heel). There have been 'near misses' to a number of modern ships which should make obvious the need to observe stability criteria and control slow flooding.

Notes
[1] The exact circumstances are unclear and may be dealt with in a later note. *Baku* suffered serious structural damage in the same gale.
[2] Pollastri says 'Strength 6–7', which is presumably Beaufort wind force in-

The destroyer Carabiniere, *sister ship to* Lanciere, *and one of the nineteen ships of the* Soldati *class. The design of the latter was based on that of the* Maestrale *class, which included the* Scirocco. (CMP)

dicating a wind speed of about 20–23kts, matching well with British accounts which say 25kts. In the North Atlantic, such a wind, blowing for a considerable time, would correspond to waves with a significant height of 2.5–4 metres. Photographs taken during the battle suggest the lower end of this band (photographs of waves are always difficult to interpret). The maximum speed of 30kts for a 350ft ship also suggests waves of about 2.5m.
[3] By DKB. I would guess, repeat guess, that she broke in half as the most likely way in which men would survive from below. These ships were highly stressed and if she got into resonance with the waves, dynamic effects could increase such stresses.

H M BATTLESHIP
AUDACIOUS, 1914

The accompanying general arrangement drawing was produced by the editor a number of years ago for no particular purpose other than

keeping himself amused. It is reproduced here as it seemed a waste to leave it locked in a tube when it might well be of interest to the readers of Warship. *The drawing, which is based on the official Admiralty 'as-fitted' drawings*

held by the National Maritime Museum, shows her appearance at the outbreak of the First World War. However, she did not, in fact, have any major appearance changes during her short career, apart from the post

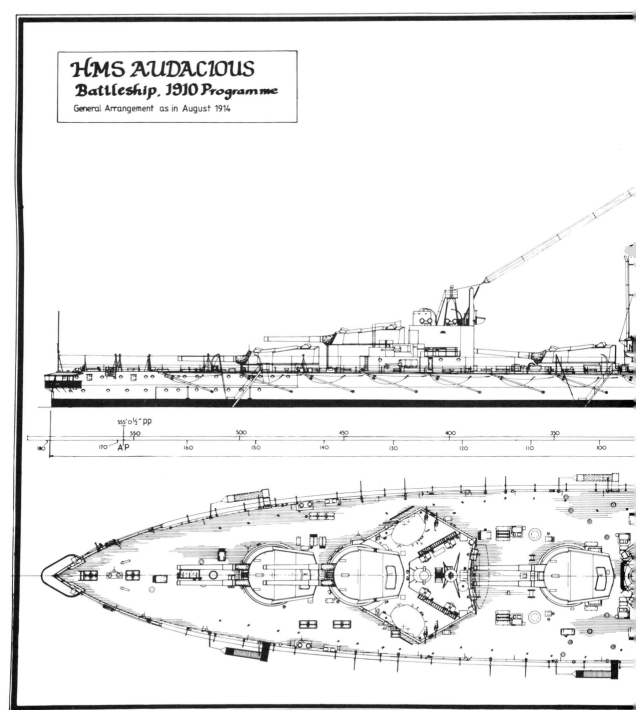

HMS AUDACIOUS
Battleship, 1910 Programme
General Arrangement as in August 1914

completion addition of her director and being camouflage painted early in the war. She was the only British dreadnought battleship to be lost to enemy action during the war, being mined on 27 October 1914 and foundering

as a result of uncontrolled flooding from what should have been comparatively minor damage (see D K Brown's note on Lanciere for a roughly related view of problems of this nature). For further details of this member

of the second group of the Royal Navy's 13.5in gun dreadnoughts and her loss, see Keith McBride, Super-Dreadnoughts, *in* Warship 1993 *and R A Burt*, British Battleships of World War One (*Arms and Armour Press, 1986*).

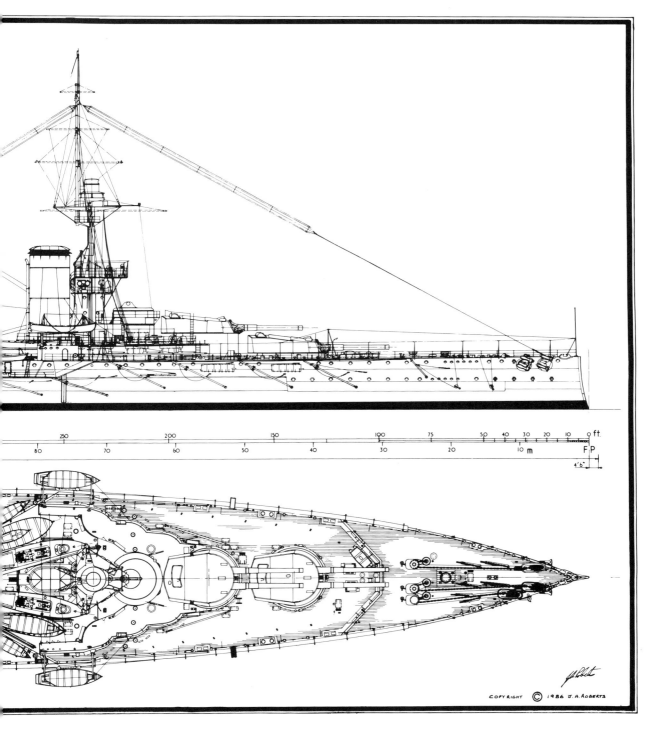

NAVAL BOOKS OF THE YEAR

As usual this section is divided into reviews proper, short descriptive notices, and a list of books announced or not actually received. In all sections place of publication is London unless otherwise specified.

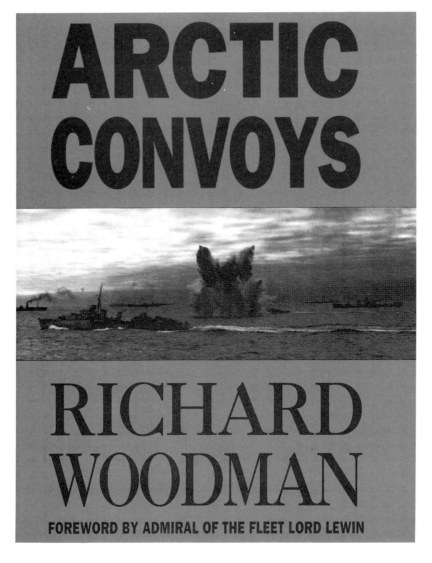

Richard Woodman, The Arctic Convoys, 1941–1945, *published by John Murray 1994.*
240 × 159mm, 528 pages, 34 photographs.
ISBN 0 7195 5079 3. £25.00.

In August 1941 the first convoy to Russia, Operation 'Dervish', sailed from Iceland to Archangel; six merchant ships with an escort of three destroyers, three minesweepers and three trawlers. This operation was comparatively uneventful and, apart from the fact that the escort outnumbered their charges, gave little indication of the major battles that lay ahead. During the next four years the thirty-nine outward and thirty-six home bound convoys that constituted the 'Kola run' had more than their fair share of misery and the worst kind of excitement.

The intensity of the battles fought for and around many of these convoys were matched only by those for the supply convoys to Malta. The Arctic, however, was a much more severe environment than the Mediterranean and gave the convoys a second enemy in the form of the weather. The best time to run a convoy was during the winter months when the long nights gave additional security from enemy assaults, but it was also a time of extreme cold and almost perpetual storms – the sea temperature was so low that those unfortunate enough to end up in it, by accident or enemy action, were unlikely to survive for more than a few minutes. Convoys *were* run in the summer, despite the increased vulnerability to enemy attack and often with the strong misgivings of the naval authorities, in order to maintain the flow of supplies to Russia, which had a political as well as a strategic importance.

Richard Woodman's book describes these events in much greater detail than any previous publication on the subject and covers all the convoys from the first, Operation 'Dervish' of August 1941, to the last, JW67, which left the Clyde shortly after the end of the war in Europe. I was a little concerned by the extent of background material which appears in the first part of the book; the first convoy not appearing until Chapter four. Apart from the necessary outline of the events which led to the initiation of the convoys, much of this seemed superficial and too lacking in detail to be of any real use. However, once the book got underway it proved both detailed and a very good read. There are some cutting remarks, normally unqualified by an explanation, about British warship design which, although not necessarily incorrect, would be likely to mislead those with a limited knowledge of the subject. These are balanced with virtually no positive remarks and left me with a feeling that some prejudice was at work. However, the book is very much operationally biased and the above complaints form a very small part of what is in other respects an excellent history.

The disastrous PQ17 operation, the low point of the Russian convoy story (and of the War as far as the Royal Navy is concerned), and the Battle of North Cape naturally form major sections in the book, but even the uneventful early and late convoys, which are normally neglected, are covered in some detail. The stories of both naval and merchant ships and seamen are recounted from both personal experiences and official documents and the author has obviously carried out some extensive original research (which is fully documented in the chapter notes and source list). One point I particularly like is that

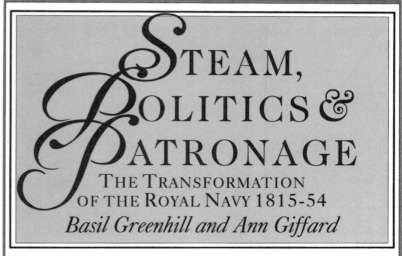

the names of *all* ships, both naval and merchant, are given (if not in the text then in the notes). The book also contains four drawings of typical (and real) convoy cruising formations. This is an excellent operational history and as such would make a valuable addition to any naval bookshelf.

John Roberts

Basil Greenhill and Ann Giffard Steam, Politics and Patronage. The Transformation of the Royal Navy 1815–1854, *published by Conway Maritime Press 1994. 240 × 159mm, 256 pages, 41 illustrations, maps, bibliography, index. ISBN 0 85177 612 4. £25.00.*

This book examines some of the major changes that occurred in the selection of equipment and recruitment of officers for the Royal Navy between the fall of Napoleon and the opening shots of the Crimean, or more properly Russian, War in 1854.

The central core of the book is provided by the career of Henry Wells Giffard, who went into action under sail as a midshipman aboard the 84-gun *Asia* at Navarin in 1827, and died of his wounds in Odessa, in the southern Ukraine, as a senior Captain in May 1854. Between times Giffard served in the first Opium War, and later specialised in steam, commanding three paddle frigates in succession: the *Penelope*, the *Dragon*, and tragically the *Tiger*. These three ships demonstrated the rapid maturing of paddle warship technology, the last being a well built and mechanically reliable vessel capable of towing two sailing battleships, at a time when the screw propeller had already made such ships obsolescent.

Giffard's career in the postwar navy was dominated by the sharp political division within the service, between whigs, with whom he was particularly well connected, and tories. Politics affected every aspect of his career, from his entrance into service to the timing of the two critical promotions, to commander, and then to Post Captain. In this case the first promotion was the direct result of the death of his maternal uncle, the whig MP for Portsmouth. Even the findings of the Court Martial held on the loss of the *Tiger* appear to have had a political character.

At the same time the advance of steam in the Royal Navy is traced, with particular emphasis on the paddle wheel fighting ships. The emphasis on personal experience and operational usage, from the anti-slavery patrol to the bombardment of Odessa, make this book a useful companion to D K Brown's recent study of British paddle warships, and other studies of the ships and technology of the period.

The loss of the *Tiger*, the largest British warship to be lost in the war, appears to have been the direct result of the Captain's orders being ignored by the First Lieutenant and the Master. However, in the middle of a war, and with the Captain dead, it was easy enough to ensure that he took the blame.

A valuable addition to our understanding of the Royal Navy in a time of transition, and a fitting memorial for a professional officer who gave his life in the service of his country.

Andrew Lambert

D K Brown, Paddle Warships, the Earliest Steam Powered Fighting Ships, 1815–1850, *published by Conway Maritime Press 1993. 267 × 186mm, 94 pages, 80 illustrations. ISBN 0 85177 553 5. £25.00.*

Until very recently there has been very little in print about the warships of the period from 1815 to 1860; the period in which steam propulsion began to supplement sails, iron to replace wood for hull construction and the paddle-powered warship had its brief span in front-line service. Andrew Lambert, a technologically-minded historian, and DK Brown, a naval architect, have between them

gone far to fill the gap. The former, with *The Last Sailing Battlefleet* and *Battleships in Transition*, has covered the development of the ship-of-the-line into the screw line-of-battle ship, with full consideration of the political, administrative and technological background. He has also, in the opening chapters of the relevant volume of Conway's 'History of the Ship' (*Steam, Steel and Shellfire* – which he edited) given an efficient, coherent and convincing summary of the development of all types of warship in this period. Astonishingly, there is no reference to any of these works in the book under review. David Brown has produced a useful book of essays on the technical developments of the period (expanded from a number of articles published over the years in *Warship*) called *Before the Ironclad* (Conway 1991). He has now provided us with a book which sets out to cover the Royal Navy's paddle warships during the period in which they were the main steam force of that navy; in other words, up to the time that screw propulsion was generally accepted.

Despite the title the book does not cover the paddle warships built in Britain for other navies, still less those built in France, the United States and elsewhere. He does, however, include the paddle packets taken over from the Post Office in 1837. These include the *Royal Sovereign*, which was renamed *Monkey* at this stage and then went on to provide the cheap and inaccu-

HMS Terrible, *the largest and most powerful of the Royal Navy's paddle frigates, from DK Brown's* Paddle Warships, *reviewed here. (Science Museum, London)*

rate jibe that the Admiralty thought so little of steamers that they named the first steamer they built *Monkey*. This vessel was the oldest steam vessel on the Navy List at the time when this oft-repeated charge was first made, but was neither built for the Navy nor with that name. Indeed, the charge of technical backwardness made by mid-nineteenth-century inventors and journalists against the Admiralty, repeated many times since by historians and others who have neither the technical understanding nor the acquaintanceship with the primary sources necessary for this subject, really will not hold water, as all the books mentioned here make quite clear.

Amongst the primary sources mentioned above are the Admiralty ships plans now held by the National Maritime Museum, and some sixty of these are reproduced in this book, plus numbers of contemporary prints, photographs of models of ships and engines and so on. These alone would make the book worth purchasing, but it is perhaps unfortunate that, as a colleague observed, 'take the plans away and you haven't got much of a book left'. The text divides into a first section which gives a chronological design history of the type, a second part which comments on such specifics as machinery, armament, trials and builders, an appendix on the packets and notes on sources. All of these are rather thin as, indeed, is the book itself. It compares rather badly in width, coverage and denseness of thought and argument with Robert Gardiner's two volumes on frigates which it is meant to resemble and which are the other books published in this series so far. There is little awareness of the political and administrative background (an area in which Lambert is the master) to the technical matters which the author covers very clearly but not perhaps at the length or in the depth that they deserve. To take just one example; the brief mention of *Flamer*'s engine change does not tell one anything about her original Morgan engine which 'did not answer', whether it was designed by the same Morgan who is elsewhere referred to in the context of paddle wheels, or what actually replaced it (a Boulton & Watt engine).

The thinness of this work becomes especially apparent when one looks at its references. Pictures are inadequately captioned – one drawing is credited to the author's collection but the name of the artist is not given, nor any other indication whether it was drawn by someone who had actually seen the ship. The model of the *Lightning* depicted here is a modern one, mostly built from the plans depicted in the book and therefore not evidence for the actual appearance of the ship, unlike the other models, which are indeed contemporary with the ships they depict. A vague reference to 'references in Admiralty files to order dates' on page 29 is very little use to anyone who is trying to check these. Perhaps the worst example of this sloppiness in the use of evidence is Table 42, which shows some representative costs but gives no references at all. Anyone who has tried chasing up ship costs knows full well that sources often disagree – often because the costs are worked out in a different way in each source. The accompanying table contrasts the figures Brown gives with those obtained from the copies of the Admiralty Progress Books held in the National Maritime Museum (the originals are in the

Table 1: *TYPICAL COSTS*

Ship	Date	Hull	Cost (£) Machinery	Total
Comet	1822	4314	5050	9364*
		8052	5050	14414
Lightning	1823			14661
			5385	15744
Dee	1832			27700
				30536
Gorgon	1837			54306
			22662	54306**
Devastation	1841			42168
				45744
Sphynx	1846	25000	25000	50000***
		16802	25578	58843
Gladiator	1844			53165
		21535	23579	57773
Furious	1850			59323
		32420	24577	64794
Terrible	1845			94650
		38346	41820	101842

Notes: *Figures underlined are from the Progress Books – with the 'total' column being the total first cost, ie the cost of building the hull and machinery plus fitting for sea (so therefore more than just the sum of hull and machinery).*

In the text the author gives the first cost of the Buzzard *of 1849 as £44134 without stating where the figure comes from. The figure from the Progress Books is £45699.*

    * *The figure of £9364 is the total first cost (ie hull plus fitting) minus the cost of machinery. Brown's figures are obviously wrong here.*

   ** *This is the only case in which the figures for total cost agree.*

  *** *These figures are obviously either approximations or guesses, and should be indicated as such (and are clearly wrong in any case).*

Public Record Office). It is not necessarily the case that the second figures are right, but at least they can be checked out, which is not the case for the ones given in the book.

It should perhaps have been made clear that the listing of the NMM plans given at the end of the book is a provisional one, and not complete. Also the museum holds numbers of plans of packets and of purchased vessels which are not included.

This is a disappointing book from an author from whom we have come to expect better. However, I do not wish to indicate that it is a bad one. There are excellent little touches coming from the writer's vast personal experience of ship design; though I, for one, would love to hear more about the proposal for paddle minesweepers. There is a very useful note about the stern-wheel turret ship built for use in New Zealand which had previously been a mystery. Above all there is a good deal of material on paddle warships which is not available elsewhere, though perhaps not quite as much, or as firmly based, as one might wish. The book is certainly worth buying.

D J Lyon

F C Lane, Venetian Ships and Shipbuilders of the Renaissance, *published by The Johns Hopkins University Press (Baltimore and London, 1992).*
233 × 156mm, 285 pages, illustrated.
ISBN 0 80184 514 9. £12.

Arguably the first 'modern navy' was that created by the Italian city state of Venice in the later Middle Ages. Certainly its Arsenal (after which all others are named) was the first modern navy yard and the premier industrial organisation of its day. This handsome 'quality' paperback is a reprint of the standard work (first published in 1934) on the ships and shipbuilders of Venice over the central period of its power – the mid-thirteenth to the early seventeenth centuries. It is a book based on much archival research. The author starts by considering the different types of ship of the period, divided between

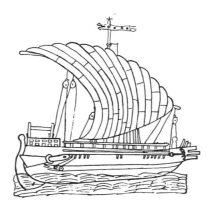

Typical illustrations from Venetian Ships and Shipbuilders.

the oared galleys and the sailing round ships. This is not a simple division between rowing warships and sailing merchantmen, however. The light galleys were, it is true, rarely used for anything but warfare, but Venice took the lead in developing the 'great galleys' which were intended for mercantile use, and became the 'liners' of the later Middle Ages. It was not until the mid-sixteenth century that Venice adapted this type for war in the form of the 'galeass'. Venice also regularly built a few very big round ships for war, with 'castles' fore and aft and heavily manned. They served as floating fortresses which could escort smaller sailing merchantmen. However, there was no easy way they could accompany fleets of galleys into battle. There are indications that the name 'galleon' came from Venice, and possibly the type was invented there. Certainly Venetian ship designers, to whom Lane devotes a chapter, were highly skilled and inventive. The next chapter describes Venetian shipbuilding methods and is

followed by a discussion of the private yards and then of the Arsenal itself, the workmen, organisation and discipline of the latter. The final chapter is on the perennial problem of timber supply. Tables and appendices cover Venetian ship numbers, dimensions, lengths of service and costs.

This is a splendid, informative and clearly written book. It was recognised as a classic of its kind when it first appeared and it retains that status after sixty years. Apart from its paperback cover the book is unaltered from the first edition. There is only one place in which it shows its age, and that is in the discussion of the earlier galleys. No serious scholar nowadays would attempt to suggest that what the medieval Venetians called a trireme bore any relation at all to the trireme of ancient Greece. The Venetian galley had oars in groups of three, but they were all rowed from the same level. Its hull was built by the 'skeleton first' method and it had a beak above the water. Its chief weapons were the bows of its archers and not a ram.

The suggestion that the ship captains of the end of the fifteenth century after the introduction of the three-masted ship 'would have little to learn before taking charge of a ship of Nelson's Day', a suggestion copied by Lane from R C Anderson, is a rather dangerous half-truth, as it underestimates the cumulative effect of many comparatively small improvements – none very major in themselves but taken together producing very radical changes in performance.

Minor niggles apart, this book is very strongly to be recommended to anyone interested in the development of oared and sailing warships. It was well worth reprinting.

D J Lyon

Yves Buffetaut, D-Day Ships *published by Conway Maritime Press 1994.*
274 x 216mm, 164 pages, 140 photographs, maps.
ISBN 0 85177 639 6. £20.

This attractively designed volume

contains one of the best selections of photographs of the naval side of D-Day yet published. These mostly come from the magnificent collections of the Imperial War Musem. The text is a translation from the French. It is clearly meant as a 'commemoration volume' to take advantage of the 50th Anniversary ballyhoo about this most impressive and important of amphibious operations. It is not something that will tell the expert anything very new about the ships and craft involved in D-Day, or about the naval side of the first month of the Allied campaign in Normandy. However, it reads and looks well and for the first time assembles the relevant information in one clear and thorough account. The author adds some useful touches from his local knowledge and experiences in sailing a small boat off the coast.

The 'meat' of this book is in the chapters on landing craft types and their development, on the supporting naval vessels, and the blow-by-blow account of the actual landings and the subsequent naval support operations. The installation of the Mulberry Harbours, the subsequent destruction of one in the 'Great Storm' (one of the most interesting parts of the book)

and the bombardment of Cherbourg complete the book.

The photographs alone make this book worth buying for any warship enthusiast. Most are unfamiliar, and the general quality of the original pictures and of their reproduction is very high. Altogether this probably is the D-Day 'best buy' for any naval enthusiast amongst the plethora of commemorative volumes which cover all aspects of this tri-service operation, usually at the expense of inadequate coverage of the maritime side.

R A Burt, British Battleships 1919–1939, *published by Arms and Armour Press 1993. 246 × 244mm, 416 pages, 216 photographs, 200 line drawings. ISBN 1 85409 68 2. £40.00*

In his preface the author says that he took soundings on what book would be popular and the answer came back – 'another battleship book, but with fresh information if possible, new drawings and different photographs'.

None of these objectives can have been easy to achieve, but there is new information, the drawings are different and there are many photographs not previously seen – though some rare ones are not of very good quality.

Coverage is generally straightforward with brief mention of the very old battleships serving into the early twenties, more on the *Iron Dukes* and full coverage of later classes. Updating and modernisation of the remaining ships of the First World War era is given full and accurate coverage. The new ships of the *Nelson* and *King George V* classes only make their appearance from page 325 onwards. There is a section on aircraft carriers which is too brief to describe their complex history adequately. The limits on time scale are strangely applied; the deadline of 1939 is taken to exclude the *Lion* class and *Vanguard*, but wartime changes and damage are included and even the postwar bombing trials against *Nelson* are covered.

LCAs landing Canadian troops on Juno Beach, 6 June 1944, from Buffetaut's D-Day Ships. *(IWM)*

The most interesting material is on the large number of full-scale trials carried out between the wars on the effects of all kinds of weapons and on protection against them. Obsolete ships, including the ex-German *Baden*, the *Superb*, *Monarch*, *Empress of India* and *Marlborough* were all used in this way, sometimes after considerable modification to simulate more modern ships. Later, an enormous pontoon, Job 74, was built to represent the protection of *King George V* (and *Ark Royal*) full size and tested successfully against modern weapons. Though other books have referred to these trials, the author has found much new material and some interesting photos. The Admiralty was certainly right, at least in the earlier years, to see the battleship as the key to naval power, and worked very hard to make it as resistant to attack as possible.

The conclusions take the form of a robust defence of British battleship design in its last years, demolishing much ill-informed criticism. The author is, however, wrong in attributing the poor endurance of the *King George V* solely to low fuel stowage. Her old-fashioned engines had a fuel consumption some 25 per cent worse than contemporary USN battleships.

The author refers to earlier books and references Roberts and Raven *British Battleships of World War II* in several places rather than repeating material in the earlier book. Oscar Parkes' classic *British Battleships* should now be regarded as a curiosity in relation to the twentieth-century British battleships as he had very little access to official documents for the more modern ships and hence there are many omissions and errors.

DK Brown, RCNC

Dr David W Chalmers RCNC, Design of Ships' Structures, *published by HMSO 1993. 498 pages, 80 figures and 90 data sheets. ISBN 0 11 772717 2. £85.00*

The dust jacket makes the need for this book very clear, as it highlights the external stiffening applied to a Type 42 destroyer to compensate for a design error. Such errors, resulting in expensive rectification, have occurred in several classes of RN ships (designed both within the MoD and in private industry) and in ships of the USN, French and former Soviet navies. The problem is that structural design is seen as easy and the effort devoted to it, particularly by senior officers, has been too small. While structural design is not difficult, there are many pitfalls and it is very easy to make an expensive mistake, often of omission.

At £85 it is unlikely that many *Warship* readers will buy personal copies of this book, but libraries should be persuaded to purchase an adequate number of copies. Everyone concerned with the design, building, maintenance and operation of warships should read chapters 1–3, 15 and 16, which set out the problem in simple terms and indicate the direction in which solutions should be sought. The aim of structural design may be summarised as deciding the nature of the various loads with their corresponding failure modes, synthesising a structure to resist both extreme loads (including wartime damage) and repeated lesser loads through life in the most efficient manner. 'Efficient' is hard to define but is roughly equivalent to minimum through-life cost (TLC), remembering that excess weight can also affect both speed and fuel consumption. Chapter 15, on vulnerability, gives an interesting glimpse of possible future ships with the primary structure concentrated in a few box girders, resistant to buckling, with very light structure between to vent the blast from internal explosions. The problem is to maintain shear strength with material which will fail rapidly under pressure.

DK Brown, RCNC

Derek Howse, Radar at Sea, *published by Macmillan (Basingstoke, 1993). 240 x 158mm, 397 pages, 60 photographs. ISBN 0 333 58449 X. £25.00.*

This is one of those classic books which should be on the shelves of all who are interested in the history of naval technology and of the Second World War. It is important in two aspects; first, the impact of radar on the war at sea – and it is now hard to imagine life without radar – and second, on the attitude of the prewar Admiralty to radically new technology.

It all began well; by August 1935, only six months after Watson-Watt's classic demonstration at Daventry, the Controller, Vice Admiral Sir Reginald Henderson, directed the Signals School at Eastney to get radar at sea. The Treasury approved the necessary staff within days, but it was the end of the year before they arrived. Progress was rather slow in 1936 though the trials ship, *Saltburn*, did take a prototype set to sea at the end of the year. The reasons for the slow progress seem complex; it is likely that the secrecy of radar (then called RDF) was a major factor; faced with so many demands for skilled staff, those not in the know cannot be blamed for not giving priority to what seemed just another radio set. There was also debate as to whether Orfordness should be a tri-service establishment or whether the Navy should go it alone. The author concludes that the advantages and disadvantages were fairly evenly balanced with a slight advantage to the Signal School, both from its geographical location and from its leadership in silica valve technology.

There are many aspects in this story which are familiar to those who have studied the period but may surprise the casual reader; the way in which Henderson crops up in pushing so many aspects of new technology; his unexpected death in April 1939 was a sad loss to the country. Active co-operation from the Treasury was also quite normal, contrary to the views often expressed. The real problem was that the Navy and industry were overwhelmed with the task of rearming the country and good scientists were very scarce and in great demand.

By early 1938 the battleship *Rodney* and the cruiser *Sheffield* had pre-production air warning sets, achieving detection at up to 53 miles against aircraft, and these were used in a major exercise in March 1939.

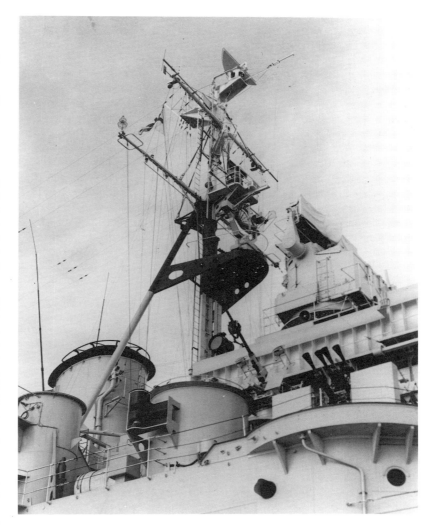

A postwar view of the foremast and upper bridge of the cruiser Superb *illustrates the growth of wartime radar, with the aerials of both air and surface search sets on the mast platforms and that for the main gunnery set above the director control tower.* (CMP)

During this exercise *Rodney* was able to detect *Sheffield*'s transmissions at 100 miles, and concern over the detection of radar signals led to severe restrictions on the use of radar in the early years of the war – one minute's transmission per hour was not unusual.

From then on, progress was rapid, spurred by the appointment of Admiral Somerville as co-ordinator on the outbreak of war, and there were a bewildering number of new sets. The Navy had been pressing for centimetric radar from 1938 but there were real problems. The first trials of Type 271 were in March 1941, and were so successful that the Signal School made a batch of twenty-five, which were fitted in July, while production sets followed quickly, with 236 sets at sea by March 1942. The office was prefabricated and fully outfitted ashore, probably the first use of such methods in the UK.

Much work had to be done in learning how to use the new sensors, and the carrier *Illustrious'* work-up off Bermuda in the spring of 1940 laid the foundations for fighter direction. The older carrier *Ark Royal*, in the Mediterranean, did not have radar and her plot relied on flag signals from *Sheffield*! By the end of the War larger ships would have an effective air warning set, a target indication set and radar on all gun directors as well as IFF and jammers, all integrated into the Action Information Organisation.

Many of the pioneer workers are still alive (many now FRS or F Eng) and following a meeting in 1985 they set up the Naval Radar Trust to collect and digest available material and, as a result, the author was persuaded to put the story together in this book. A somewhat similar approach, some years ago, led to Hackmann's excellent history of

underwater sensors and weapons – *Seek and Strike*. (Attention has been drawn to the need for a good history of naval engineering which could be approached in the same way.) The author is well qualified for his task, having navigated a destroyer during the War and served as a curator of the Maritime Museum postwar. The book is not always easy reading as there are so many set numbers and names of individuals, but the story is so fascinating that I had great difficulty in putting it down. There is a nice tribute to the many Canadian physics graduates who served in the RN as Radar officers.

Each chapter concludes with some light-hearted tail pieces – noting that flagships were not originally given radar (for fear it might interfere with communications), it is said that cynics claimed it was because Commanders-in-Chief could not bear to see their flag displaced! I also like the story of the crew of the destroyer *Westminster*, who welded a set of pawnbroker's balls to the bridge and described it as Type 298, later used as the theme for a successful film. The photographs are well selected but they are not well reproduced. However, the captions are unusually informative. Books on radar generally concentrate on the airforce applications and this book tells the complete naval story for the first time; it is very highly recommended. (The David Brown who wrote the annex on airborne radar is the head of Naval Historical Branch and not the reviewer.)

DK Brown, RCNC

Graham Spinardi, From Polaris to Trident: The Development of US Fleet Ballistic Missile Technology, *published by Cambridge University Press (Cambridge 1994).*
262 pages.
ISBN 0 5521 41357 5. £35.

The subtitle is a very precise description of this book; it is about the missile, with little mention of the submarines, and the US programme, with only passing mention of the UK purchases. Within these limits, it is an intriguing account of the political background, aims and technology of the FBM system beginning with the philosophy of the deterrent, a passage which would delight medieval theologians.

The aim of the programme is not always clear. One US admiral described it as to '– go out and clobber the enemy. The enemy being the [US] Air Force.' Rivalry with the Air Force, so much more bitter than in the UK, greatly affected the choice of targeting between cities (Polaris) or counter-force as in Trident II. There were also internal problems; not all the USN wished to see so much of their budgets going on missiles and there were, inevitably, problems with Rickover.

However, the Special Projects Office has an enviable record of promising only what could realistically be achieved, of having few failures and being closer to budget than most weapon systems. One could wish for more information on the management systems which led to this result. The last chapter is a fascinating debate on whether advances were requirement-led or due to technological push. The author's conclusions are not entirely clear and he could have given more weight to mutual interaction between these two explanations. He does point out that, in many aspects, engineers had got the widget working some five years before science came up with an explanation of why it worked.

The book is based on a doctrinal thesis and is not light reading but it is clear. Anyone interested in ballistic missile politics and technology will find it fascinating. One is left with the impression that Congress is much better informed than the House of Commons, but maybe the grass is greener.

DK Brown, RCNC

Robert Gardiner, The Heavy Frigate, Eighteen-Pounder Frigates: Vol 1, 1778–1800, *published by Conway Maritime Press 1994.*
267 x 186mm, 128 pages, 90 illustrations.
ISBN 0 85177 627 2. £25.

For the last quarter century those researchers specialising in the history of ships have had good cause to know the name of Robert Gardiner. This is for two reasons. The first is his vital role in developing the publishing activities and reputation of Conway Maritime Press. The other is his pioneering work on the design history of sailing warships and particularly of British frigates. Some of his deeply researched, searchingly analysed and clearly stated conclusions have appeared in articles in *The Mariner's Mirror, Model Shipwright* and *Petit Perroquet*. It is not until very recently, however, that his work has begun to appear between hard covers at the sort of length and with the sort of illustrations its importance and originality deserves. His chapters on frigates and on smaller warships in the Conway History of the Ship volume on *The Line of Battle* are outstanding and the best in a (mostly) good bunch. More important still, however, was the pioneer volume of Conway's Ship Types series on *The First Frigates* which covered those of the Royal Navy's sailing frigates which were armed with 9- and 12-pounder guns. This was published at the end of 1992. Just over a year later the volume now under review appeared, to begin the story of the 18-pounder frigates of the Royal Navy.

Unusually for a sailing warship type, this was pioneered by the Royal Navy and not taken over from foreign prototypes. Probably it was the unusual experience of being on the defensive against the numerically superior combined French and Spanish fleets in the late 1770s which caused the building of a more powerfully armed frigate; both 38- and 36-gun prototypes appeared at much the same time. Numbers of both types were completed or under construction by the end of the War of American Independence in 1783, but it was the construction programme of the 1790s which made the 18-pounder ships of 36 or 38 guns the major part of the navy's frigate force, with the decline of the lighter 9- and 12-pounder armed ships (none of the former and only a scattering of the latter being ordered after 1783).

A further development of the 1790s was the introduction of the 32-gun, 18-pounder frigate. As the author points out, this appears to have been intended to be built in yards or on slips too small to tackle the bigger types (like the *Weapons* class destroyers of the 1940s). The story of British designs ends with the last of the varied designs produced in small numbers to the order of Lord Spencer's Admiralty Board in 1800. The following administration, that of Lord Saint Vincent, would change both designs and the way they were ordered, and so 1800 makes a logical break point to finish this volume in respect of ships designed for the Royal Navy. In the case of the 18-pounder frigates taken by that Navy, however, the natural dividing date is that of the Treaty of Amiens a year later, and so that story only ends with the brief period of truce with France.

Part of the problem of writing about the development of British sailing warships is that very little of the crucial reasoning and argument which lay behind the development of designs was ever committed to paper (unlike the case of the Danes, for example). Robert Gardiner's acute intelligence and wide knowledge makes him particularly fitted for working out the evolution of policy from hints in the documents and the record of what was done. He succeeds in producing a closely reasoned, well illustrated, eloquently argued and totally convincing account of why particular designs were the way they were, and of the general design philosophy behind the developments in the period under discussion.

Equally convincing and subtle is the further development of his argument on the subject of the persistent and simplistic assertion that French ship design was 'better' than British and that French ships were faster. Anyone who continues to believe these myths (which like all myths have a certain basis of original truth) is encouraged to read this book and its predecessor to find out that reality is more complex and variable, that different navies have different requirements, that performance can vary according to conditions. They will also find a great deal of material to help them make up their own minds, from the large number of original Admiralty plans illustrated to the substantial extracts from the Navy's sailing reports.

Robert Gardiner's books on frigates are an example of history at its best; of careful research, well presented, put firmly in context and intelligently analysed. They are a pleasure to read, and a splendid example for other writers to follow. They cannot be too highly recommended, and one looks forward with interest and excitement to the promised second volume on 18-pounder frigates, and a sequel on the heaviest frigates, those armed with 24- or 32-pounders.

DJ Lyon

Raymond L Wheeler, From River to Sea, the Maritime Heritage of Sam Saunders, *published by Cross Publishing (Newport, 1993).*
280 × 205mm, 316 pages, c900 photographs and plans.
ISBN 1 873295 05 7. £30.

Ray Wheeler's first book, *Sea to Air*, published in 1989, dealt with the aircraft activities of Saunders-Roe. This new book is concerned with the water supported craft built by the company, including hydrofoils and hovercraft. It opens with a family history of Sam Saunders, covering the growth of the company from the family boatyard at Goring. It soon gained a high reputation for fast river launches with minimum wash. It is interesting that Saunders' recipe for minimum wash was long, narrow and lightweight hulls, supported by research 100 years later. In 1890 Saunders began to use Daimler Benz internal combustion engines.

At about the same time Saunders developed a very successful form of lightweight construction which he called *Consuta* (Latin–sewed). This used three to four thin wood laminates sewn together with copper or annealed brass wire. Canvas impregnated with a rubbery adhesive was placed between the laminates to ensure watertightness. The first such launch achieved 27½kts with a 100hp steam engine.

The company moved to Cowes in 1901 and soon became involved in building racing craft such as S F Edge's Napier Minor in 1904. It also won an exclusive contract for RNLI boats in 1913. During the First World War the company was almost entirely occupied with aircraft work, but once the War was over it returned to building racing boats, family cruisers and a few weird experimental craft. Saunders' death in 1927 had little effect on the output of the company. It built *Miss England II* in 1930 which won the world speed record three times, leaving it at 110mph. Later it designed and built *Bluebird*, which put the record up to 130mph in 1938. This speed, and the later record by the *Bluebird II*, were predicted with incredible accuracy by A E W Haslar, who must have had an excellent crystal ball in those days.

After the Second World War the company built its first ships for the RN with four inshore minesweepers followed by four *Dark* class fast patrol boats with laminated wood skins over aluminium frames. A modified craft, *Dark Scout*, was built in 1958 with all welded aluminium construction. Saunders-Roe built the successful research hydrofoil *Bras D'or* for the Canadian Navy in 1959 – she may be seen today in an Ottawa museum.

The rest of the story is mainly that of the hovercraft which began so well but failed to win the success that the author (and reviewer) think it deserved. Cockerell's early model tests led to the building of SRN 1 in 1959, which crossed the Channel the same year. The big SRN 3 for naval use followed in 1963 and was proved in a number of roles including ASW, amphibious operations and MCM. The commercial SRN 5 was completed in 1964, the first car ferry, SRN 4, in 1967 and the naval BH 7 in 1969.

By this time naval interest was centred on MCM, and it was demonstrated in full-scale trials that the hovercraft could carry out every function of conventional MCMV, usually better and often more cheaply. A series of explosion trials against the old SRN 3 in 1974 showed that the air cushion made hovercraft almost invulnerable to underwater explosions. The air cushion decoupled the craft from the sea, giving very low acoustic and pressure signatures. Trials in 1977 with a hired SRN 4 and with BH 7 showed that track keeping in severe wind and sea was better than that of a *Hunt*. In 1983 a 193M sonar was installed on a retractable strut under BH 7 and worked very well. This craft was fitted up as a full MCM demonstrator and was very successful, but in 1985 the company was informed that naval hovercraft work was to be dropped as a savings measure, a decision which the author describes as incredible.

It is not possible to mention all the various topics dealt with in this book in a review of reasonable length. The many illustrations are well selected, showing craft under construction as well as in use. It is a fine record of a high-technology company, written by an engineer who was involved (latterly as technical director) in most of the postwar work.

DK Brown, RCNC

John Lambert and Al Ross, Allied Coastal Forces of World War II, Volume II, Vosper MTBs and US ELCOs, *published by Conway Maritime Press 1993.*
296 x 248mm, 256 pages, 200 photographs, 700 line drawings.
ISBN 0 85177 602 7. £35.

Volume II covers in great detail some

sixteen designs of Vosper MTB, together with those built in the USA, and three types of USN ELCO boats, some of which served in the RN. There is a brief history of each company followed by a detailed description of each design. Rightly, much attention is paid to Vosper's private venture craft, eventually purchased for the RN as *MTB 102*. Her general design style was followed in virtually all later Vosper designs and influenced those of some other companies. Though her structure was generally well conceived, it did need additional strengthening, as did that of most designs. It seems to be a natural law that fast craft will be driven by their keen CO's until something does break, and extra stiffening merely increases the speed at which this happens. *MTB 102* was also used by *Vernon* for trials of different methods of torpedo launching, ending with the sided and slightly angled pair of tubes used in almost all RN 'short' boats. She was also used, probably at the instigation of Lord Mountbatten, for demonstrations of the 20mm Oerlikon gun. Happily, this historic craft is preserved and may be seen at various naval functions.

MTB 102 was originally fitted with Italian Issotta-Fraschini engines, as were a few of the follow-on craft, but these ceased to be available when Italy entered the War. After some under-powered stop gaps, the American Packard, which is described in detail, became available and was used in most craft. There are always problems in matching propeller and machinery power curves in fast craft, and the author pays tribute to the work of AEW's new cavitation tunnel in solving this problem. (Though the 'E' is Experiment, not Experimental)

Altogether 127 Vosper design craft were built in the UK, whilst the USA built sixty-four more for the RN, one hundred for the Soviet Union and a few for other countries. The majority were derivatives of 102 though there was a substantial revision in 1943 with four torpedo tubes, changed again in 1944 to increase gun armament at the expense of torpedoes. Experimental types, such as the stepped hull 103 and the bigger 510, both of which were completed but not used operationally, are well covered. Re-

ference is made to the Denny hydrofoil 109 which the author says was not completed – some details of her trials appear in Conway's own *Warship 14*, together with a drawing. There is also some confusion between boats built by J S White to their own design and those they built to Vosper design.

The ELCO boats derive from Scott-Paine's British Power Boat design (to be described in Volume III) though later, bigger boats were considerably altered. A number of the earlier boats served in the RN, mainly as gunboats, whilst a few of the later and better MTBs served in the Mediterranean. The book concludes with a number of essays on specialist topics such as hull construction, engines, weapons, etc. There is a fascinating annex on the boats which remain, mainly as house boats.

The illustrations form an important part of the book. The drawings are beautifully done but, as in volume I, one may wonder if quite so much detail is necessary, eg. a thimble eye. The photographs are well selected and well reproduced but the captions show some signs of haste. The authors have put together a vast mass of material which is not readily available elsewhere. Volume III is awaited with interest.

DK Brown, RCNC

Ken Macpherson and Marc Milner, Corvettes of the Royal Canadian Navy, *published by Airlife (Shrewsbury, 1994).*
280 × 215mm, 173 pages,
197 illustrations.
ISBN 0 920277 83 7. £19.95

Part I tells in 87 pages the story of the design and building of the corvettes of the RCN which contributed so much to victory in the Battle of the Atlantic. The story is very well told as the authors are not content merely to list the differences between Canadian ships and those built in the UK but give clear reasons for these differences – we are even told why RCN ships were more rusty (they were built so quickly that there was no time for the mill scale to be removed by weathering).

During the War 121 corvettes were built in Canadian shipyards, a wonderful achievement considering that there was only a small industry before the War. Many of the excellent photos show ships under construction, a fine tribute to the builders. Part I also outlines the operational history, showing how well the ships did even with very inexperienced crews. Equipment was very scarce, an important reason for the delay in modernisation which so greatly hampered Canadian corvettes later in the War.

In part II, each ship has a photograph and a short note on its building and fate. There is a complex chart from which it is possible to obtain the wartime movements of each ship. This book is essential reading for anyone studying the Battle of the Atlantic, the contribution of Canadian shipyards or the valour of their crews.

DK Brown, RCNC

Paddy Gregson, Ten Degrees Below Seaweed, A true story of World War II Boat's Crew Wrens, *published by Merlin Books (Braunton, Devon, 1993)*
210 × 147mm, 131 pages,
22 photographs.
ISBN 0 86303 660 0. £9.95

Wren boat's crews were employed during the Second World War to operate harbour service craft for such duties as carrying stores and mail and running liberty boats. The idea was initiated, despite some opposition from 'Their Lordships', in the early part of the War and the crews were disbanded in 1945; during which time the service provided some much needed relief to the problems of manning the fleet. This book is not, however, a history of the boat service, but the personal wartime recollections of one of its members. It does not contain much for the warship enthusiast, although several warships are mentioned, either from an operational or technical point of view. It does, however, provide a very readable account of wartime life in the

Wrens and the day-to-day operation of the boat's crews.

Harry Holmes, The Last Patrol, *published by Airlife (Shrewsbury, 1994). 218 × 149mm, 212 pages, 124 photographs. ISBN 1 85310 414 0. £19.95*

The operations of the United States Navy's surface ships, particularly the carriers, in the naval battles and island-hopping campaign of the Pacific War have, to a great extent, overshadowed the contribution made by the US submarine service. Like Britain, Japan is an island nation particularly vulnerable to an assault on its seaborne lines of supply. A few well chosen words on the dust jacket of this book describe very succinctly the great contribution made by America's submariners in stating that while absorbing only 2 per cent of the Navy's personnel they were responsible for the destruction of 55 per cent of Japanese merchant shipping. This was not, however, achieved without loss, and almost one in five US submarines failed to return from patrol. *The Last Patrol* details the complete operational histories of all fifty-two of these lost vessels and as such provides the reader with a valuable source of information. It did seem a shame that the treatment could not have been expanded to include those boats that were not lost – thus providing a complete work of reference – but it has to be admitted that, for the same coverage, the result would have been a large and expensive publication. The book also contains some useful appendices and a full index which adds to the value of a very worthwhile and interesting read.

David J Hepper, British Warship Losses in the Age of Sail, 1650–1859, *published by Jean Boudriot (Rotherfield, 1994). 295 × 205mm, 220 pages. ISBN 0 948864 30 3. £24 (incl p & p).*

This book gives a brief account of the circumstances of the loss of every British warship, large and small, between 1650 and 1859. The most striking fact is that it is a slim volume; in fact there are 1700 losses described, which is not a large figure for 200 years of near-continuous war. There is a list of conflicts at the beginning of the book which suggests 75 years without naval action.

The principal source is the record of courts martial, as in those days the senior survivor was automatically brought to trial – which might result in a knighthood or severe punishment. For example, the loss of the 74-gun *Alexander*, nearly 200 years ago on 6 November 1794 rates about 230 words to describe her surrender to the *Jean Bart* en route to Gibraltar.

There is a statistical analysis which shows that in the great wars from 1793–1815 the majority of losses were accidental and there were no losses in the big battles. The RN surely has a proud tradition of victory. It is a fascinating book in which to dip and should be at the bedside of all those interested in the sailing navy.

DK Brown, RCNC

Garry E Weir, Forged in War, *published by the Naval Historical Center (Washington DC, 1993). 331 pages, 42 illustrations. ISBN 0 16 038258 0.*

This book describes the procurement of USN submarines from 1940 to 1961 and, in particular, the relation between the Department of Defense and industry. The war time years were dominated by the need to produce very large numbers of similar vessels. After the War the need for fast submarines led first to the *Guppy* conversions, which were very successful, and then to the *Tangs* which were not, mainly because of unreliable diesels. The development of the *Albacore* is well covered.

The nuclear submarine brought new problems and made others more serious, such as flow and cavitation

noise, Helmholtz cavity resonance and singing propellers. The requirement for increased diving depth brought HY-80 steel with initial welding problems. The author does not attempt to deal with the technology of these problems, which is just as well – he seems to think that HY-80 means it can withstand 80,000 psi of water pressure. It is surprising that there is no mention of the very active collaboration between US authorities and AEW and NCRE.

The author is clearly of the opinion that technical innovation is more likely to be initiated in-house rather than in industry, and that a partnership led by the Navy with industry using its production expertise is desirable. However, he sees such a partnership as impossible in today's climate where, as he says, 'The bean counters have inherited the earth'.

DK Brown, RCNC

Januz Skulski, Anatomy of the Ship Series: The Heavy Cruiser Takao, *published by Conway Maritime Press 1994. 240 x 254mm, 256 pages, 30 photographs, 700 drawings. ISBN 0 85177 628 0. £25.00.*

The *Takao* is a typical example of Japanese warship design of the interwar period and as such is an ideal vessel for the Anatomy series. She was the nameship of the second group of the Imperial Navy's 8in-gun Washington Treaty cruisers and, like many Japanese ships, combined both design brilliance and technical shortcomings. Compared with the ships she was intended to counter, the US and British 8in-gun cruisers, she was faster, more heavily armed and better protected. This was, however, achieved by exceeding the Washington Treaty limit of 10,000 tons; the completed ship being of 11,350 tons standard – US and British ships generally completed below limit as a result of the careful application of weight saving techniques. The Japanese also applied extensive weight saving methods (including the integration of the non-cemented side

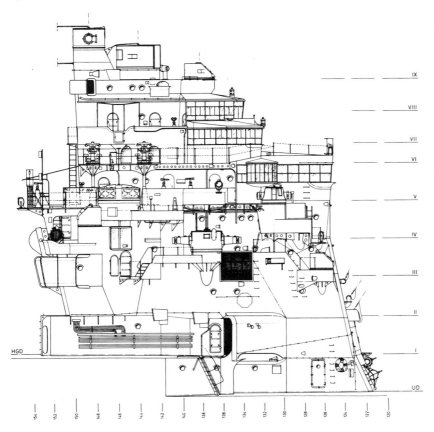

and deck armour into the hull structure) and the *Takao* class *were* originally intended to be designed to the Treaty limit. That this goal was not achieved was largely the result of a strong Naval General Staff, which, in imposing its will on an often reluctant design section, were constantly pressing for additions and improvements. As a result, the *Takao* and her sisters completed overweight, low on stability and lacking in freeboard. Those shortcomings were, however, corrected during major refits in the late 1930s by the addition of bulges – albeit at substantial cost and with a further increase in displacement.

Whatever the problems of the original design, the *Takao* class were powerful ships and they were to see a good deal of action during the Pacific war. The *Takao* herself saw extensive service before being seriously damaged by torpedoes from the US submarine *Darter* in October 1944. After incomplete repair she spent the last year of the War out of action at Singapore, where she was further damaged by the British midget submarines *XE3* and *XE1*. She was eventually surrendered to British forces in September 1945 and, after use as a base ship, was scuttled in the Malacca Strait in October 1946.

This Anatomy follows the standard pattern, with an introductory text, photographic section and a large number of drawings – which occupy over 80 per cent of the book. The introduction comprehensively covers the design, construction, technical details, modifications and service his-

ory of *Takao* in both written and tabular form. It also manages to provide a good general background to Japanese cruiser design of the period and the problems of Japanese designers in the face of a strong naval staff. There is a good photographic section and those taken while *Takao* was under construction are particularly interesting. The drawings are, however, as with all the Anatomy series, the principal part of the book, and these are of remarkable quality. Most are two-dimensional, although there are a few perspective views, and they could have been further enhanced with some more extensive keys and explanatory notes. Apart from the general arrangement drawings and sectional views of the twin 8in gun mounting, there is little detail on the ship's interior and structural arrangements, although the general arrangement sections do show details (with thicknesses, etc) of the hull structure. However, one cannot have everything, particularly with Japanese ships which are notoriously difficult to research, and this substantial addition to the series definitely has no 'padding'. The exterior of the ship, its equipment and fittings are covered in minute detail and (from one who knows just how much is involved in producing an Anatomy) represent an enormous amount of work. These drawings are a modelmaker's delight and there would be no difficulty in producing a highly detailed model of the ship solely from the information provided in this book. It is a masterpiece of the draughtsman's art and is highly recommended to warship enthusiasts and modelmakers alike.

John Roberts

BOOKS ANNOUNCED

The Battle of the Atlantic, *published by Alan Sutton, 1994, £17.99.*
A view of the battle in the words of those who were there.

Paul Beaver, Britain's New Navy, *published by Patrick Stephens, 1994, £19.95.*
Details the changes taking place in the RN to face the challenges of the new world order.

Rahul Roy-Chaudhury, Sea Power and Indian Security, *published by Brassey, 1994, £35.00.*
A study of the Indian Navy from 1947 to date.

Conway's All the World's Fighting Ships, 1947–1995, *published by Conway Maritime Press, 1995, c£75.00.*
A revised and updated version of this standard work, previously published in two volumes.

Conway's 'History of the Ship' series:
Robert Gardiner (ed)
The Earliest Ships: The Evolution of Boats into Ships, *1994, £28.00.*

The Golden Age of Shipping: The Classic Merchant Ship 1900–1960, *1994, £28.00.*

The Age of the Galley: Mediterranean vessels since pre-classical Times, *1994, £28.00.*

Jack Green, The Midway Campaign, *published by Combined Books, 1994, £17.95.*
The Pacific war from Pearl Harbour to Midway.

Eric Grove (editor), Great Battles of the British Navy, As Celebrated in the Gunroom, Royal Naval College Dartmouth, *published by Arms and Armour Press, 1994, £25.00.*

Paul G Halpern, A Naval History of World War 1, *published by UCL Press, 1994, £25.00.*
A comprehensive history of the First World War at Sea.

A A Hoehling, The Lexington Goes Down: A Fighting Carrier's Last Hours in the Coral Sea, *published by Stackpole, 1994, £9.95.*

Stephen Howarth and Derek Law (eds), The Battle of the Atlantic, 1939–1945: The 50th Anniversary International Conference, *published by Greenhill, 1994, £35.00.*
A collection of writings from thirty-six international naval historians on all aspects of the Battle of the Atlantic.

Bernd Langensiepen and Ahmet Güleryüz, The Ottoman Steam Navy, 1828–1923, *published by Conway Maritime Press, 1994, £35.00.*

Aiden McIvor, A History of the Irish Naval Service, *published by Irish Academic Press, 1994, £25.00.*

John Niven, Gideon Welles: Lincoln's Secretary of the Navy, *published by Louisiana State University Press, 1994, £16.95.*

Captain William J Ruhe, War in the Boats: My Submarine Battles, *published by Brassey (Washington), 1994, £19.95.*

The Royal Navy: An Illustrated Social History, *published by Alan Sutton, £19.99.*
Life in the Royal Navy from 1919 to present.

John Slader, The Fourth Service: Merchantmen at War, 1939–45, *published by Hale, 1994, £25.00.*

Lawrence Sondhaus, The Naval Policy of Austria-Hungary, 1867–1918: Navalism, Industrial Development and the Politics of Dualism, *published by Purdue University Press, 1994, £37.95.*

Paul Tarrant, The Last Year of the Kriegsmarine, May 1944 – May 1945, *Published by Arms and Armour Press, 1994, £16.99.*

John M Taylor, Confederate Raider, Raphael Semmes of the Alabama, *published by Brassey (Washington), 1994, £19.95.*

Geoffrey Till (ed), Coastal Forces, *published by Brassey, 1994, £15.00.*
Review of present-day situation in the development and employment of FPBs, patrol craft and mine-sweepers.

John Walter, The Kaiser's Pirates, German Raiders of World War One, *published by Arms and Armour Press, 1994, £19.99.*

Chris Ware, Bomb Vessels, *published by Conway Maritime Press, 1994, £25.00.*
Technical history of the bomb vessel from the 17th to the mid-19th century.

THE NAVAL YEAR IN REVIEW

The events covered by this review stretch from approximately May 1993 to May 1994, with some reference before and after. Compiled by Ian Sturton.

A. INTRODUCTION

Improved East-West relations were maintained during the year, despite weak and vacillating American leadership and a more prominent Russian profile in Europe. Russia, so often invaded in history, fears encirclement and objects to any eastward expansion by NATO; membership of the 'Partnership for Peace' military co-operation programme is acceptable.

Further afield, the Far East arms race continues; the North Korean nuclear question produced considerable tension, while Russia and Japan failed to decide ownership of the Kurile Islands, which protect Russian SSBN bases and safe operating areas in the Sea of Okhotsk, and guard the routes to the Pacific Ocean. A treaty to demilitarise the frontier between Russia and China is expected in 1994 but regional disputes over attempts to extend control of ill-defined EEZs continue. The Gulf remained in conflict, with renewed military operations against Iraq, while America's unwillingness to accept casualties in Somalia was exploited there, and in Haiti.

World defence spending fell by an estimated 15 per cent in 1992, mainly because of a sharp decline in expenditure in the former Soviet Union, and again in 1993; armed forces continue to be reduced in almost all industrialised nations, China remaining the big exception.

The strengths of the major naval powers are listed in Table 1.

B(i). THE STRATEGIC BALANCE

The strategic balance changed little, although the superpowers became militarily less formidable, NATO more disunited and the influence of

Table 1: *MAJOR WARSHIP TYPES OF PRINCIPAL NAVIES, 1 APRIL 1994*

Type	USA	Russia	UK	France	China	India	Japan	Italy
CV (large)	13	1	–	–	–	–	–	–
CV (medium)	–	1	–	2	–	1	–	–
CV (small)	–	–	3	–	–	1	–	1
Cruiser (helicopter)	–	1	–	1	–	–	–	1
Cruiser (missile)	37	10	–	–	–	–	–	–
Destroyer	30	33	12	15	18	5	41	4
Frigate (fleet)	55	37	23	1	38	9	20	14
(escort)	–	95	–	23	–	9	–	9
SSBN	19	48	3	5	1	–	–	–
SSGN		22	–	–	–	–	–	–
	84							
SSN		53	12	6	5	–	–	–
SS (all types)	–	70	2	7	c40	18	17	9
MCMV (ocean and coastal)	17	c140	23	15	c120	12	32	14

Note: *Russian totals exclude Ukraine.*

The Australian submarine Collins *is the first of six Kockums Type 471. Seen on the day of launch, 28 August 1993, she is due to commission in May 1995.* (1993, RAN)

the rapidly-industrialising Far East more pervasive. Within a fragmenting Europe, the NATO southern region (a flank in the Cold War) is now a front region, while the central region is now a logistics base; extensive forces have been committed to the Bosnian conflict, and NATO aircraft took part in the first ever NATO military strikes, but there is no political will for a peace settlement. In the unlikely event of a major

European conflict, NATO would have a serious sealift/airlift shortfall.

B(ii). DISARMAMENT

The superpowers continued implementing the terms of the START 1 Treaty and the informal START 2 agreement. The American seaborne deterrent will shortly be carried in

eighteen *Ohio* class submarines, and plans to retrofit Trident II D-5 missiles in the eight earlier boats have been shelved. The most recent published Russian fleet plan suggests that by the end of the decade its ballistic missile fleet may be limited to five 'Typhoon' class and seven 'Delta IV' class boats. Ukraine has agreed to dismantle former Soviet nuclear weapons on its soil. From mid-1994, the USA and Russia, and Britain and

The Belgian frigate Weilingen. *Two of this class are to remain operational; the fourth,* Westhinder, *was disarmed and deleted after grounding off Norway in 1993.* (Belgian Navy)

The Belgian coastal minehunter Crocus. *Although modern, three of the ten Belgian vessels of this class were for sale in 1993.* Crocus *has been modified to transport ammunition.* (Belgian Navy)

Russia, agreed to 'detarget' their strategic nuclear missiles.

The American moratorium on nuclear tests provided no other country conducts tests was extended into 1995. The moratorium may affect UK Trident development, as three British and three American tests to check fail-safe mechanisms had been planned. The USA also suggested a world ban on production of enriched uranium and plutonium for military purposes, which might hinder production of British Trident warheads.

B(iii). THE ENVIRONMENT

Marine pollution by radioactive materials and other chemicals continued to receive attention. A Russian-American monitoring group may be formed to trace leaks from the 'Yankee' class submarine that sank 500 miles east of Bermuda, after an explosion of its liquid rocket-propelling fuel in October 1986. An international team has studied the

possible sealing of two badly damaged nuclear warheads in the hull of the 'Mike' class submarine *Komsomolets*, sunk off Norway in 1989; the wreck is leaking small amounts of radioactive caesium from its reactor, and plutonium from the warheads. Corrosion of the warheads is accelerating, while the reactor might soon go critical, causing a rapid release of radioactivity that would present a sudden, very widespread danger to fisheries.

The Russian naval special tanker *TNT 27*, with naval escorts, was detected pumping low-level liquid nuclear waste (from scrapped SSN) without containment into the Japan Sea, 105nm SE of Vladivostok, on 17 October. The waste had previously been stored in tankers near the coast; at least one tanker was in disrepair, and the safety of depots on land could not be guaranteed (after an officer had been killed in a raid on an arms depot, guards in the Russian Far East were given a 'shoot-to-kill' order). Japan, South Korea and the USA protested strongly, and Russia dropped plans for a second dumping.

C. BUDGET PROPOSALS AND NEW PROGRAMMES

C(i). USA, NATO and Allies

Major NATO Navies

(a) United States. The defence authorisation bill for FY94, beginning 1 October 1993, was finalised at $261.0b, some $13b below the FY93 level. The Defense Department requested $252.2b for FY95, reflecting a sharp drop in procurement, the US Navy's share being $78b; details of shipbuilding programmes are given in Table 2. The new administration's 'Bottom Up Defence Review' (BUDR) provided for a future force total of twelve aircraft carriers (one in reserve), eleven air wings (one reserve) and 346 major combatants; the USN plans to have 330 major combatants by removing some support and repair ships. Older ships continue to be withdrawn or transferred to allies, while A-6 and P-3A/B aircraft are being retired. New weapon

ʜᴍᴄѕ Fredericton, *the eighth* Halifax *class frigate, on sea trials, February 1994.* (Saint John Shipbuilding Ltd)

нмсѕ Preserver, *showing the two 20mm Phalanx CIWS systems fitted during refit in 1992.* (Canadian Maritime Command)

priorities include the NAS submarine, successor to *Seawolf,* and the F/A-18E/F, JAST and MV-22 aircraft programmes or projects. Details of new construction programmes are given in Table 2. The USN continue to oppose attempts by the USAF to increase its role in long-range strike missions.

The review of force structure and requirements is intended to enable the United States to fight two major regional conflicts almost simultaneously, keeping the second on 'hold' until the first is won, permitting the transfer of resources; this is the so-called 'win-hold-win' scenario, replacing the previous 'win-win'

plan, the main differences being in the extent of use of reserves and in the amount of sealift and airlift available. New fast sealift ships will enter service later in the decade, replacing the leased or chartered tonnage relied on in the meantime.

The SOSUS fixed underwater arrays system are on 'standby' be-

Table 2: *USN Shipbuilding Programmes, 1992–1995*

New Construction	Approved (authorised and funded)			Proposed (subject to amendment)
	FY92	*FY93*	*FY94*	*FY95*
SSBN	–	–	–	–
SSN-21	1	–	–	–
CVN	–	*	*	CVN-76
DDG-51	5	4	3	3
MHC	3	2	–	–
LHD	–	1**	–	–
LSD	1***	–	–	–

Notes: * *Advance funding for CVN-76.*
  ** *LHD-6 authorised in FY93 but only partly funded. Remainder of funding in FY94.*
  *** *LSD-52, authorised in FY92, funded in FY93. Conversion of* Inchon *to Mine Warfare Command Ship funded in FY94.*

cause of reduced funding, with the closure of onshore processing facilities; the number of operational T-AGOR oceanographic research ships has been reduced. As part of US counter-narcotics efforts, three T-AGOS ocean surveillance ships have had their towed sonar arrays replaced by 2D air search radars.

A second carrier may be based overseas permanently if carrier numbers are reduced below the presently intended twelve.

(b) United Kingdom. The 1993 Autumn Statement reduced 1993-94 defence spending by £110m to £23.4b; the figures for 1994-95 and 1995-96 were set at £23.5b and £22.7b respectively, less by 3.5 per cent and 6.7 per cent than the allocations proposed in

1992. Economies introduced in 'Options for Change', in the 1992 and 1993 Autumn Statements and in the 1993 Defence White Paper 'Defending our Future' continued; the *Upholder* class was laid up and the destroyer and frigate total reduced to 35. In the coming year, a further SRMH batch will be ordered. invitations to tender (ITT) for the next batch of frigates issued, and the decision on the first ITT for the replacement LPD taken. Arrangements for the collaborative development of the new-generation air defence frigate progressed, but work on a possible future joint SSN with France would be restricted by the 1958 agreement between Britain and America. On 1 January 1993 the total of Royal Navy and Royal Marine personnel was

60,300; one year later it was 56,339, reducing to 52,500 in April 1995 (the 1995 figure was further reduced to 51,000 in the 1994 Statement on the Defence Estimates). The WRNS ended as a separate service on 1 November, after 75 years.

The results of the 'Front Line First' study, to be announced in the summer, are expected to include recommendations that Rosyth Naval Base be closed, and that Rosyth and Devonport dockyards be sold; the Navy is unhappy with the decision in 1992 to keep both naval bases. HMS *Malabar*, the Bermuda naval base, will close in 1995. As another economy, the royal yacht *Britannia* will be decommissioned in 1997.

(c) Canada. Future defence alloca-

A cut-away drawing of a Type 212 submarine for the German Navy. The pressure hull aft has a smaller diameter than forward; the boat will be fitted with combined fuel cell/battery underwater propulsion derived from the experimental system tested in U1 *between 1988 and 1989.* (HDW)

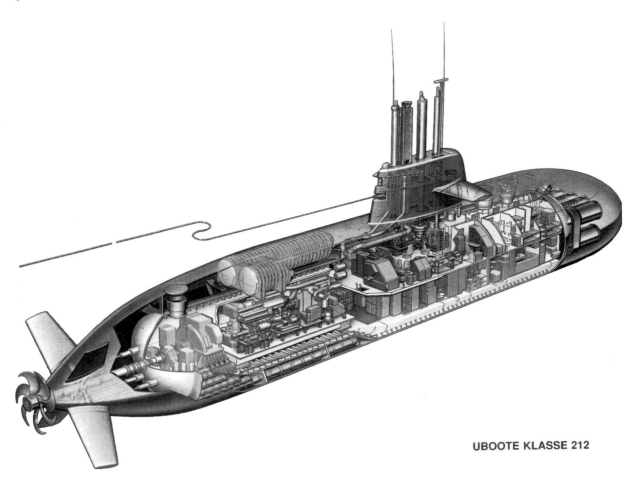

UBOOTE KLASSE 212

The missile-armed patrol craft Bakassi, *completed for Cameroon by SNCF at Villeneuve-la-Garenne in 1984. Sources state that the MM 40 missiles have been removed.* (SNCF)

The French ballistic missile submarine (SNLE) Le Foudroyant, *the oldest French SSBN in service, completed refitting with M4 missiles in February 1993.* (ECP Armées)

tions (the 1993–94 figure was $9.0b) are to be reduced by $1.2b over the next three years, savings being mostly in personnel and overheads; this is in addition to reductions announced previously and to the $1.3b saved over the same period by cancellation of the EH 101 helicopter programme, the first official act of the incoming Liberal administration.

(d) Germany. The 1994 defence budget was set at $27.5b, a reduction of $1.5b on 1993. Too much money is still being spent on personnel costs; the allocation for new equipment and R&D, increased to 21.8 per cent of the total, remains much less than the desired 30 per cent. Three instead of four Type 124 frigates will be ordered, so that the four-unit *U-212*

submarine programme can be fully funded. In the long term, it is hoped to replace all fast attack craft with between ten and fifteen corvettes of a new type.

(e) Italy. The new political order and resulting economies in state spending have meant a dearth of new equipment orders.

(f) Netherlands. In addition to the reductions announced in the Defence White Paper of 12 January 1993 (naval forces would be reduced by 25 per cent by 2002), the 1994 defence budget cut naval allocation by $41m; the additional reduction will be absorbed by stretching the project definition phase for the two planned air defence and command frigates

from 18 to 24 months; it is now intended to let their construction contract in mid-1995. The Dutch and Belgian Navies plan to merge their headquarters at Den Helder in the Netherlands and to integrate their surface forces operationally.

The South-Eastern Flank. Greece continued to acquire surplus American and Dutch tonnage; the indigenous frigate, fast attack craft and LST programmes are being delayed by financial problems at the Greek shipyards. **Turkey** balances increased Greek strength with ex-US frigates and her own programme of new construction. Five teams have delivered final bids for the $360m contract for six minehunters.

The French SSN Rubis *was one of three French nuclear attack submarines involved in accidents or collisions during the year. In 1993* Rubis *completed modernisation, to reach the same ASW standard as the later* Amethyste *and* Perle. *(ECP Armées)*

The German Type 123 frigate Brandenburg *began first-of-class initial sea trials in late 1993; commissioning is scheduled for October 1994.* (German Navy)

The German missile-armed fast attack craft Puma *was the first Type 143A to receive the Rolling Airframe Missile (RAM) 21-cell PDMS. All ten of the class are to be fitted between 1992 and 1995.* (German Navy)

Lesser NATO Navies

Norway. The proposed naval procurement programme includes from six to eight surface effect FAC(M), while some units of existing classes (except *Storm* class) will be modernised, three new coastguard patrol ships, with the existing three being modernised, and up to six new escort frigates - which might overtake the FAC(M) as first priority. **Belgium.** Severe cuts in defence spending will lead to a reduction in personnel from 4000 to 2500 by the end of 1994. One

frigate and five MCMV will be put up for sale, but four coastal minesweepers were ordered and three frigates are to be modernised. **Portugal** has prioritised new submarine construction; second-hand or new construction minesweepers and OPVs are lower on the list.

France and Spain

France and Spain co-operate with NATO but are not full military members

France. The 1994 defence budget rose by 3.6 per cent to $34.9b; new proposals aim to raise defence spending eventually to the 1990 level of 3.4 per cent of GNP. The Defence White Paper proposes a reduced nuclear role in French defence. At least $106b is to be spent on defence equipment in 1995–2000, with an annual rise of 0.5 per cent before inflation, perhaps rising to 1.5 per cent from 1997 if the economy permits. Continued funding was approved for all major equipment programmes, although there will be minor stretch-outs for the nuclear carrier *Charles de Gaulle*, the Rafale M and the multinational NH-90 helicopter (the audit committee stated that stretching-out military contracts wastes money instead of saving it), and the M5 missile will enter service in 2010 instead of 2005. A second *Foudre* class LPD was ordered; a decision will be taken on the second nuclear carrier in 1997.

Closer ties are sought with NATO, but there are no plans to rejoin the integrated command system.

The German Type 332 coastal minehunter Frankenthal, *first of a class of ten. The class generally resemble the earlier Type 343* Hameln *class sweepers.* (German Navy)

The German large patrol craft Neustrelitz, *begun as a* Volksmarine *Type 153 (NATO 'Balcom-10')* Sassnitz *class FAC(M). Re-engined and fitted with new electronics in 1992–93, she was armed with a 40mm/70 Bofors gun and transferred to the Border Guard (Bundesgrenzscutz – See).* (German Navy)

Spain. The proposed 1994 budget increases defence spending by 6.3 per cent to $6.1b, after continuous falls since 1990. Material spending made up 46 per cent of the total, an increase of 15 per cent on the 1993 equipment figure. At present, ships have insufficient sea time, steaming for 70 days annually against the desired 110 days.

Major US Allies

Japan. The FY94 defence budget increase was agreed at a real 1.95 per cent or $900m, the lowest increase for thirty-three years; the 1993 increase was only 3.2 per cent. These figures will mean less new equipment, more upgrading and modernisation of existing JDF systems, and less training. The JMSDF will continue developing capabilities to protect sea lanes. The

1993 Defence White Paper provided an extensive review of the PACRIM situation, but proposed no major changes in the current five-year programme; proposed changes in the National Defence Programme Outline were not addressed. The future control of the Russian armed forces, and North Korea's SSM and nuclear programmes, cause concern. Some warships homeported at Yokosuka are to be dispersed elsewhere to attract naval recruits and reduce congestion round the port.

Australia. The 1993–94 defence budget was $6.65bn, a real 0.75 per cent less than in 1992–93, and spending is projected to fall by 0.5 per cent annually for the next five years. The major submarine and frigate programmes remain, but the projected training and helicopter support ship has been deleted – second-hand US

tonnage may be modified for these roles. The contract for up to six coastal minehunters was awarded to ADI/Intermarine, and a possible collaborative programme with Malaysia for Offshore Patrol Vessels (OPVs) is being investigated.

C(ii). Neutral European Nations

(a) Finland. Recession continues to reduce defence spending and delay modernisation. The 1993 defence allocation of $1.94b was 20 per cent less in real terms than the 1992 figure, itself down by a real 5 per cent on 1991; new minelayers and SSM-armed fast attack craft have improved naval capabilities, but future orders are uncertain.

The Irish offshore patrol vessel Emer, *one of four similar ships completed to Nevesbu design between 1972 and 1980.* (Irish Navy)

The flight deck of INS Vikrant, *before fitting of ski jump. This ship is to remain in service until at least 1997; funds permitting, she may be replaced by a* Garibaldi *type carrier.*

(b) Sweden. The June 1992 five-year defence resolution approved a spending increase of $1b over five years; despite reductions in social welfare spending, the defence budget increased by an annual $150m from 1992 to 1994, the latter figure being $4.6b. The Navy's new programme submitted in August proposed eight new stealth warships, as the start of a programme of up to 28 new ships in the next decade.

C(iii). Eastern European Nations

Russia, CIS and Succession States. According to US estimates, Russian defence spending for 1992 was one half that of 1991 for the whole USSR; the 1993 aim is to match 1992 spending, but with procurement up by between 10 per cent

and 30 per cent. A Swedish report suggested that the defence allocation, some 18 per cent of GNP in later Soviet years, is now around 11–12 per cent of the (much lower) Russian GNP. Russia's conventional forces are in very poor condition: fewer manoeuvres, fuel shortages, falling weapon procurement, deteriorating maintenance, low morale and poorly qualified conscripts. Recent production levels include 20 submarines and major surface warships in 1990, 13 in 1991 and eight (Russia only) in 1992.

According to a published Fleet Plan, the intention is ultimately to retain the following current submarine types for the stated purposes:
a) the 'Typhoon' and 'Delta IV' classes in the strategic deterrent role;
b) the SS-N-21 armed 'Akula' class in the substrategic land attack role;
c) the 'Sierra I/II', 'Kilo' and around one-third of the 'Victor III' classes for ASW;
d) the 'Oscar I/II' and the bulk of the

'Victor III' classes for anti-surface ship warfare.

Similarly, the reduced surface fleet will include the carrier *Admiral Kuznetsov, Udaloy* and *Sovremenniy* class destroyers, and 'Krivak III' and *Neustrashimy* class frigates. More 'Tarantul' class missile-armed fast attack craft will be ordered.

Ukraine. Attempts to divide the Black Sea Fleet between Russia and Ukraine continued to sour relations, an issue complicated by the wish of the Crimean people to secede from Ukraine and rejoin Russia. The 1992 agreement to share control of the fleet for three years having become untenable, the two nations agreed on a 50-50 division of the fleet and other assets, with Russia continuing to use the Sevastopol naval base. A further agreement for Russia to take over the Ukrainian share of the fleet in return for cancelling Ukraine's energy debts was challenged in Parliament in

The Israeli corvette Eilat, *first of three, on builder's trials in the Gulf of Mexico.* (Ingalls)

Kiev. Skirmishing was reported around naval installations in Odessa and Ismail. The situation remains tense, and Ukraine's economy and independence shaky; its navy in 1994 possessed four frigates and various auxiliaries.

Kazakhstan proposed renovating two ex-Soviet bases, on the Caspian and Aral Seas, but the required funding is not yet approved; one-quarter to one-third of the former Caspian Flotilla may be taken over, and requirements will focus on coastal areas and adjacent inland waterways.

Bulgaria. Proposals to modernise the navy include cutting manpower by around 20 per cent over the next three years. Funds permitting, the strike force will be improved, air defence capabilities increased and mine warfare expertise developed. Thirty older warships and auxiliaries will be deleted.

C(iv) Middle East

In general, the progress of orders is hindered by the low price of oil. **Oman's** contract for three Project Mawj fast patrol craft, with lead-in training for new corvettes, went to CMN, Cherbourg, which will supply P400 type craft; Swan Hunter, the other yard in line for the contract, laid off 200 workers almost immediately. **Saudi Arabia's** cash flow problems have limited orders and the navy has the lowest priority among the services. Orders for frigates and the three further MCMV have not been confirmed; the frigate design may be optimised for ASW in place of air defence. The **UAE's** new construction plans now appear to comprise four FFGs, and smaller corvettes or fast attack craft. **Egypt**. The US State Department authorised HDW to prepare proposals for Ingalls to build two Type 209 submarines, for which US funding may be required.

C(v). 'PACRIM' and Indian Ocean

(a) China. The official defence budget for 1994 was $6.2b, a drop in real terms (after devaluation) from the 1993 figure of $7.4b, and less in real terms than in 1980; in 1980, defence spending was (officially) about 4.5 per cent of GNP, in 1993 about 1.5 per cent. Foreign observers consider that the true defence spending is very much higher, SIPRI suggesting a figure of $45b. Naval capabilities are being increased to support Beijing's moves towards a more positive offshore defence strategy covering China's EEZ and extending it to include the Spratly Islands. High-technology air-defence purchases from Russia stimulated by the lessons of the Gulf War may be followed by attempts to obtain crucial carrier technology from Moscow or elsewhere; a report indicates that two 48,000-ton carriers are planned to be in service by 2005. A mock-up of a

The Italian submarine Nazario Sauro, *commissioned in 1980. The second pair of boats of the improved* Sauro *class were completed in 1993–94.* (Italian Navy)

carrier flight deck has been built on shore and over 100 pilots for fixed-wing carrier aircraft are to be trained by 1997.

(b) India. The 1994-95 defence budget of $7.4b represented a real increase of about 8 per cent on the 1993–94 figure; the increase is to stem the long decline in defence capabilities, and is partly meant for replacing obsolescent and unmaintainable former-Soviet equipment; the naval allocation, excluding capital outlays, was $430m. The indigenous naval new construction programmes continue slowly.

Lesser Navies

South Korea's submarine programme is complete, and the prototype KDX destroyer may be ordered shortly, when the command and fire control systems are chosen. **Taiwan** continued its military build-up; the navy is spending over $10b in replacing its older warships, and new and modern second-hand frigates have

begun entering service. However, attempts to acquire Dutch or German technology for the local construction or assembly of submarines seem to date to have been unsuccessful. **Malaysia** will be able to keep defence spending at 4.5 per cent of GDP to boost defence capabilities because recent financial constraints have been lifted; in future, less reliance may be placed on the Five Power Defence Arrangement. Likely naval orders include the first batch of up to twenty-seven OPVs. **Singapore's** defence spending in 1994-95 is set to rise by 8.6 per cent to $2.7b. **Indonesia** is using limited funds to modernise its ex-*Volksmarine* warships (according to a Djakarta press report, the deal was approved against Indonesian Navy advice), while ordering four more PB 57 large patrol craft to be built at Surabaia. **Pakistan** spent $3.0b on defence in 1992-93, a crippling burden for a very poor nation; the ex-US frigates returned under the nuclear proliferation Amendment were replaced by the RN's Type 21 class, and the tripartite minehunter programme is in hand.

C(vi). Africa

South Africa. The first step towards regaining a blue-water presence and ASW capability may be an order for up to six 2000-ton corvettes equipped with helicopters; replacement submarines, strike craft and MCMV will also be required during the next 15 years.

D. WARSHIP BUILDING

D(i). New Designs and Principal Orders

Multinational. In Britain, the GEC/Marconi bid to become UK prime contractor for the tri-national Common New Generation Frigate (CNGF) – 'Project Horizon' – was chosen in preference to VSEL and Swan Hunter; Yarrow, BAe and Vosper Thornycroft are part of the successful team. The French prime contractor is DCN (International),

The Italian LPD San Marco, *funded by the Ministry of Civil Protection and fitted for disaster relief but operated by the Navy. The third unit,* San Giusto, *built to a modified design with more accommodation, was completed in mid-1994.* (Italian Navy)

The Italian offshore patrol vessel Cassiopea, *first of four units funded by Italy's Merchant Navy Ministry but operated by the Navy.* (Italian Navy)

the Italian a Fincantieri/Finmeccanica consortium. The three national partners will negotiate to form an international joint venture company to bid for the design contract and for the construction of the first three, one for each navy, which might begin in 1997.

Dutch, German and Spanish shipbuilders signed a MoU for their future tripartite frigate, the other major joint European programme; a common design, possibly an enlarged *Karel Doorman*, with systems chosen by the individual navies, is predicted. Germany and Spain approached the USA for possible AEGIS systems, while the Dutch units will have VLS Standard missiles.

(a) United States. The options for futher USN submarine construction are reopening the SSN-688 production line, more SSN-21 *Seawolf*s (two are building, a third will be requested in FY96), and the New Attack Submarine (NAS), presently envisaged at around 6800-7000 tons and perhaps to begin construction in 1998. Major post-Cold War roles include the covert collection of intelligence and detection of mines, the operation of special forces, an increased strike performance and improved ASW performance against very quiet non-nuclear submarines. For example, *Seawolf* could be equipped to land sixty special force troops ashore, while the NAS might be fitted with

from 75 to 100 'Tomahawk' cruise missiles.

Looking further ahead, preliminary studies are in hand for the next multi-mission surface combatant, designated SC-21, which would complement and perhaps eventually replace the CG-47 and DDG-51 classes. The present AEGIS fleet has partly corrected older ships' difficulties in engaging very small or over-the-horizon targets, and their lack of design flexibility for modernisation.

Five Ro-Ro conversions were ordered for transport and pre-positioning of US Army armour and helicopters, three from National Steel and Shipbuilding and two from Newport News Shipbuilding. One new

The Italian replenishment tanker Stromboli, *seen on exercises with* Vittorio Veneto. *The Iraqi* Agnadeen, *of this type, has been laid up in Alexandria since 1986.* (Italian Navy)

$265m Ro-Ro sealift ship for US Army pre-positioning requirements was ordered from Avondale, New Orleans, and a second from National Steel and Shipbuilding, with options for five more; 49-month construction periods were specified. Six new strategic sealift ships ordered from National Steel and Shipbuilding Co, San Diego, at a cost of $1.3b.

The contract for completion of two fleet oilers was terminated because of severe financial and performance problems at Tampa Shipyards; the incomplete hulls of T-AO-191 and T-AO-192 were removed from the shipyard and inactivated.

The Libyan LST Ibn Harissa, *one of two completed by CNI de la Mediterranée in 1977 and 1978.* (Breda)

The Malaysian light frigate Kasturi, *completed in 1984.* (HDW)

(b) United Kingdom. HMS *Vanguard* was accepted by the RN in September and should make her first operational patrol from late 1994; *Victorious* was rolled out and named in October. The fourth of the class will be named *Vengeance*. Swan Hunter remained open to complete the three Type 23 frigates building, and give a lifeline to possible bids (and orders) from the UK and overseas. *Ocean* will be equipped with the Ferranti ADAWS 2000 command system. The new RFAs *Fort Victoria* and *Fort George* will enter service without VLS Sea Wolf.

(c) Norway released details of its new

Table 3: *NEW AMPHIBIOUS WARFARE SHIP TYPES*

Country	Netherlands/Spain	UK	USA
Type	LPD	LPH	LPD
Class	Rotterdam/–	Ocean	LPD-17
No in class	1 each	1	12
Builders	Royal Schelde/ Bazan	Kvaerner/ VSEL	–
Building dates	1994–98	1994–97	c1996–2007
Displacement (max)	12,000	20,000	23,000
L × b × d (max), metres	150 × 25 × 5.9	203 × 32.6 × 6.6	213 × 31.4 × 6.4
Missiles	–	–	2 RAM
Guns	2 CIWS, 4–20mm	8–30mm/73 3–20mm CIWS	3–20mm CIWS
Helicopters	4 large or 6 small	12	1 (hangar) + 1 (deck)
Military lift	6 LCVP	4 LCVP	2 LCAC
Troops	600	480	750
Machinery	Diesel	Diesel	Diesel
Max bhp	–	–	40,000
Speed (kts)	20	18	23

Table 4: RECENT MINE COUNTERMEASURES VESSEL TYPES

Country	Belgium	Germany	Spain
Type	Sweeper (coastal)	Hunter (coastal)	Hunter (coastal)
Class	–	Frankenthal	–
No in class	4	10	4
Builder(s)	–	Lurssenwerft Abeking & Rasmussen Krogerwerft	Bazan
Building dates	c1995–2001	1989–1995	1995–c2000
Displacement (max)	620t	650t	530t
L × b × d (max), metres	52.4 × 10.4 × 3.1	54.5 × 9.2 × 2.6	54.0 × 10.7 × 2.3
Missiles	–	2 Stinger	–
Guns	1–20mm	1–40mm/70	1–20mm
Machinery	Diesel	Diesel	Diesel
Max bhp	–	5550	1520
Speed (kts)	15	18	14

AGI *Marjata*, a remarkable 5300-ton ship 82m long and 40m wide, which will replace the previous *Marjala* in the Barents Sea.

(d) Belgium. The four coastal minehunters to be built between 1996 and 2003 at a cost of $353m will be fitted with a mine avoidance sonar and a full suite of mechanical, acoustic and magnetic sweeps; the design will resemble that of the aborted joint programme with the Netherlands and Portugal.

(e) France. The new ballistic missile submarine (SNLE-NG) *Le Triomphant* was rolled out on 13 July and lowered into the water in October. Weld faults discovered in the hull may delay sea trials by two months, until February 1994. The diesel *Scorpene* CM 2000 submarine project, designed by DCI and Bazan to replace the Spanish *Daphne* class, will incorporate technology from the French nuclear fleet and an AIP system. The carrier *Charles de Gaulle* was floated out on 7 May 1994 (a brief earlier flotation in 1993 had been to reposition the ship on its blocks).

(f) Spain. The F 100 timetable has been revised; construction of the first-of-class, now part of the tripartite frigate programme, is now planned to begin in 1997 for delivery in 2001, and the fourth should be completed in 2004. Fears have been expressed over Dutch and German domination of the programme. In December, DCN (International) and Bazan signed an accord for the former to assist in the construction of four GRP minehunters, possibly to a Spanish design that uses the UK *Sandown* class as baseline. In 1989, Vosper Thornycroft transferred design and technology

The Malaysian logistic support ship Sri Indera Sakti, *completed by Bremer Vulkan in 1980.* Mahawangsa, *the second unit of the class, was built by Korea Tacoma and has no funnel.* (Bremer Vulkan)

details of *Sandown* under a six-month contract.

(g) Australia. The first new submarine, *Collins*, was ceremonially rolled out on schedule and on budget. However, delivery has slipped by six months, mainly because of systems integration problems.

(h) Sweden. Four limited stealth, GRP-hulled, Type YSB coastal minehunters were ordered from Karlskronavarvet (KKV) on 11 February. Details of four larger, full stealth Type YSM (or YS 2000) fast attack craft also to be ordered from KKV are being finalised: following a displacement increase to 400 tons and length increase to almost 60m, a monohulled ship may be preferred to the surface-effect design first proposed. The new design will include the latest technology to counter, for example, laser guided bombs.

(j) Russia. Russian new construction continued slowly. Current ballistic missile submarine programmes are complete (a new SSBN may begin construction around 2000), but the SSGN 'Oscar II' (Antyev) class continues building at Severodvinsk, the only yard now building nuclear powered submarines, at the rate of about one per year. The 'Victor III' and 'Sierra II' programmes are complete, the 'Akula' class remains in production. The first *Severodvinsk* class (Projekt 885) steel-hulled fourth-generation SSN was begun in December and may be launched in 1996-97

(new SSN construction seems to be limited to finishing boats already started, or for which material has been collected). Wider markets are being sought for the 'Kilo' class diesel submarines, described as cheaper to buy and easier to operate than Western equivalents. A small number of updated 'Kilos' (Model 636) were ordered, fitted with improved electronics and control systems and an uprated wire-guided torpedo, TEST-96. The 'Amur Project' is a follow-on 'Kilo'. The *Pyotr Velikiy*, fourth nuclear-powered missile cruiser of the *Kirov* class, is to be completed; with the 'Udaloy II', *Neustrashimy*, 'Krivak III' and 'Grisha V' classes apparently all complete, terminated or greatly slowed, construction of major surface combatants seems limited to about one *Sovremenniy* class a year. The 21st *Sovremenniy* is to have a new SSM, smaller than the SS-N-22, which will be launched from a VLS box aft. Surface combatants available for export include frigates, corvettes and a fast attack craft of existing modern types armed with Russia's latest weaponry. The fourth *Slava* class cruiser has been renamed, and is to be completed as flagship of the Ukrainian Navy.

(k) Iran. The second 'Kilo' class submarine was delivered in August 1993, the third is expected in September or October 1994.

(l) Israel. The first Sa'ar 5 corvette completed initial sea trials in October.

(m) Oman. The keel of the first corvette was laid, 21 May 1993; the pair will be fitted with an active towed array sonar (Thomson Sintra ATAS), and possibly with ASW torpedo tubes.

(n) Taiwan. The first *La Fayette* class frigate was reported launched at night with minimal ceremony, for 'technical reasons', 12 March.

D(ii) Ships Entering Service During the Year

These are listed in Table 5 (the figures for Russia and China are approximate).

D(iii). Reconstructions

(a) United Kingdom. Four *Trafalgar* class submarines are to be refitted with Ferranti-Thomson Type 2076 integrated sonar suites, under Phase 3-4 of the SSN update programme.

(b) Netherlands is to upgrade four *Alkmaar* class minehunters with propelled VDS and modify three others for guidance of improved Troika minesweeping drones; the modernisations are intended to compensate for the decommissioning of eight *Dokkum* class MCMV and the cancellation of six new coastal minesweepers. Four other *Alkmaar* class

Table 5: *NEW SHIPS ENTERING SERVICE, 1 APRIL 1993 TO 31 MARCH 1994 (RUSSIA, CHINA IN 1993)*

Type	USA	Russia	UK	France	China	India	Japan	Italy
CV (large)	–	–	–	–	–	–	–	–
CV (medium)	–	–	–	–	–	–	–	–
CV (small)	–	–	–	–	–	–	–	–
CAH	–	–	–	–	–	–	–	–
CG	3	–	–	–	–	–	–	–
DD	2	1	–	–	1	–	–	–
FF (fleet)	–	1	2	–	4	–	–	–
(escort)	–	–	–	2	–	–	–	–
SSBN	1	–	1	–	–	–	–	–
SSGN	3	1	–	–	–	–	–	–
SSN		1	–	1	–	–	–	–
SS (all)	–	2	1	–	–	–	1	1

The Moroccan large patrol craft El Maher, *one of six built in Spain between 1987 and 1989, is employed on coastal fisheries protection.* (Bazan)

The Dutch air defence frigate Jacob van Heemskerck, *showing the prominent SHF SATCOM terminals fitted in 1993. The four* Kortenaer *being retained will be fitted with these terminals.* RNethN)

will be refitted later for deeper-water operations.

(c) France. The three *Tourville* class (Type F67) ASW destroyers are receiving mid-life updates; the 11-month refit of *Duguay-Trouin* included an ASW update, removal of Malafon and provision for female crew. The other two in the class will be more extensively refitted, to include installation of the SLASM ASW combat suite. The MILAS ASROC-type stand-off ASW weapon system will replace Malafon from 1997.

(d) Chile. Two of the ex-RN 'County' class destroyers have been fitted with the Israeli Barak PDMS in boxes located on the former Seacat director platforms, in addition to the extended flight decks and enlarged hangars. The frigate *Condell* has been modified with enlarged hangar and flight deck to operate a Super Puma helicopter.

The Dutch frigate Karel Doorman, *showing SATCOM terminals.* (RNethN)

D(iv). Fleet Depletions (decommissionings, transfers, etc)

(a) United States. The decommissioning list for FY 94 included the carrier *Saratoga*, fifteen SSN, the nuclear-powered cruisers *Virginia* and *Long Beach*, seventeen CG and eight frigates. Some nuclear-powered vessels are being retired as they become due for expensive refuelling. All older CG will go by the end of FY94, except *Belknap*, Sixth Fleet flagship. All the *Knox* class will also go: transfers or proposed transfers on lease to allies are as follows (numbers in parentheses): Brazil (4), Egypt (2), Greece (3), Morocco (1), Oman (1), Spain (2), Taiwan (6 + 6), Turkey (8, including one on a grant basis to replace *Muavenet*), Venzuela (2). Congressional approval is being

The Nigerian corvette Erinomi, *completed in 1980. Many (if not most) Nigerian warships are of doubtful operational value*. (Vosper Thornycroft)

sought for the transfer of *Newport* class LSTs to Australia (2) and Spain (2).

(b) United Kingdom. The six Type 21 frigates were acquired by Pakistan for around £48m ($76.2m), at the rate of about two every six months, starting in July 1993; plans for refitting them are believed to include Harpoon SSM and replacement of Seacat with Phalanx from discarded destroyers. *Challenger* was sold for £2m to a Scottish cable-laying company. The MCMV *Nurton*, the Navy's last active wooden warship, arrived at Portsmouth to decommission on 3 December and the last steam combatant, the frigate *Sirius*, was withdrawn in January. Six *River* class minesweepers are on the sales list, and the OPV *Jersey* went to Bangladesh.

(c) Italy. The acquisition of the four ex-Iraqi *Lupo* class frigates was finally approved; new legislation was required, as the Italian Navy declined to release its own funds for the purchase. Two-year refits will be required to re-equip the ships as Fleet Patrol Ships.

(d) Netherlands. The naval sales list includes three more *Kortenaer* class frigates, available in 1995-96, two *Zwaardvis* class submarines (1996), eight *Dokkum* class MCMV (1995) and the support ship *Poolster*.

(e) Russia continues to scrap older units and those too expensive to maintain. Only the damaged *Admiral Gorshkov* remains from the *Kiev* class; five 'Karas' remain, the two refitting in Ukraine having been listed for sale or scrap; all 'Krestas', 'Kyndas' and 'Kashins' are going or have gone. The earlier 'Krivaks' and 'Grishas' are paying off. Chaos in the shipyards and dockyards is such that even modern ships damaged in accidents are not being repaired. Over 150 SSGN and SSN, and 30 SSBN will be laid up, scrapped or sold by 2000. **Ukraine** cannot afford to continue with construction of *Ulyanovsk*, and will turn the unfinished hull into tankers; *Varyag* will also be sold for scrap.

E. NAVAL WEAPON SYSTEMS

E(i). Missiles, including Ballistic Missiles

(a) United States. The USN's requirement for a submarine-launched long range precision-guided weapon (PGW) able to attack deeply buried targets may be met by a non-nuclear

Trident. Continuing army and navy participation in the tri-service, very advanced TSSAM missile programme is in doubt despite reduced orders (the navy's order was 1050 out of a total of 7450 in mid-1993), and further Stand-off Land Attack Missiles (SLAMs) may be ordered instead. A new extended range SLAM will reach 120km rather than 95km, and the navy's existing SLAM inventory will be uprated to this standard (SLAM-ER).

(b) United Kingdom. Britain's nuclear firepower is to be reduced by at least 20 per cent, from a maximum of 128 warheads per submarine to a maximum of 96, and maybe significantly fewer. With the abandoning of the RAF's proposed new tactical air-launched stand-off nuclear missile (TASM), work began on a substrategic Trident: British D-5 missiles could be deployed with fewer, or a single, nuclear warheads as theatre nuclear weapons. There are no plans to deploy Trident missiles with non-nuclear warheads, but Tomahawk cruise missiles with conventional warheads might be purchased for the *Trafalgar* class. The first Trident firings from *Vanguard* took place in mid-1994; operational missiles will be loaded in the United States, their warheads fitted in Britain. The House of Commons Defence Committee continued investigating the safety of the Trident missile system.

(c) French and **German** companies are planning a joint supersonic anti-ship missile to replace Exocet. It might combine the warhead and sensor system of the aborted ANS (Anti-Navire Supersonique) with the airframe of the French tactical nuclear missile ASMP.

(d) Taiwain's Hsieung Feng II anti-ship missile, which has a dual IR/active radar seeker and a range of between 70 and 80km, is entering service.

E(ii). Maritime Aircraft

Multinational. The planned orders for the NFH 90 NATO frigate helicopter are: sixty-four for Italy, sixty for France, thirty-eight for Germany and twenty for the Netherlands.

(a) United States. The FY94 budget approved $1.45b for research and development for the F/A-18E/F, which faced an important design review in June 1994, and $1.5b for thirty-six F/A-18C/D Hornets. $110m would be spent on increasing the strike capability of the F-14 Tomcat. The USN's proposed A/F-X and the Air Force's multirole fighter (MRF) were terminated, and replaced by a new multimission project, the Joint Advanced Strike Technology (JAST) programme, for which initial study contracts are expected. The F/A-18E/F and JAST will provide a continuing naval deep strike capability. Only twenty-seven new production radar-equipped Harrier II Plus are funded, and remaining USMC requirements will be met by remanufacture of existing Harriers. A Boeing study for a relatively modest STOVL concept, to compete against more sophisticated proposals, was funded. 68 P-3C Orion aircraft will receive ASuW updates. The decision on possible production of the V-22 Osprey was deferred. The last active Seasprite squadron was disbanded; two reserve squadrons remain.

Norway's first surface effect minehunter, the Kvaener Mandal-built Oksoy, *seen on trials.* (RNoN)

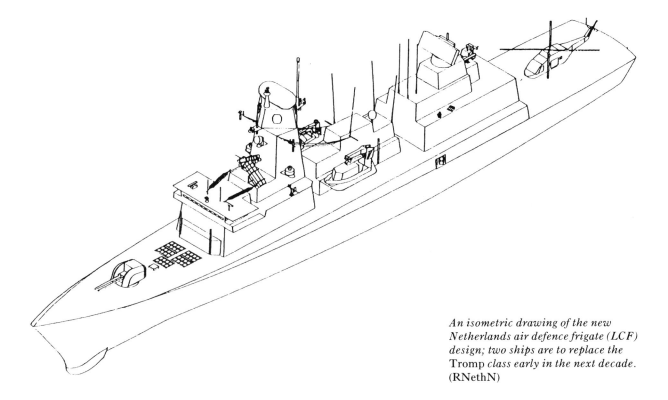

An isometric drawing of the new Netherlands air defence frigate (LCF) design; two ships are to replace the Tromp *class early in the next decade.* (RNethN)

(b) United Kingdom. The order for eighteen new Sea Harrier FRS2 to cost £200m ($300m) was confirmed. The Anglo-Italian EH 101 resumed flight trials in June 1993, following a fatal crash in January caused by an uncommanded engagement of the rotor brake system in flight.

(c) Canada reduced its purchase of thirty-five naval EH 101 helicopters to twenty-eight in September, to save $775m, the order for fifteen SAR versions being unaffected. The entire order was cancelled in November.

(d) France. The latest in-service date for the Rafale M is now 1999, to coincide with the commissioning of *Charles de Gaulle*. Rafale M carrier trials aboard *Foch*, planned for between 24 January and 4 March, were suspended for two months while the carrier was diverted to the Adriatic. Two Hawkeyes will be purchased for the new carrier, and possibly two more later in the decade. Fixed-wing pilots will be trained in America from 1994, when the Fouga-Zephyr trainers are withdrawn.

(e) Russia. The Su-33 (formerly Su-27K) intended for the *Admiral Kuznetsov* will probably initially be based ashore; intensive deck landing trials are being carried out aboard the carrier, presently operating from Murmansk.

(f) Thailand wishes to purchase surplus Spanish AV-8S and TAV-8S Harriers (replaced in Spanish service by the Harrier II Plus) for its future carrier; the USA is considering the request. Six S-60B Seahawk helicopters have been ordered for delivery in 1997.

(g) Brazil is to be the third client for Super Lynx: nine new, five upgrades ordered, at cost of $220m. Brazil's carrier conducted joint operations with the Argentine Navy Super Etendards, to give Argentine pilots experience while their carrier is rebuilding.

E(iii). Anti-Aircraft and Anti-Missile Warfare (AAW)

(a) United States et al. The 'Star Wars' programme was terminated on 13 May 1993 and replaced by the Ballistic Missile Defence Organisa-tion (BMDO). Proposals for possible future defences include use of a modified RIM-67 Standard-ER Block 4 missile fired from an AEGIS-equipped ship; the ship's SPY-1 radar and systems would be modified to search at higher altitudes and to receive data from early-warning satellites. In a simulation, two AEGIS cruisers in the Western Mediterranean, armed with Standard Block IV missiles with LEAP seekers and working with a land-based phased array radar, were able to protect an area from Rome to London against missile attack. In addition, AEGIS-equipped ships fitted with the SPY-1 radar will be given an over-the-horizon capability against stealthy, supersonic, low-flying cruise missiles by new airborne radar technology. This will use an MPA platform to increase radar range from 30km to 130km. A non-AEGIS programme to improve anti-missile defences will integrate RAM, Phalanx, radar, IR sensors and electronics warfare suites.

(b) United Kingdom. BAe is to supply a further 450 VLS Seawolf at a cost of $100m.

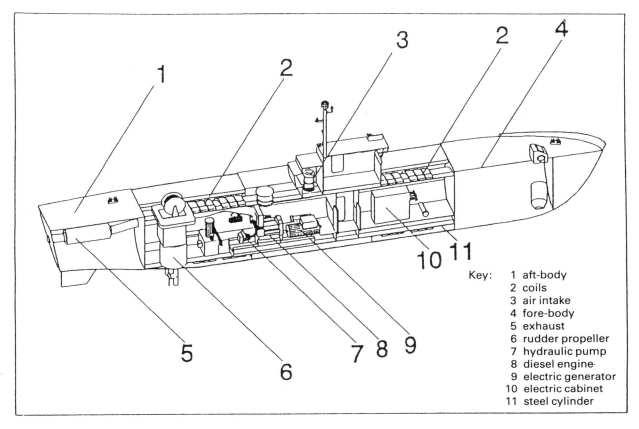

Key:
1 aft-body
2 coils
3 air intake
4 fore-body
5 exhaust
6 rudder propeller
7 hydraulic pump
8 diesel engine
9 electric generator
10 electric cabinet
11 steel cylinder

A cut-away drawing of a Dutch Troika minesweeping drone, similar to the type developed for Germany by SIGNAAL; four such drones will be controlled by modified Dutch Alkmaar class minehunters. (RNethN)

The Alvares Cabral, second of Portugal's three ASW MEKO 200 type frigates completed in 1991. (Portuguese Navy)

The Russian frigate Neustrashimy. *The second-of-class may be completed in 1994, the third was launched without superstructure.* (BMVg/MoD, Bonn)

E(iv). Guns

(a) United States. Plans put forward to overcome the USN's fire support shortfall included redesigned rounds and new propellants for the existing 5in/45 Mod 2 gun, the introduction of precision-guided munitions and eventually an entirely new 155mm gun.

(b) United Kingdom. A new ER round of the 'base-bleed' type is being sought for UK Mk8 4.5in guns, to increase the 22km range by up to 25 per cent.

E(v). Mine Warfare Systems

Multinational. NATO is studying methods of clearing shallow (0-10m depth) minefields before amphibious landings. The methods include carpet bombing, use of autonomous underwater vehicles (UAVs) and a naval version of an army explosive line system.

(a) United States. The USN's top mine warfare priority is covert mine watching. Both the upgrade for the CAPTOR mine and the projected helicopter-launched missile for mine clearing were cancelled.

F. NAVAL EVENTS

F(i) Areas of Conflict and Naval Actions

(a) The Gulf. UN sanctions against Iraq and air exclusion zones in the north and south of the country remained in force. At 2022 hours GMT on 26 June, twenty-three Tomahawk cruise missiles were launched by USS *Chancellorsville* in the Gulf (nine missiles) and USS *Peterson* in the Red Sea (sixteen missiles) against Iraqi military intelligence headquarters in Bagdad; sixteen missiles arrived on target. The attack was in retaliation for the abortive assassination attempt against ex-President Bush in Kuwait. Recent withdrawals of US carriers meant no carrier battle group was in

the Gulf between the departure of the *Nimitz* in June and the arrival of the *Abraham Lincoln* in late July. The *Theodore Roosevelt* CVBG, with the NATO force off Bosnia, was therefore temporarily sent through to the Red Sea on 29 June.

(b) The Mediterranean. The five-nation Operation 'Deny Flight', maintained by land air forces and twelve aircraft from the *Theodore Roosevelt* CVBG, was generally successful; violations were generally by communications helicopters, without direct impact on the ground war. In July, attack aircraft tasked to protect UN ground forces included fourteen from the CVBG, recalled from the Red Sea. As diplomatic attempts to halt Serb advances and bombardments failed, NATO strikes were conducted on 10 and 11 April, and on 16 April a Sea Harrier from *Ark Royal* was downed by a Serb SAM while attempting an attack. The pilot ejected with minor injuries and was rescued by helicopter. An Etendard IVP, slightly damaged by

The Spanish frigate Reina Sofia. *The fifth and sixth ships of this class are to commission in 1994.* (Spanish Navy)

A Lurssen-built 45m FAC(M) *on trials. Such fast, well-armed craft were exported to Gulf states in the 1980s, but Operation 'Desert Storm' showed their limitations. More modern units fit short-range SAMs and/or CIWS, while older craft are being refitted.* (Breda)

A recent outboard profile of the Dutch LPD Rotterdam. *The first steel was cut in early 1994, and the ship will be completed in 1997. A similar ship is to be built by Bazan for Spain, entering service about one year later.* (RNethN)

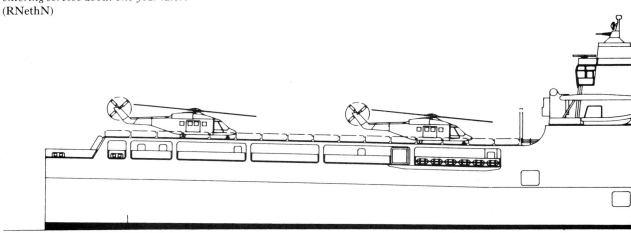

The attack transport Aragon *(ex-USS* Francis Marion, *LPA 249), is flagship of Spain's Amphibious Command.* (Spanish Navy)

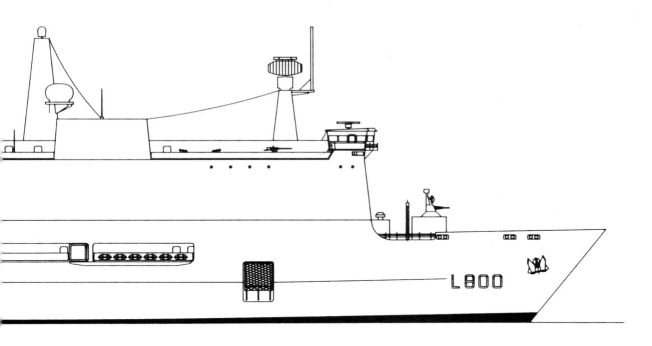

The Thai frigate Naresuan, *photographed after launch on 24 July 1993, is already fitted with some weapon systems.*
(Royal Thai Navy)

The frigate Northumberland, *seen fitting out at Swan Hunter's Wallsend shipyard, will commission in autumn 1994.* (Swan Hunter)

HMS Revenge, *the first British SSBN to pay off (1992).* Resolution *followed in June 1994, and the other two will go as the Trident boats enter service.*

RFA Fort George. *Goalkeeper may be fitted to replace the deleted VLS Seawolf.* (Swan Hunter)

ground fire, was able to return to *Clemenceau*.

Maritime patrol aircraft operating north of the Otranto Straits were authorised to carry two live ASW torpedoes and a full load of sonobuoys; in the southern area, no live weapons were carried. In May 1994, the tanker *Lido II* was boarded and taken into an Italian port as a suspected blockade runner; three Yugoslav warships attempted to interfere with the operation.

The 'November 17' organisation attempted to damage the *Ark Royal* by mortar fire during an April 1994 visit to Piraeus; the missiles failed to fire because of damp.

(c) The Black Sea. In the Caucasus, the Abkhazi insurrection against Georgia was supported by Russia. In June, a freighter apparently supporting the insurgents was sunk by a helicopter and a frigate, both of which were damaged. At dawn on 2 July, the Abkahzis landed 600 commandos to isolate Sukhumi; during further operations there in September civilian airliners were shot down by SAMs from Abkhazi gunboats

offshore. Georgia turned to Russia for help in suppressing further unrest, in return rejoining the CIS. On 4 and 5 November, 500 Russian Marines with armoured vehicles were landed at Poti by nine Russian warships to secure communications centres.

(d) The Baltic. Underwater incursions into Swedish waters continued in 1993; the degree of certainty was high in several cases, but the nationality of possible intruders was not stated. Norway chased a submarine intruder near Narvik for two days in April; sightings of submarines off Norway have dropped more than tenfold since 1987.

(e) 'PACRIM' and Indian Ocean. Russia ordered Pacific Fleet warships to protect merchant ships in the East China Sea after the freighter *Valeri Volkhov*, carrying metal from Vladivostock to China, was fired on by a Chinese warship, the second such incident reported in a month.

The Tamil insurgency in Sri Lanka's northern area erupted periodically into major violence. In August, the Indian Navy escorted

returning refugees and the Tamil Tigers claimed the destruction of two Sri Lankan patrol boats with explosive suicide craft, themselves losing five. In September the Tigers destroyed two Israel-built *Dvora* class patrol craft, but in the following month Government troops captured a Tiger sea base and destroyed 120 boats.

(f) Caribbean. The UN ban on oil and arms shipments to Haiti (23 June) led to an agreement for the return of democratic rule. However, when on 11 October USS *Harlan County* attempted to land American support forces at Port-au-Prince, dockside violence prevented disembarkation, and the LST returned to Guantanamo Bay. The blockade of Haiti was lifted and then reimposed, and the six American warships sent to enforce it were reinforced by British, Canadian, Dutch, French and Argentine units. In mid-1994, the lack of progress towards democratic rule and a flood of refugees seemed to be signals for future US military intervention.

USS Port Royal *(CG 73), the last of twenty-seven* Ticonderoga *class AEGIS guided missile cruisers, on predelivery sea trials in the Gulf of Mexico, 6 December 1993; she will be commissioned for the Pacific Fleet.* (Ingalls)

F(ii). Major Accidents and Incidents at Sea, 1 April 1993 to 31 March 1994

(a) An enquiry was ordered at Faslane into a nuclear submarine alert, 20 June, when a minute leakage of radioactive coolant from HMS *Repulse* sprayed three men working on deck.

(b) On 8 July a machinery compartment fire aboard HMS *Broadsword* off Sicily, while returning from Adriatic deployment, killed two crew members and injured one.

(c) The French SSN *Rubis* collided with the French 277,735-ton supertanker *Lyria* when surfacing off the Riviera on 17 August, causing no injuries but slight damage to the submarine's bow; the crew of the tanker were unaware of the collision, but some cargo was lost through a 5m gash in the hull. The collision might have been due to a malfunction of the submarine's sonar in warm surface water. The accident cost an estimated $7m and the submarine captain was relieved of his command.

(d) Thirty-two submariners from HMS *Torbay* were hospitalised after inhaling toxic diesel fumes at Devonport; there was no fire.

(e) The Norwegian frigate *Oslo*, refloated by tugs after grounding, sank in tow south of Bergen on 24 January. The grounding was attributed to contaminated fuel, causing fuel pump failure and loss of power; one crew member died and ten were injured.

(f) On 2 February a burst steam-pipe and subsequent boiler-room fire in *Admiral Gorshkov*, while alongside at Murmansk, left six crew members dead and two injured.

(g) The French SSN *Amethyste* was slightly damaged by grounding at slow speed while submerged on 2 March; she returned to Toulon with a damaged bow, without assistance.

(h) A turbo-alternator in the French SSN *Emeraude* exploded, killing ten crew members while the boat was submerged off Toulon on 30 March; she surfaced safely and returned to port under her own power. Nuclear installations were unaffected and there was no release of radioactivity.

F(iii). Footnotes

(a) The deaths were announced during the year of:

i) Lieutenant-General James Doolittle, at age 96, leader of the April 1942 raid on Japan by sixteen B-25s flown from USS *Hornet*.

ii) Captain Henry Denham, aged 95, whose intelligence reports from wartime Sweden started the hunt for the *Bismarck*.

iii) Captain Yevgeny Ivanov, aged 68, the Russian naval attaché and intelligence officer in the Profumo affair.

The remains of Admiral Miklos Horthy (1868-1957), last Commander-in-Chief of the Austro-Hungarian Navy and longtime Regent of Hungary, were taken from Portugal to Budapest for reburial on 4 September.

(b) Four sunken submarines were discovered or investigated:

i) The wreck of *UB30*, rammed and sunk by the armed trawler *John Gillman* on 13 August 1918, was located off Whitby in July; another was discovered in 1991 in the same area.

ii) *U 534*, sunk by a British Liberator 13 miles north of the Danish island of Anholt on 5th May 1945, was raised 23 August; press speculation that the hull might contain valuables, secret documents or other war loot proved incorrect.

iii) The hull of a small German submarine, scuttled in 1918 or perhaps 1944, was discovered by Turkish miners in an open-cast mine on reclaimed land at Akpinar, Black Sea, late August/early September.

iv) An unmanned Norwegian submersible found the remains of the Dutch submarine *O-22*, a mine

USS Stout *(DDG 55), the fifth* Arleigh Burke *AEGIS guided missile destroyer, ran trials in January and February 1994 and will be delivered later in the year for Atlantic Fleet service.* (Ingalls)

USS Kearsarge *(LHD 3), commissioned on 16 October 1993 for Atlantic Fleet service. A seventh ship of this class, planned for FY95, has been postponed.* (Ingalls)

casualty in the North Sea sometime after 5 November 1940.

(c) A complete diving ban was imposed on the wreck of the battleship *Royal Oak*, torpedoed in Scapa Flow in 1939 with the loss of 843 lives.

(d) The Pentagon released declassified reports and film relating to the losses of the nuclear-powered submarines *Thresher* and *Scorpion* in 1963 and 1968 respectively; it is believed that a fractured joint in the *Thresher* allowed water at full diving pressure (the boat was at 300m depth) to spray on the electrical system controls, automatically closing down the nuclear reactor, while in *Scorpion*

a faulty torpedo, jettisoned because the propulsion motor accidentally started up, became fully armed and homed on its nearest target, the host submarine.

(e) HMS *Valiant* was damaged by grounding off the coast of Norway during a NATO exercise, due to navigational error; the commander, who failed to report the accident for six weeks, was dismissed from his base and forfeited four years' seniority.

G. MISCELLANEOUS

(a) Five scientists with a full complement of equipment and operating from a US *Sturgeon* class submarine performed a range of experiments below the Arctic icecap in the summer of 1993; the unidentified submarine's military capability was unaltered, and dives to its full (classified) diving depth were not permitted. The Russian Navy, perhaps more desperate for hard currency, was prepared to go further, and allow foreign scientists to work from a 'Victor III' class SSN for up to three

uss Cyclone *(PC 1), first of thirteen coastal patrol craft built to a design based on Vosper Thornycroft's 52m* Ramadan *class missile-armed fast attack craft. Stinger SAMs will be fitted.* (Bollinger)

USCGC Orcas *(WPB 1327), one of forty-nine Island class patrol craft, is a modified version of the Vosper Thornycroft's 110ft patrol craft design.* (Bollinger)

years; one forward torpedo flat would be converted to a floating laboratory and the scientists could spend up to six months a year at sea doing research.

(b) Investigations into the Tailhook sexual harassment episode led to the court martial of five officers, the formal censure of three admirals and administrative action against 29 other officers. The CNO, Admiral Frank Kelso, retired two months early because of the affair.

(c) The US Navy is retiring around twenty-five dolphins and five seal lions trained for Cold War missions such as locating hostile mines off naval bases; it is hoped they can be found homes in aquariums or marine parks.

INDEX

Page numbers in italics refer to illustrations; those in bold refer to tables.

251